A Most Desperate Undertaking: The British Army in the Crimea, 1854-56

Edited by Alastair Massie

A Most Desperate Undertaking:
The British Army in the Crimea, 1854-56

Edited by Alastair Massie

A Special Exhibition at the National Army Museum from October 2003

Designed by Sarah Glaves and Graham Smith

Conservation and display of objects by Erica Arnold, Susan Beale,
Lorraine Finch, Martin Hinchcliffe, Vince Prior and Ray Seabrook

Book design by Deborah Harris

Photography by Ian Jones and Nigel Armstrong

All the above are members of staff of the National Army Museum

© National Army Museum 2003

ISBN 0 901721 38 7

Printed by Nuffield Press

Origination by Blue Cube

Contents
Catalogue sections in **bold type**

Contents

Maps

The Theatre of War in the East, 1854-56

**Dedicated to the memory of Ian G Robertson, MA FMA
Director of the National Army Museum, 1988-2003.**

Foreword

The fourth of October 2003 is the 150th Anniversary of the declaration of war by the Ottoman Empire on Russia. So began the conflict generally known as the Crimean War, on account of the fact that from September 1854 the Crimean Peninsula in the Black Sea became the principal theatre of operations. The National Army Museum is marking this memorable occasion with a Special Exhibition, to which this publication is a companion. Once again the Museum has drawn on its remarkable Collections, many of them never before displayed to the public and the remainder newly conserved and freshly interpreted.

The Foreword to this book was to have been written by Ian G Robertson MA FMA, Director of the National Army Museum since 1988. Ian Robertson died suddenly on 1 August 2003. During his 15 years as Director he had overseen many Special Exhibitions - projects close to his heart, being a museum professional dedicated to providing access to the national treasures in his care. He was keen that every Special Exhibition be accompanied by a publication which would reach beyond the precincts of the Museum to give a lasting record of what had been achieved. He took a close interest in preparations for this Exhibition, chairing planning meetings and involving himself in the production of the book - insisting that both should be as thoroughly researched, detailed and visually attractive as possible. It is the hope of everyone involved that Ian Robertson would have been happy with the outcome of these endeavours and this publication is dedicated to his memory.

The British Army's painful experiences in the Crimea will be familiar to many. Less well known is the extent to which the difficulties it found itself in had been foreseen. It was one thing for the Royal Navy to dust off plans to attack the French naval arsenal of Cherbourg for use, with French assistance no less, against the Russians at Sevastopol - in 1911 the naval historian Sir Julian Corbett declared that in its conception and organization the attack on the Crimea was perhaps the most daring, brilliant and successful thing of its kind Britain ever did. But for the soldiers, always trepidatious about being landed on a hostile shore - and they knew very little indeed about this one - things looked rather different. Our title, *A Most Desperate Undertaking,* thus reflects widespread disquiet among the Army's upper echelons, those very words having come from Lieutenant-General Sir John Fox Burgoyne, a military engineer of vast experience, in a querulous memorandum written as late as August 1854. Unsurprisingly perhaps, Burgoyne's prophecy was self-fulfilling. Had he not, in the aftermath of victory on the Alma a month later, advised the allies to besiege Sevastopol from the south rather than risk an immediate assault on the northern sector of the town, it is possible that the British Army would have been spared the disastrous loss of much of its equipment in the Great Storm of 14 November 1854 and the luridly-reported horrors of a Crimean winter.

The Team Leader for the Exhibition and editor of this publication is Dr Alastair Massie, Head of the Department of Archives, Photographs, Film & Sound. Dr Massie is also the author of *The National Army Museum Book of the Crimean War: The Untold Stories,* to be published in February 2004 by Sidgwick & Jackson. He has been assisted by Miss Emma Armstrong, Miss Sara Jones and Mrs Gill Brewer of the Departments of Fine & Decorative Art, Weapons, Equipment & Vehicles, and Uniforms, Badges & Medals respectively. All the essays in the book are by Museum staff; their names appear at the head of each one. Mr Keith Miller, Head of the Department of Weapons, Equipment & Vehicles and his colleague Ms Sophie Stathi provided extra captioning, likewise Mrs Lesley Smurthwaite and Miss Natalia Wieczorek of the Department of Uniforms, Badges & Medals. Dr Peter Boyden, Assistant Director (Collections), assisted with editorial conventions. Mr Mike O'Connor, Strategic Facilities Manager, oversaw the budget. The index was prepared by Mr Simon Moody of the Department of Archives, Photographs, Film & Sound and the bibliography by Mr Michael Ball, Head of the Department of Printed Books. The Head of the Department of Computer Services, Mr David Collens, and his colleague Mr Phil Sharp installed audio-visuals in the Gallery. Mr Julian Farrance of the Department of Education and Miss Jo Woolley, Head of the Department of Public Relations, Marketing & Corporate Hospitality organized location filming with The History Channel. External assistance was kindly given by Major Roger Chapman, Curator of the Green Howards Museum at Richmond, North Yorkshire, who unearthed important information about the mysterious Arthur Wellesley Kirby (see p306), as well as by Miss Elizabeth Talbot Rice and Mrs Etain Casey who helped obtain translations from the Russian.

Alan J Guy
Acting Director   October 2003

Britain, the Army and the Crimean War

Alastair Massie

The British Army was unprepared in 1854 for the outbreak of a European war. Since the final defeat of Napoleon forty years before it had possessed two purposes: to garrison the Empire and provide homeland security. Balancing these two requirements had not been easy. There was a shortage of both manpower and money. Politicians had preached the virtues of economy. The Army budget fell from £43 million in 1815 to £8 million in 1836. Its personnel declined to a total of 109,000. The garrisoning requirements of India and the colonies meant that there were rarely more than 50,000 troops left in the British Isles. In 1841 there were only nineteen battalions of infantry present. This was clearly unacceptable, particularly as the 1840s were a time when French sabre rattling across the Channel gave rise to periodic invasion scares. In 1847, the Whig Secretary for War and the Colonies, Henry George Grey, 3rd Earl of Grey (1802-94), attempted reform. While endeavouring to reduce commitments overseas, he at the same time introduced short-service enlistment. The aim was to create a pool of trained manpower so that, in the event of an emergency, the Army could be rapidly augmented by recalled reservists. Unfortunately, the Army's own immediate need was for long service regulars who could be sent overseas for a decade or more, not soldiers on limited enlistment. The experiment was not a success.

The death in September 1852 of the country's foremost soldier, Field Marshal Arthur Wellesley, 1st Duke of Wellington (1769-1852), proved a landmark. Fearing that it would be used as an excuse for further economy and political control, he had long opposed army reform, especially the type of administrative reform proposed by Lord Howick (the future Lord Grey) in 1836. If only by comparison, his successor as commander-in-chief of the Army, Lieutenant-General Henry Hardinge, 1st Viscount Hardinge (1785-1856), had a reputation as a reformer. Even this might not have led to much, until circumstances forced Hardinge's hand. In France there was a new ruler, a Bonaparte no less. The Emperor Napoleon III was a nephew of the great Napoleon. It was thought that he wished to undo the effects of his uncle's defeat at Waterloo. Threatening noises had been made towards Belgium. Once again there was an invasion alarm. Hardinge was painfully aware that to repel a French invasion the Army, ordinarily dispersed around the country, would need to concentrate rapidly; yet it was completely unused to conducting operations on a brigade, let alone a divisional, basis. Hence the innovation between June and August 1853 of holding a summer camp of exercise at Chobham in Surrey. Generals were given the opportunity to conduct large-scale manoeuvres. The men learned to live under canvas. Land was purchased at Aldershot to build a permanent camp. To equip the Army better for field service, the artillery received more field guns. The Enfield Rifle Musket, a handier and smaller-calibre successor to the Minié, itself only adopted in 1851,

was approved for production. A School of Musketry was established at Hythe. 'We have done more in two years than during the last century', Hardinge wrote in November 1854.[1] Although intended to improve the Army's state of readiness for home defence, it was also the kind of preparation that the expeditionary force which departed Britain's shores in 1854 would desperately need.

As it transpired, rather than threaten Britain, Napoleon III looked in other directions to further his ambition of overthrowing the Vienna settlement of 1815. Championing the rights of the Latin monks over the Holy Places in Palestine not only propitiated the Roman Catholic vote in France, but challenged the prestige of Tsar Nicholas I of Russia, the protector of the rights of the rival Orthodox monks and guardian of the status quo in Europe. Throughout 1852 the Ottoman authorities in Palestine were buffeted by claim and counter-claim made by each side until, following a show of naval power by the French, the keys to the Church of the Nativity in Bethlehem were handed to the Latin monks in December. Tsar Nicholas was outraged: aside from the religious rebuff, it conceded to Napoleon III diplomatic pre-eminence at Constantinople, something which he considered to have been his ever since the Treaty of Unkiar Skelessi in 1833. Troops were moved to the Turkish border. In February 1853 a browbeating mission under the incredibly undiplomatic Prince Menshikov was despatched to Constantinople to claim for the Tsar a protectorate over all the Orthodox subjects of the Turkish Empire. Until this point the British Government had been vaguely sympathetic to the Russian position. The Prime Minister, George Hamilton-Gordon, 4th Earl of Aberdeen (1784-1860), had been prepared not to take seriously Tsar Nicholas's musings to the British ambassador about Turkey being 'a sick man', carrying with it the implication that arrangements should be made for the Ottoman Empire's partition; after all, he had spoken the same language on a visit to England in 1844. But the claim for a protectorate threatened Turkish independence too explicitly. The possibility was conjured of the Russians gaining control of Constantinople and securing access to the Mediterranean for their Black Sea fleet. In Cabinet, the Home Secretary, Henry John Temple, Viscount Palmerston (1784-1865) urged a forceful response. British suspicion of the Russians displaced that of the French. In June the British Mediterranean fleet was ordered to Besika Bay outside the Dardanelles. The French fleet followed.

The Tsar knew that the British Cabinet was divided and he had great faith in the pacific intentions of Lord Aberdeen. He did not countermand the orders that he had given his forces following the final failure of the Menshikov mission in May to occupy the Ottoman Empire's Danubian Principalities, Moldavia and Wallachia. Palmerston wanted to send the fleet through the Straits but was overruled. Instead, Britain and France, in conjunction with Austria and Prussia, attempted to resolve the crisis by means of the Vienna Note, tendered by the Austrian foreign minister, Count Buol. By this the Turkish Sultan was to promise to protect the Christian religion in his domains in accordance with past treaties. Although the Turks bristled at the idea that the Russians and French should police the agreement, it eventually foundered because the Russian Chancellor, Nesselrode, suddenly reasserted his country's claim to a protectorate over Orthodox Christians in the Ottoman Empire. In response, Britain and France ordered their fleets through the Dardanelles. This encouraged the Turks, who on 4 October presented an ultimatum to Russia demanding the withdrawal of its forces from the principalities within two weeks. It was a declaration of war.

The pacific Lord Aberdeen: seeing the aftermath of the Battle of Leipzig in 1813 had given him a horror of war.
NAM. Negative 98117

Britain and France were horrified by the Turkish action. The British ambassador at Constantinople, Stratford Canning, 1st Viscount Stratford de Redcliffe (1786-1880), led the efforts to secure a truce. Fighting however broke out along the Danube. When the Turks attempted to ship supplies across the Black Sea to the Caucasus front - where fighting had also begun - their flotilla was intercepted by the Russian fleet at Sinope on 30 November and destroyed. The war clamour in Britain, already loud, became deafening. Bullied in Cabinet by the bellicose Palmerston and Lord John Russell (1792-1878), Aberdeen agreed to send the fleet into the Black Sea in co-operation with the French; the Russians were told to confine their ships to harbour at the naval base of Sevastopol. A joint ultimatum to withdraw from the principalities was issued on 27 February 1854. No answer being forthcoming, on 28 March Britain and France declared war.[2]

The 'drift' to war, to use a phrase coined at the time, caught the British Army as much by surprise as anybody. On 8 February 1854 the Government decided to send 10,000 troops to Malta. They would act as the nucleus of any future 'Army of the East'. The subsequent expansion of this force to a total of 27,000 upon its commitment to the Balkans posed problems. It had never been envisaged that in addition to its twin responsibilities of Imperial and Home defence, the Army would have to supply a European expeditionary force as well. Of its 153,000 men, nearly two thirds were already overseas; and among these were the Army's most experienced troops. Depots were ransacked for soldiers. The 63rd (The West Suffolk) Regiment was just one of many that had to recruit heavily before departure, beating the drum in Dublin. During the course of 1854 over 12,000 men were found from the Militia, which had providentially been recast as a volunteer force two years previously. Even so, the 4th Division, ostensibly the reserve, had to be sent to the Balkans as early as July. It was nothing less than the truth when the Secretary at War, Sidney Herbert (1810-1861), wrote in November 1854: 'The army of the east has been created by discounting the future. Every regiment at home, or within reach, and not forming a part of that army, has been robbed to complete it.'[3]

Hardinge encountered similar difficulties in finding generals for the expeditionary force. During the invasion scare of 1850 it had been discovered that there were no generals in England under the age of sixty-one. The continued dearth of generals of sufficient youthful vigour meant that all the Army of the East's infantry brigades had to be given to colonels furnished with the brevet rank of brigadier. Among divisional commanders, half had not seen any active service - if they had seen any at all - since the Napoleonic Wars of their youth. Fitzroy James Henry Somerset, 1st Baron Raglan (1788-1855), the sixty-six year old overall commander, was no exception. The commander of the 4th

The application of British seapower: the Baltic fleet off the Aland Islands, August 1854.
NAM. 1976-05-33

Division, sixty year old Sir George Cathcart (1794-1854), who had just returned from the Cape, was given a dormant commission to succeed Raglan in the event of his incapacitation simply because he was the only general with recent experience of independent command. Such was the gravity of the situation that a commission on promotion met in February 1854 to bring forward younger officers. A large brevet promotion followed in June to try and improve the pool of officers for the Crimea.

By June 1854 the British and French armies had advanced as far as Varna in Bulgaria. However, the Russians' raising of the siege of Silistria and subsequent retirement from the Danubian Principalities left the Allied expedition lacking a purpose. Without the co-operation of Austria, neither Russia nor the Allies could act decisively in the Balkans; and although the threat of intervention in the war by Vienna

had forced Russian withdrawal, the Austrians were otherwise determined to remain neutral, as they would inevitably bear the brunt of any fighting if they became involved. The British contemplated an amphibious warfare strategy instead. Ever since Sinope the First Lord of the Admiralty, Sir James Robert George Graham (1792-1861), had urged the necessity of destroying the Russian naval base at Sevastopol. The ministers of Aberdeen's coalition Government proved to be as divided on this issue as they had been on the question of war or peace. During the following months even those who - like Palmerston - were in favour of strong measures periodically turned their gaze towards Circassia and the Caucasus as a more tempting theatre for Black Sea operations. But by the end of June 1854, after *The Times* had printed a fiery editorial, the tide was running strongly in favour of Sevastopol. On 27 June Henry Pelham Fiennes Pelham Clinton, 5th Duke of Newcastle (1811-1864), the Secretary for War, brought the

proposal for an invasion of the Crimea before the Cabinet. According to Kinglake, most of the Cabinet fell asleep during the course of the meeting, but at its close the proposal was approved.[4] Lord Raglan was given definite instructions to proceed to the Crimea.

Sevastopol was pre-eminently a naval objective.[5] After the Inspector General of Fortifications, Lieutenant-General Sir John Fox Burgoyne (1782-1871) - who returned from Constantinople in April - submitted an unfavourable report, military opinion had been against the expedition. But the Army possessed nobody to match the lobbying skills of Sir James Graham. Both Hardinge and Raglan had imbibed the Wellingtonian precept that their opinion should only be offered to politicians when asked. The wrangling over administrative reform during the years before the outbreak of war completed the estrangement of the civilian-led War Office from the military hierarchy. There was little communication. When Raglan received orders to attack Sevastopol he and at least three of his divisional commanders - Cathcart, Lieutenant-General Sir George Brown (1790-1865) and Lieutenant-General George William Frederick Charles, 2nd Duke of Cambridge (1819-1904) - privately opposed the enterprise. As Brigadier-General Richard (later General Lord) Airey (1803-1881) complained: 'The Press in England is pushing us forward very violently! A strong Press and a weak Government are the worst enemies any Army can have.'[6] There was moreover a crippling lack of intelligence. Where was the best place to land in the Crimea? What was the number of Russian troops? How were they disposed? No one knew. 'A most desperate undertaking', was Burgoyne's verdict on the projected expedition.[7]

With too few troops - 27,000 British, 30,000 French and 7000 Turks - and land transport which had proved inadequate even in Bulgaria, the expedition to the Crimea in September 1854 took on the character

Sir John Fox Burgoyne: he disliked the idea of an expedition to the Crimea from the beginning.
NAM. Negative 46924

collapsed. Although only twelve kilometres from their base at Balaklava, the troops besieging Sevastopol were cut off from their supplies by a sea of mud. Already suffering from overwork and exposure, they lacked the fuel to cook their meagre rations; and when the soldiers fell sick, the medical provision was woefully inadequate. Among the many reasons for the breakdown of supply, the failure to achieve administrative reform before the war bulked large. There was too much division of responsibility. Too many branches of Government were involved. The Ordnance Office provided greatcoats; the Treasury supplied provisions and transport; the Army Medical Department was distinct; the War Office was the recipient of their collective goods and services. There was bureaucratic procedure to match. Commissaries refused to issue equipment and food at Balaklava unless over-complex regulations were complied with. Ships left the Crimea with their cargoes unloaded. A requisition for 2000 tons of hay issued in September 1854 was met by the Treasury eight months later.[8]

In December 1854, with the Army running out of men and recruitment poor, an emergency session of Parliament passed the Foreign Enlistment Bill. German, Swiss and Italian recruits would form auxiliary 'legions'. At the same time, reports appeared in *The Times* of the deplorable condition of the Army in the Crimea. There was an outcry. When Parliament reassembled in January 1855 an opposition motion for an inquiry into the condition of the army before Sevastopol was carried overwhelmingly. Aberdeen's Government resigned. A Ministry led by Palmerston eventually emerged to replace it. Administrative reform was swiftly implemented. The Commissariat had already been removed from Treasury control. Existing plans for a Land Transport Corps were put in place. The Board of Ordnance was abolished. Commissions of investigation were installed. To increase the Army's manpower short service enlistment was offered; an increased bounty and the inducement of additional pay while on active service followed. A convention was concluded to take a Turkish contingent into British pay. The services of 15,000 men from Piedmont-Sardinia were secured with the aid of a £2 million loan.

In spite of the perception that Palmerston would prove masterful - perhaps even a second Chatham - his government was in many respects no stronger than the Aberdeen administration. Parliament forced upon him the Roebuck, or Sevastopol, Committee of Inquiry, leading to the resignation of the Government's Peelite ministers. In July 1855 Lord John Russell was compelled to resign. The crucial guarantee of a loan to Turkey was passed by only three votes on 20 July.[9] However, the Opposition was divided, and the Radicals – Austen Henry Layard (1817-94) in particular - over-played their hand when they criticised the 'aristocratic' composition of the Army.[10] The fall – thanks to

of a grand raid. If, like the expedition to Copenhagen in 1807, it were to succeed, it needed to do so quickly. But the opportunity presented by victory at the Alma was wasted. Rather than storm Sevastopol, which was ripe for the taking, the Allies settled down to conduct a siege. The failure of the bombardment of 17 October, and the Russian counterstrokes at Balaklava and Inkerman, condemned the British Army to wintering in the Crimea. It was hopelessly unprepared. Whereas the French could expand their army in the Crimea four-fold, in Raglan's army casualties went largely unreplaced. The land transport system

Lord Palmerston: he would discover that bellicosity had its limits.
NAM. 1960-12-323-23

The plenipotentiaries to the Paris peace conference. The British, French and Russian delegates, seated in the middle, occupy centre stage.
NAM. Negative 98120

the French - of Sevastopol on 8 September brought to an end this period of parliamentary instability; it was now a question of bringing the war itself to a successful conclusion. Its denouement, generally speaking, has been perceived as a purely diplomatic process. The war, as A J P Taylor suggested, was one 'in which diplomacy had only occasionally been interrupted by battles'.[11] True, the Austrian ultimatum in December threatening to break off diplomatic relations was pivotal in persuading Russia to accept Allied peace terms. But Palmerston's preparations to send a massive naval armament to the Baltic, reduce the fortress of Kronstadt and lay the Russian capital St Petersburg under the guns of the British fleet, provided another strong incentive for the new Tsar, Alexander II, to end the war.[12] The British were insistent that the peace congress meet early: if the Russians proved obdurate, the fleet could still be sent to the Baltic in the spring. Peace preliminaries were signed on 1 February 1856; the Congress of Paris concluded a treaty on 30 March. Russia agreed to the neutralization of

the Black Sea – which meant the end for the time being of Sevastopol as a naval base – and ceded southern Bessarabia at the mouth of the River Danube. Yet the wider effects of the Crimean War were more significant. With Russia weakened by defeat, its ability to influence events in central Europe – so apparent as recently as 1848-49, when it played the leading role in subduing revolutionary insurrection – disappeared. A power vacuum arose. Napoleon III continued his efforts to overthrow the Vienna settlement of 1815. Yet ironically, his victory over Austria in the Italian War of 1859 gave Otto von Bismarck's Prussia the opportunity to assert itself within Germany, and inflict in turn a crushing defeat on France in the War of 1870-71. The balance of power in Europe changed forever.

In these momentous events the British Army played no part. The impetus of the administrative reforms enacted during the Crimean War was not maintained. Even if it had been, the changes would not have given Britain an army of a size sufficient to intervene on the continent. Witnessing Britain's inability to field more than 30,000 of its own troops in the Crimea, Europe came to the conclusion that British military prowess was much over-rated. When Palmerston threatened to intervene on the side of the Danes in the Schleswig-Holstein dispute of 1864, Bismarck made the riposte that if the British Army landed in Germany he would send the police force to arrest it. Fifty years later, on the outbreak of the First World War, such disdain found its echo in Kaiser Wilhelm II's dismissal of Britain's 'contemptible little army'. Only with the deployment of Kitchener's volunteers in 1916 could Britain achieve a continental sized army, and only then would the recollection of the British Army's quixotic – if nonetheless heroic - participation in the Crimean War be erased.

Notes

1   Quoted H Strachan, *Wellington's Legacy. The Reform of the British Army 1830-54*, Manchester (1984) p42.

2   The story of the preliminaries to war has been told most recently in T Royle, *Crimea. The Great Crimean War 1854-1856*, London (1999).

3   Quoted Strachan *op. cit.* p221.

4   A W Kinglake, *The Invasion of the Crimea*, Edinburgh & London (6th edn. 1877) Vol 2 pp249-250, 407-411.

5   The significance and consequences of this are explored in H Strachan, 'Soldiers, Strategy and Sebastopol' *The Historical Journal*, 21, 2 (1978) pp303-325 and A Lambert, *The Crimean War. British Grand Strategy 1853-1856*, Manchester (1990).

6   NAM. 1962-10-94-1 Airey to Major-General George Augustus Wetherall, 22 July 1854.

7   G Wrottesley, *Life and Correspondence of Field Marshal Sir John Burgoyne,* London (1873) Vol 2 p69.

8   The problems with the Commissariat are dealt with in J Sweetman, *War and Administration. The Significance of the Crimean War for the British Army*, Edinburgh (1984) pp41-59.

9   For the difficulties faced by Palmerston's new government see J R Vincent, 'The Parliamentary Dimension of the Crimean War', *Transactions of the Royal Historical Society*, 5th Series, Vol 31 1981 pp37-49 and O Anderson, *A Liberal State at War. English Politics and Economics during the Crimean War*, London (1967).

10   G Waterfield, *Layard of Nineveh*, London (1963) pp250-277.

11   A J P Taylor, *The Struggle for Mastery in Europe 1848-1918*, Oxford (1954) p79.

12   The contention that the naval threat was instrumental in forcing peace on Russia is a major component of Lambert's work cited above.

The British Army of 1854

The British Army, on the eve of the Crimean War, was the product of forty years of peace in Europe. Although it was 150,000 strong, over two-thirds of it was posted overseas garrisoning the Empire. A large number of its generals had not seen active service - if they had seen any at all - since they fought Napoleon's France in their youth. Army administration had ossified: the War Office, Commander-in-Chief, Board of Ordnance and Treasury all possessed competing responsibilities. The Army, too, was intensely hierarchical. Officers generally purchased their commissions and this ensured social exclusivity. The other ranks, drawn from a stratum of society which saw little alternative to enlistment, were nearly all long service regulars. Many had been brutalised by harsh discipline and poor living conditions. There were only a few stirrings of change. In appearance, the troops looked much as they had done at Waterloo, but new and more practical styles of uniform were under consideration. Soldiers were also in the process of being issued with new weaponry. The Minié Rifle in particular was a significant advance on the Pattern 1842 Percussion Musket in terms of both its range and accuracy. Chobham Camp, held in 1853, was a praiseworthy if belated attempt to familiarise the home army with large scale manoeuvre and life under canvas. Yet none of this could disguise the fact that the British Army of 1854 remained an unreformed Army and one ill-prepared for a European war.

Pattern 1842 Smoothbore Percussion Musket, .753in., 1845

Tower of London Arsenal, 139 cm. l

NAM. 1974-07-32

The Pattern 1842 Smoothbore Musket was one of the first percussion firearms adopted by the British Army for the infantry. This type of weapon was used by several infantry regiments of the 4th Division at the beginning of the Crimean War and had an effective range of about 200 yards (182 metres). During 1855 their muskets were gradually exchanged for new Pattern 1853 Enfield Rifle Muskets, which had been sent out to the Crimea.

All Pattern 1842 muskets have the year of manufacture stamped on the lock and this example is dated 1845. It was produced at the Tower of London arsenal by the gunmaker Proctor, whose name is marked on the stock.

Paper Cartridge, Smoothbore Percussion Musket

Generously donated by Mr A Beadle

NAM. 1978-11-175

Of a type that was used with the Pattern 1842 Smoothbore Musket, the paper cartridge contains a spherical lead ball of .685in. (1.74cm.) and 125 grains (8.1g.) of powder. The cartridge was torn open and the powder, wadding and ball rammed down the gun barrel prior to firing.

Socket Bayonet for Pattern 1842 Smoothbore Musket, post-1842

S Hill, 53cm. l

Generously donated by the Horniman Museum

NAM. 1979-07-11

The Pattern 1842 Musket incorporated a new bayonet spring catch, invented by George Lovell, Inspector of Small Arms at the Royal Small Arms Factory, Enfield. It was designed to hold the bayonet in place more securely.

The bayonet was based on the standard design of the time, with a different shaped collar so that it would fit the new spring catch. This type of bayonet was also initially issued for the pattern 1851 Minié Rifle Musket, and was replaced in 1853 by the Enfield bayonet.

This example is engraved to the 92nd (Highland) Regiment of Foot and the blade is stamped with the maker's name, S Hill.

Pattern 1851 Minié Percussion Rifle Musket, .702in., 1852

139cm. l

NAM. 1994-06-3

The Pattern 1851 Rifle Musket, or Minié, named after the French inventor of the rifling system, was a major leap forward in the design of the British service arm. Before its introduction in Britain, the Duke of Wellington had been adamant that the 'armament and equipment of each individual soldier should be the best that can be found' and he was consequently urged by the Marquess of Anglesey, Master-General of the Ordnance, that all infantry soldiers should carry a rifle. The Duke agreed, on condition that the weight of the bullet should remain the same as the musket ball, that fifty of the new cartridges should weigh no more than sixty of the old, and that it should be named a 'rifled musket', not a rifle, to make clear the distinction between the infantry and rifle regiments. A French and a Belgian Minié were trialed against other firearms, and in April 1851 the report concluded that the Belgian Minié was the superior weapon. Four British prototype Miniés were manufactured based on the Belgian design. With Wellington's approval, 500 were then manufactured for testing by ten regiments, selected as having suitable range facilities.

The ammunition of this new weapon was unique. It fired a conical-shaped projectile with a hollow base, fitted with an iron cup, which expanded on firing to take the four rifling grooves in the barrel. This vastly improved range and accuracy.

Externally the Minié was very similar to the Pattern 1842 Musket, but can be distinguished by the elevating tangent backsight, required for firing at greater range. The Minié had an effective range of about 800 yards (731m.) and played an important role during the early battles of the Crimean War. This particular example is dated 1852.

Detail: Pattern 1851 Minié Percussion Rifle Musket, .702in., 1852

Minié bullets used by the 88th Regiment of Foot (Connaught Rangers) before going to the Crimea, 1854

Generously donated by Lieutenant-Colonel HFN Jourdain

NAM. 1960-05-75

The 88th Regiment of Foot (Connaught Rangers) was one of ten regiments selected to test the Pattern 1851 Minié Rifle Musket. The Minié bullet was made from lead, a soft metal that easily distorted upon hitting a target. With its iron cup, the bullet weighed 680 grains (44g.) and measured .690in. (1.75cm.) in diameter.

The seventeen bullets were recovered from the range of the 88th Regiment of Foot (Connaught Rangers), having been used as practice rounds before the regiment left for the Crimea.

Pattern 1842 Percussion Lancers Pistol, .753in., 1845

40cm. l

NAM. 1980-03-6

Pistols for cavalry had largely been abandoned in the British Army in 1838, except for lancers, trumpeters and sergeant majors. In 1842 a new pattern percussion single shot pistol of the same calibre as the Pattern 1842 Musket was introduced. It was issued to lancers and used by them during the Crimean War, whereas dragoons and hussars carried carbines. It comprises a 9 inch long smoothbore barrel, percussion lock and a sharply cut-down butt, with a brass butt plate. This example is dated 1845 and marked on the butt plate to the 12th (Prince of Wales's) Royal Regiment of Lancers. An ammunition pouch for 20 rounds of pistol ammunition was also issued.

Pattern 1821 Light Cavalry Trooper's Sword, *c*1838

Birmingham, 103.5cm. l

NAM. 2000-09-18

A lighter version of the heavy cavalry sword but with three-bar guard, this sword bore the brunt of the cavalry's criticism of the 'cut and thrust' blade. Most cavalrymen and many experts thought it inferior to the Pattern 1796 Sword. In 1828 a committee recommended several improvements to the sword but in the 'long peace' nothing appears to have been done. Further complaints were investigated in the mid-1830s but again little was done. This sword was of the type carried by many troopers in the Crimea.

Pattern 1853 Cavalry Trooper's Sword

104cm. l

NAM. 1972-05-7-38

Introduced as the first universal pattern cavalry sword for both light and heavy cavalry, this sword came in for heavy criticism during the Crimean War, much of it ill-informed. Regiments often carried out unofficial bending tests on the blades, which severely weakened them.

It is possible that up to 50% of the cavalry who fought in the Crimea carried the new sword while the others had to use the Pattern 1821. At the Battle of Balaklava it is known that some troopers at least of the 11th (or Prince Albert's Own) Regiment of Hussars and 2nd (Royal North British) Regiment of Dragoons were armed with the new sword.

Pattern 1821 Heavy Cavalry Trooper's Sword, *c*1835

105cm. l

NAM. 1995-08-2

Although officially accepted in 1821, production of the sword only began in 1827. Both this type and the light cavalry sword had the new 'cut and thrust' blade which was heavily criticised by the cavalry. Modifications were suggested and the heavy cavalry sword and scabbard were improved in the mid-1830s from which time it remained relatively free from complaints.

The sword itself was an improvement on the old 1796 Pattern. The bowl guard gave good protection to the hand and such guards became standard later in the century.

Lord Cardigan in the uniform of Colonel, 11th (or Prince Albert's Own) Regiment of Hussars, *c*1855

Photograph of an artistic depiction, produced by G West & Son, Gosport, 16.5cm. h x 10.8cm. w

Generously donated by Mrs A Monro

NAM. 1958-04-32-2

By 1854 James Thomas Brudenell, 7th Earl of Cardigan (1797-1868) had long been among the most notorious officers in the British Army. Although he first joined the Army in 1824 at the relatively advanced age of 27, his family was wealthy and by purchasing his commissions he had, within eight years, risen to command the 15th (The King's) Regiment of Light Dragoons (Hussars). His ill-temper ensured that he constantly quarrelled with his officers and matters did not change when he received the lieutenant-colonelcy of the 11th Hussars in 1836. The so-called 'Black Bottle' affair in May 1840, when he ordered one of his officers under arrest for placing bottled wine on the mess table rather than having it decanted, became a *cause célèbre*. He followed it up by challenging to a duel and wounding another officer who had written critically on the affair to the newspapers.

Cardigan was tried for attempted murder before the House of Lords, only to be acquitted on a technicality. In the years that followed Cardigan was able to escape the same degree of public scrutiny and was promoted major-general on 20 June 1854, but the events of the Crimean War were dramatically to restore him to the headlines.

Letter from Captain William Charles Forrest to the Adjutant, 11th (or Prince Albert's) Regiment of Hussars, 28 October 1842

Manuscript, 33.5cm. h x 20.5cm. w

Generously donated by Mrs A Monro

NAM. 1958-04-32-1-2

One of the officers to suffer at Lord Cardigan's hands was Captain (later General) William Charles Forrest (1819-1902), who in September 1840 was placed under arrest for failing to surrender, during an absence of a week, the key to his room in barracks. Cardigan continued to persecute Forrest thereafter by making it difficult for him to take leave, a state of affairs which culminated in 1843 in Cardigan's attempt to recall Forrest to his duties while the latter was attending his wife in the wake of a difficult birth. On this occasion the Commander in Chief himself, the Duke of Wellington, reprimanded Cardigan for his conduct. As this letter shows, however, Forrest had begun to lose patience with Cardigan's behaviour the previous year.

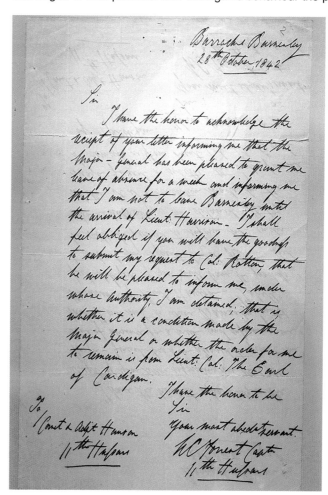

'Funeral of the Duke of Wellington. The funeral car passing the archway at Apsley House, Novr 18th 1852.'

Colour lithograph by T Picken after Louis Haghe (1806-85), published by R Ackermann & Son, 30 April 1853, 48.2cm. h x 59.9cm. w

NAM. 1974-02-167

The death of Arthur Wellesley, 1st Duke of Wellington (1769-1852) on 14 September 1852 marked the passing of an era. The victor of Waterloo and vanquisher of Napoleon, Wellington was perhaps Britain's greatest ever soldier, but as commander-in-chief of the Army in his old age, his belief that past methods were the best had acted as a brake on progress. Although his death provided the opportunity for military reform, the outbreak of the Crimean War just over a year later meant that the time available for any reforms to take effect would be limited.

The procession of Wellington's funeral cortège to St Paul's Cathedral was watched by a million and a half people. The artist has depicted the funeral car – which weighed eighteen tons and was of a design inspired by Prince Albert - passing the Duke's London residence, Apsley House, Hyde Park Corner.

'The Right Honble. Vicount [*sic*] Hardinge G.C.B. P.C', 1849

Mezzotint J Faed after Sir Francis Grant (1803-78), published by Paul & Dominic Colnaghi, London, 1 November 1851, 55.3cm. h x 43.5cm. w

NAM. 1979-04-13

A veteran of the Corunna retreat (1809), who lost a hand while serving as a liaison officer with the Prussians at Ligny (1815), in later years Lieutenant-General (later Field Marshal) Henry Hardinge, 1st Viscount Hardinge of Lahore (1785-1856) showed himself an able military administrator. Upon the death in 1852 of his mentor, the Duke of Wellington, who in 1816 had presented him with the sword reputedly worn by Napoleon at Waterloo (and which he is here depicted as wearing), Hardinge succeeded to the command of the Army. He had a reputation as a reformer and established the School of Musketry at Hythe, as well as overseeing the introduction of the Enfield Rifle. However, the shortcomings of the Army during the Crimean War clouded his reputation and he resigned as commander-in-chief in July 1856, dying two months later.

Full Dress Coatee and Epaulettes, *c*1854

39th (The Dorsetshire) Regiment of Foot

Wool cloth, gilt metal buttons, gilt metal epaulettes

Generously donated by Lieutenant-Colonel J B Slade Baker

NAM. 1960-08-250, -1, -2

Captain (later Major) Robert Broome Baker purchased an ensigncy in the 39th (The Dorsetshire) Regiment of Foot in 1849 and his captaincy in 1853. His uniform is of the coatee style which, by the 1850s, with its skirts cut away to the front, was looking distinctly old-fashioned when set against the tunic worn by an increasing number of continental armies. Although the introduction to the British Army of the tunic was announced in August 1854, the expeditionary force which sailed for the Crimea the following month was still garbed in the coatee.

The narrow silk stripes in the regimental facing colour (in this case green) on Baker's epaulette straps denote someone of company officer rank.

Major-General's Coatee and Epaulettes, 1845-54

Wool cloth, body and sleeves lined with silk, tails faced with kerseymere, metal thread embroidery

Generously donated by the Trustees of the Middlesex Regimental Museum

NAM. 1992-09-51

George William Frederick Charles, 2nd Duke of Cambridge (1819-1904), a first cousin of Queen Victoria, had gained a solid grounding as a regimental officer before being promoted major-general on 7 May 1845. He succeeded his father as Duke of Cambridge in 1850. His uniform is of the general officer's full dress pattern of 1828-55; the arrangement of gilt buttons in pairs and the width of embroidery on the cuffs is distinctive to a major-general. The epaulettes are of gold lace in a French check pattern, trimmed with gold round cord and boxed gold bullion tassels, but the general officer's rank insignia is absent from the straps. Cambridge was promoted lieutenant-general on 19 June 1854, by which time he was already in Turkey with the Army of the East and in command of the 1st Division.

Officer's Pelisse, c1848-53

11th (or Prince Albert's Own) Regiment of Hussars

Blue cloth, gold lace and braid, fur trim, gilt metal buttons

Bequeathed by Mr W E Brinkley

NAM. 1967-06-32-1

Worn by Lieutenant Walter Stephens Brinkley, who retired in 1853. Both officers and men of hussar regiments wore the pelisse, or over jacket, which reflected the Hungarian origins of the hussar's style of dress. To enable the pelisse to be worn over the left shoulder, a yellow cord loop fitted at the collar. In the Crimea, hussars were expected to wear pelisses in place of greatcoats; however, upon landing, pelisses of both the 8th and 11th Hussars were left on board the transport ships and not returned until November 1854.

Lord Cardigan had taken command of the 11th Regiment of Light Dragoons in 1836. On 11 February 1840 the regiment was chosen to escort Prince Albert from Dover to London for his marriage to Queen Victoria. In recognition of this, the regiment's title was changed to the 11th (or Prince Albert's Own) Regiment of Hussars. With the change of designation came a change of uniform - the extravagant new one was reputedly chosen by Prince Albert himself - which, given that it was made by a Bond Street tailor, suggests that the report Cardigan lavished £10,000 a year on clothing and mounting his regiment is perhaps not fanciful.

Sabretache, *c*1848-53

11th (or Prince Albert's Own) Regiment of Hussars

Crimson Morocco Leather, gilt metal stud fastenings, gold wire and lace

Bequeathed by Mr W E Brinkley

NAM. 1967-06-32-3

The trousers of the hussar were traditionally so tight that they could not accommodate pockets, and consequently hussars were issued instead with bags which hung from the same belt as their sabres, hence sabretache (from the German *tasche*, meaning pocket). This example belonged to Lieutenant Walter Brinkley; the flap of the sabretache bears the Royal cypher 'VR'. In 1854 the sabretache of the dragoon guards, dragoons and lancers, which over the years had also adopted them, were officially abolished, leaving only the light dragoons and hussars carrying them.

Pattern 1821 Light Cavalry Officer's Sword, *c*1847-53

104cm. l

Bequeathed by Mr W E Brinkley

NAM. 1967-06-40-3

Carried by Lieutenant Walter Brinkley, 11th (or Prince Albert's Own) Regiment of Hussars, this sword has the earlier pipe-back blade, which was heavily criticised for its flimsiness. An elegant weapon, it was of little use on the battlefield.

Farriers of the 17th Regiment of (Light) Dragoons (Lancers) shoeing a horse from a mobile forge, Chobham Camp, 1853

Oil on board by Samuel Henry Alken (1810-94), 1853, 15.3cm. h x 35.5cm. w

NAM. 2002-03-179

From 14 June to 25 August 1853, 10,000 men, 1,500 horses and 24 guns mustered on Chobham Common in Surrey for drill, field operations and parades, under the command of Lieutenant-General (later Field Marshal) John Colborne, 1st Baron Seaton (1778-1863). Known as the 'Great Camp', Chobham was the scene of the first large-scale manoeuvres in mainland Britain since the Napoleonic Wars. The object of the encampment was to improve the efficiency and discipline of the British Army, which had not seen active service in Europe in nearly forty years. These preparations proved invaluable in the Crimean War of 1854-56.

Beyond the training for the then unforeseen war in the Crimea that this major exercise provided the Army, it also tested the logistics of maintaining a large force in the field. Soldiers adapting to living under canvas for a period also acquired certain extra skills. According to *The Illustrated London News*, 'some very awkward attempts at cookery characterised the earlier stages of the bivouac; but, after a little drilling, the men became more expert in handling the camp kettle...'

This painting is the original for a coloured lithograph in the set of six prints by Vincent Brooks after Alken entitled 'Chobham Reminiscences of the Camp', published by Messrs Preston, 31 Burlington Arcade, London, *c*1853.

'The military review - the camp at Chobham. The troops returning to their encampment after a field-day', 1853

Coloured tinted lithograph by Edmund Walker after Louis Haghe (1806-85), published by Ackermann & Co, 8 October 1853, 51.5cm. h x 102.5cm. w

Generously donated by the Royal United Service Institution

NAM. 1968-06-295

In addition to providing practical training for the Army, Chobham Camp was designed to be a military spectacle entailing splendid royal reviews. Lord Hardinge credited Prince Albert with the formation of the camp and the royal family visited it frequently. A number of marquees and small tents were erected on Magnet Hill, the camp Headquarters, which served as a banqueting hall and suite of apartments for the royal party and distinguished guests.

Even before the camp was complete, it had become part of the social 'Season', attracting crowds on their way to the Ascot Races. Once the regiments had arrived, Chobham drew large numbers of visitors who flocked to witness this exhibition of British military prowess with its glittering array of uniforms. In an attempt to profit from the huge popularity of Chobham Camp, a number of artists and printmakers produced pictorial souvenirs whilst *The Illustrated London News* published a diary of each day's events.

Chobham Camp, 1853

Oil on canvas, signed and dated lower left, 'E M Ward 1853', by Edward Matthew Ward (1816-79), 1853, 30.3cm. h x 35.7cm. w

Generously donated by Mr R P K MacMahon

NAM. 1999-09-39

In an encampment of a battalion of infantry - in this instance a Highland Regiment - regulations stated that the camp kitchens were to be built in front of the Rear Guard, with the sutlers in front of them in turn. The Army relied on private entrepreneurs, or sutlers, to sell provisions to the troops, licensing and accommodating them within the encampment.

Although the 42nd (The Royal Highland), the 79th (Cameron Highlanders) and the 93rd (Highland) Regiments of Foot were not brigaded together at Chobham, they nevertheless camped in the same area on the heath. Queen Victoria had expressed herself particularly satisfied with the conduct and appearance of the Highland soldiers and her enthusiasm for all things Scottish made their camp a particular attraction for visitors.

'The Court-Martial on Lieut. Perry of H. Majesty's 46th Regiment, in the Mess Room at Windsor Barracks, August, 1854'

Coloured lithograph after artist unknown, published by Read and Co, London, 9 September, 1854, 29.7cm. h x 43.5cm. w

Generously donated by the Trustees of the Estate of Countess Roberts

NAM. 1955-04-57

The hierarchical and socially exclusive nature of the early Victorian officer corps was thrown into sharp relief by the court martial of Lieutenant James Edward Perry of the 46th (The South Devonshire) Regiment of Foot. The son of a tradesman, Perry had been subject to severe bullying until, losing all restraint, he attacked Lieutenant Thomas Greer with a silver candlestick. Both officers were eventually required to sell their commissions and leave the Army, but the proceedings of the court martial exposed the unsavoury atmosphere in at least one officers' mess and generated much adverse publicity.

Reporters.   Lieut. Perry.   Sergeant.   Mr. Darvill.   Sergeant.   Major Daigetty,   Lieut. Waldy.   Col. Kelly,   General Wetherall,
Legal Adviser.   Members of the Court.   Deputy Judge Advocate.   President.   Prosecutor.

The Court-Martial on Lieut. Perry of H. Majesty's 46th Regiment, in the Mess Room at Windsor Barracks, August 1854.

EXAMINATION OF LIEUT. W. T. WALDY.

LIEUT. WALDY DENIES HAVING EVER HEARD CAPTAIN NICHOLAS MAKE USE OF OPPROBRIOUS LANGUAGE TO ANY YOUNG OFFICER, OR THAT HE HAD EVER SO STATED IN WRITING. LIEUT. PERRY HANDING HIS LETTER TO THE PRESIDENT WHEREIN HE (LIEUT. WALDY) DISTINCTLY STATES THAT CAPTAIN NICHOLAS APPLIED THE DISGUSTING LANGUAGE REFERRED TO, TO ENSIGN COOTE. LIEUT. WALDY IS UNABLE TO PERCEIVE THE DISCREPANCY BETWEEN HIS WRITTEN LETTER AND HIS STATEMENT ON OATH; AND ALSO *TOTALLY UNABLE TO RECOLLECT*, AS IS THE CASE WITH ALL HIS OTHER *GALLANT* BROTHER OFFICERS, ANYTHING PREJUDICIAL TO CAPT. NICHOLAS OR TO THEMSELVES, OR IN THE SLIGHTEST DEGREE ADVANTAGEOUS TO THE PRISONER

Uniforms of the British Army, 1854

Gill Brewer

For many years before the Crimean War, the Board of General Officers at Horse Guards had discussed the suitability of the dress worn by the British soldier. Field Marshal the Duke of Wellington had, since Waterloo, been promoting the necessity for change, and his appointment as Commander-in-Chief in 1842 gave him the opportunity to instigate this. While it is true that the Duke's main concern had been to reduce the expense involved in clothing the Army rather than addressing the practicality of the clothing the men had to wear, it does not invalidate the fact that the Crimean War, far from being the watershed for uniform change - especially the abolition of the top-heavy shako and the tight fitting coatee –which it is often perceived to be, came instead at the end of a long period of debate on the subject of the Army's uniform.

It was as early as 1828 that *The Naval and Military Magazine* commented: 'Of the two purposes of uniform - to give the soldier convenient clothing, and to distinguish him from the enemy - neither is attained by the present system.'[1] Many writers of this period were questioning why the soldier's dress should do so much to restrict their movements. More and more, officers were choosing to wear their less distinctive blue frock coats, both on the parade ground and in the field.

The author and tactician Colonel John Mitchell was another critic who had suggested a 'root and branch' overhaul of uniforms as early as 1838:

> We can promise the best thanks of the soldiers to the first authority that shall rid the service of bear-skin caps, infantry and light cavalry chakos, the ill-shaped helmet of the dragoons, the jack boots, cuirasses, and leather-breeches of the life guards, the stiff leather stocks of the whole army … Why a soldier's dress should be as much as possible calculated to cramp his exertions … we leave to the ingenious to discover.[2]

In terms of ostentation and the expenditure lavished upon them, 1830 marked the zenith of the British Army's uniforms. After this, however, sheer cost led to their rationalisation. The Board of General Officers, in 1833, made a significant contribution towards redesign of the cavalry helmet on grounds of practicality. Their conclusion was that the existing helmet was

'cumbrous' and inconvenient, both in its weight but especially in its height. Their template would see a reduction in both, combining 'strength and utility with moderate weight and compactness of form'.[3] Although changes in detail had been made to uniforms generally by the 1840s, these had produced only a marginally lighter shako, looser fitting coatee and clothing that was slightly more generously cut. Consequently, the use of undress items had increased considerably in day to day wear. In tropical environments in particular, the shell jacket superseded the dress coatee on mess occasions. In 1847, Major-General Lord Frederick Fitzclarence suggested to the Deputy Adjutant-General that this style of dress would be appropriate for home stations, as well as abroad. Reports that shell jackets could be worn at home when dining were dispensed as qualified orders in 1846. 'The officers of every regiment in the Army dine in shell jackets and white waistcoats… unless, indeed, when, some provincial Adjutant General makes himself peculiarly obnoxious'.[4]

By the summer of 1855 in the Crimea the shell jacket was the undress attire of choice. Officers of the 90th Regiment of Foot (Perthshire Volunteers) (Light Infantry) express their preference.
NAM. 1964-12-151-6-30

Frock Coats

In domestic situations, officers wore the pre-eminent style of dress - namely the blue frock coat - as their preferred garment. A report in the *Naval and Military Gazette* stated: 'The blue frock coat has become almost the real uniform of the officer; that in which he works and performs his duties on parade and in the field'.[5] However, high casualties amongst officers in the Seventh Cape Frontier War of 1846-47 were attributed to the blue frock coat being easily identifiable against the red coats of the men (in fact, the officers wore shell jackets). The potential for officers being killed or injured during battle was considered too great a risk and the blue frock coat was abolished in favour of the shell jacket on 2 June 1848. Yet four years later there was a measure of backtracking. On 9 July 1852, authorisation was given for infantry officers to wear a plain double-breasted frock coat '…when riding or walking in the neighbourhood of their quarters'. And in the auxiliary regiments, the frock coat remained a standard item of wear, unhindered by debates as to its suitability of purpose. Diverse groups such as the Enrolled Pensioners, the Dockyard Battalions, and the District Military

Even on active service in the Crimea, Sir George Brown liked to see his staff in frock coats and cocked hats.
NAM. 1964-12-151-6-3

Prison Staff wore several different styles. During sea voyages, the Army continued to wear smock frocks made of loose fitting canvas to protect dress uniforms against wear and tear. Many regiments adopted this type of garment and Strachan notes that 'at Varna in June 1854, the Guards Brigade paraded in smock frocks, arms and accoutrements for drill, and apparently all parades of the Scots Fusilier Guards at this period were in smock frocks'.[6]

Helmets

The debate over frock against coatee had been constant over decades and the design of headwear had continued in parallel for as long. In 1838, Colonel John Mitchell suggested a Grecian helmet to replace the shako that was as outlandish as it was bold. A more realistic and acceptable prototype was promulgated in 1842, in the form of a Prussian-style design. The Royal Regiment of Horse Guards adopted a helmet of this mode in 1843, and a similar version was approved for the regiments of heavy cavalry of the line in 1847.[7] The auxiliary forces were not slow to adopt the Prussian version and multifarious types appeared in their ranks.[8] In general, the Prussian helmets were light and many had a hollowed spike on top for ventilation, tufts or a curved crest. A sketch of those planned for British infantry usage detailed the diversity of styles on the Prussian theme.[9] Another proposal was the 'Roman Helmet', which was relatively low and circular, with a plume instead of a spike on top. This type of helmet was reported and proposed in the *Naval and Military Gazette*, on 23 March 1850.[10]

Uniform in the Crimea

In 1854, when the British forces landed in the Crimea, the *Dress Regulations* in force were those issued in 1846. They had superseded the 1834 *Regulations*, the main change being the introduction, in most regiments, of the 'Albert' shako, named after Prince Albert, the Prince Consort who is said to have designed the new style headwear. *Dress Regulations* detail officers' dress and accoutrements, where they were responsible for the ordering and buying of them for themselves; to ensure that the *Regulations* were adhered to the various military tailors kept pattern books that showed the relevant details. A set of amendments to the 1846 *Dress Regulations* was issued in June 1848, designed to reduce the expense of the uniforms. However, as Mollo & Mollo point out, *Dress Regulations* 'have their limitations; they refer only to Officers' uniforms and they describe only what was supposed to have been worn, whereas soldiers are notorious for ignoring regulations in matters of dress, particularly when on active service'.[11]

No dress regulations were issued for other ranks; instead, the Consolidated Board of General Officers approved the design, cut, and construction of each article of clothing worn by the men. Once

WHAT THE "BRITISH GRENADIER" IS
INEVITABLY COMING TO.

'What the "British Grenadier" is inevitably coming to': *Punch* magazine's view of the foreign influences on British military fashion. 'Some talk of Alexander, and some of Pericles,/ Of Hector and Lysander, and such old Guys as these;/ But of all the horrid objects, the "wust" I do declare,/ Is the Prusso-Russo-Belgo-Gallo-British Grenadier.'
NAM. Negative 98766

approved, sealed patterns of the items were sent to the Office of Military Boards for the guidance of manufacturers. Each regiment was then sent a memorandum from Horse Guards, informing them of the changes. Some detailing, such as that on cap-plates, buttons, and belt-plates was decided by the regiments themselves; the facing colour of the coatee had, of course, been established for many years. Another change, introduced as a cost-cutting exercise, was the decision made in 1852 to stop the one shilling per man allowance for the alteration and fitting of uniforms. Instead it was decided to issue a greater range of set, standard sizes, that could be altered, if required, 'locally' at no extra cost to the Army. Commanding officers were each sent a sealed pattern so that they could ensure the items had been made up correctly.

Cavalry

Those regiments of dragoons and dragoon guards present in the Crimea, (except the 2nd Regiment of Dragoons), wore brass helmets of the 'Albert' pattern. The 2nd (Royal North British) Regiment of Dragoons had a bearskin cap with a nine inch white hackle to the left. In undress, officers wore peaked caps with gold lace bands and embroidered peaks; other ranks had blue pillbox caps. All wore single-breasted coatees of red cloth (the 6th wore blue) with facings of their regimental colour and eight regimental buttons for the men and nine for officers. Overalls were blue, with a gold lace stripe for officers (scarlet for the men). All ranks wore scarlet cloaks lined in white (the 6th wore blue lined in white). Stable jackets were scarlet, with the officers' jackets having hook and eye fastenings and the men's having buttons.

All the hussar regiments present during the Crimea Campaign wore a busby (named after W. Busby, a London hatter), or fur cap. Officers normally wore white egret plumes on scarlet bases (the 11th (or Prince Albert's Own) Regiment of Hussars wore crimson at the Prince's behest), the plumes of other ranks being made of horsehair. In undress, officers had a blue (crimson for the 11th) cloth forage cap with a gold lace band and black leather peak; other ranks wore a blue cloth (crimson for the 11th) pillbox with a yellow band. Other ranks wore blue, single breasted cloth jackets extensively laced with yellow cord and braid, with three rows of buttons. Pelisses were in blue cloth, with an imitation lambswool trimmed collar, bottom edge, and cuffs; pelisses were used as substitute great coats but were not as effective. Officers had more luxuriant jackets and pelisses, both in blue. Jackets were five

The cookhouse of the 8th Hussars, photographed by Roger Fenton in the Crimea. Two hussars, wearing busbies, are in full dress; the remainder wear undress stable jackets and pill box forage caps.
NAM. 1964-12-151-6-36

rowed buttoned, with dead gold gimp chain loops, gold pattern lace (regimental) for collars and skirt and 'racking braid'. Pelisses were fur trimmed at skirt and cuffs, with complete fur collars. Overalls were of dark blue cloth (crimson for the 11th – hence their nickname 'The Cherry Pickers') with single gold stripes (8th) and double lace stripes (10th and 11th).

Both regiments of light dragoons which served in the Crimea wore the 'Albert' Shako of black beaver, with a yellow band for officers. Attire for

other ranks consisted of a black felt version with a leather sunken top and peak. In undress, officers wore a blue cloth cap, with lace band and embroidered peak; other ranks wore a pillbox cap. Men of the light dragoons wore blue double-breasted coatees with regimental facings, the front decorated with two rows of brass regimental buttons. Officers' coatees were similar, but with eight buttons in each row. Ornamental features were of gold basket braid and Russia braid, plus cloth welting and gold bullion crescents, fringes and back-pieces. Overalls were blue cloth with a double yellow stripe for the 4th (The Queen's Own)

Regiment of (Light) Dragoons and double white for the 13th Regiment of (Light) Dragoons (from March 1854 the 13th's overalls were issued in grey with the same marking). Officers had blue cloth overalls with two gold stripes in full dress, but in undress theirs was similar to the men's, the 13th adopting grey.

In the Crimea both the 12th (The Prince of Wales's) Royal Regiment of Lancers and the 17th Regiment of Light Dragoons (Lancers) wore chapkas (lancer caps) that measured eight inches deep at the front and nine inches at the back. The lower body and peak were black leather, with the square upper body covered in white (17th) or red cloth (12th). The top was in black leather and reinforced with brass and a yellow lace band. Officers had theirs made in a finer cloth, with round gold braid at the seams. Officers and men wore similar double-breasted jackets with regimental facing colours. Regimental buttons were in two rows (front) and three on each skirt, with two at the back waist. The 12th wore blue overalls with double yellow stripes and the 17th grey with a double white stripe. Officers wore overalls of the same colour as

the men and had similar blue stable jackets (single-breasted) but with greater ornamentation.

Artillery

The Royal Horse Artillery wore a bearskin busby, with a white plume and scarlet bag. In 1855 the officers' busby was reduced in height and made of sable fur instead of black beaver. Other ranks wore a smaller sealskin version. A peaked forage cap and pillbox cap, both in blue, were worn in undress by officers and men respectively. Small white chevrons, to the front of the pillbox, denoted ranks below sergeant. All wore single-breasted shell jackets in blue cloth, but while officers had hook and eye fastenings with scarlet collar and cuffs, the men's shell jackets were fastened with regimental buttons. A full dress jacket of blue cloth was worn, richly decorated with gold cord frogging, five rows of ball and half ball buttons and Russia braid. Overalls were blue, with scarlet stripes on the outside seam.

The officers and men of the Royal Artillery wore the 'Albert' shako with a plate unique to the regiment. Unusually, oilskin covers were issued in the Crimea, along with a calico cover and quilted neck-flap. Officers wore blue double-breasted coatees with scarlet collar and cuffs; the single breasted coatees of the men had edged yellow collars and blue cuffs. Officers' collars and cuffs were heavily embroidered with strap epaulettes comprising bullion crescents and fringes.

Lieutenant Shadwell Grylls, Royal Horse Artillery, resplendent in his busby and full dress jacket. Photograph by Roger Fenton. NAM. Negative 19094

Infantry

Standard headwear for the infantry of the line was the 'Albert' shako of black felt for the men and black beaver/patent leather for officers; undress was a blue Kilmarnock bonnet, or forage cap. All other ranks wore a single-breasted, red coatee with different button configurations for officers (who wore a double-breasted coatee) and the men. All facings were of the regimental colour. Rank was displayed on epaulettes for battalion companies and on wings for flank companies, fusiliers, and light infantry. Undress wear consisted of a shell jacket with collars and cuffs in regimental facing colours.

Five Highland regiments served in the Crimea, all of which wore the feather bonnet, except for the 71st (Highland) Regiment, which wore shakos. Officers' bonnets were cocked and feathered, but two inches deeper than the men's. Undress wear was a blue cloth, peaked, forage cap (green for the 71st) for officers, whilst the 42nd (The Royal Highland) Regiment's rank and file wore a blue Kilmarnock (green with diced band for the 71st). The other three regiments, the 72nd (The Duke of Albany's own Highlanders), 79th Regiment of Foot (Cameron Highlanders) and the 93rd (Highland) Regiment of Foot, wore the Glengarry. The coatee differed from other line infantry in that the tails were shorter and without ornaments for the rank and file, except for a triangle of white lace in the centre back at the waist. The cloth of the coatee was red for the rank and file and scarlet for the officers; the latter also had buttons and gold loops, plus skirt ornaments. All the regiments except the 71st and 72nd (which wore trews) wore kilts of regimental pattern tartan and sporrans. In undress, other ranks wore a white shell jacket.

The Rifle Brigade wore the 'Albert' shako, similar to that of the Infantry, but with a 'corded rosette or boss' at the top front and a black ball tuft above. Officers wore a beaver shako with bronze chin chain (black leather chinstrap for the men). The rank and file wore 'rifle' green, double-breasted coatees with a Prussian collar and cuffs, faced in

Coldstream Guardsmen in the trenches before Sevastopol. They have dispensed with their bearskins and wear field service caps. NAM. 1973-09-1-11

Foot Guards

Battalions of all three regiments of Foot Guards - the Grenadier, Coldstream, and Scots Fusilier - served in the Crimea. Initially they wore twelve-inch high bearskin caps, but thereafter the Field Service Cap, introduced in 1854, was more commonly worn; it provided cover for the ears and had front and rear peaks. Officers wore peaked forage caps with black or, in the case of the Scots Fusilier Guards, tartan braid, with a regimental badge to the front. A scarlet cloth, double-breasted coatee was worn by the rank and file, while officers wore a double-breasted coatee, similarly buttoned but with a Prussian collar carrying the Regimental badge to the front. Rank dictated the size and shape of epaulettes, as it did the badges on the strap. 'Oxford' mixture trousers, with a scarlet welt down the seam for the men and a scarlet stripe for officers, completed the ensemble. Undress wear was a waist-length jacket in white cloth for the men and a blue frock coat (braided at the front) for officers.

black. Officers had single-breasted, short jackets, with three rows of buttons, black Russia braid loops, and trimmings. The officers also wore a single-breasted, 'rifle' green pelisse, which was ornamented with olivettes, cord loops, and trimmed in black fur. A stable jacket with cording was worn in undress and trousers of 'rifle' green (as for full dress) were worn.

A soldier's kit was divided into Clothing, Necessaries, and Accoutrements; the provision of this kit, who should pay for it and how often, was governed by the Royal Warrant and Regulations regarding Army Service issued by the War Office on 1 July 1848. Colonels of regiments were allowed sums of money, known as 'off-reckonings' to equip their men, these sums varied according to where a regiment was stationed. Clothing was supplied at the expense of the respective colonel from the off-reckoning. If for any reason the colonel was not entitled to these sums, the public met the cost of the clothing. Greatcoats were listed separately on the Warrant; they were to be supplied at public expense to all non-commissioned men.

Notes

1   *The Naval and Military Magazine* vol. III xxii, quoted in H F A Strachan, 'The Origins of the 1855 Uniform Changes', *Journal of the Society for Army Historical Research* vol 55, 1977, p85.

2   J. Mitchell, *Thoughts on Tactics and Military Organization,* London (1888) pp230-232, quoted *ibid.*

3   The National Archives: Public Record Office WO 7/58 pp17-26.

4   *United Service Magazine* 1846 part 3 p119, quoted Stachan *op. cit.* p87.

5   *Naval and Military Gazette*, 2nd August 1845 p491, quoted *ibid.*

6   *Ibid.* p89

7   *Ibid.* p108

8   *Ibid.* p109-110

9   *Ibid.* p109

10   *Ibid.* p111

11   J. Mollo & B. Mollo, *Uniforms and Equipment of the Light Brigade,* London (1968), p4.

Weapons and Equipment of the British Army in the Crimea, 1854

Sara Jones

When the British Army entered the Crimean War in 1854, it had not faced a major European opponent since the Battle of Waterloo in 1815. Nevertheless, time had not completely stood still for the British Army during these years. Colonial campaigning had taken place and new weapons were gradually being introduced in Europe. It was a time of innovation, which triggered a leap in the development of firearms and new possibilities for artillery. Yet despite progress in Europe, the British Army under the Duke of Wellington was slow to embrace advances in technology. Only after his death in 1852 was change in the British Army's weaponry able to accelerate. By the outbreak of the Crimean War the Army was in the midst of modernisation.

Small Arms

At the end of the Napoleonic Wars the British infantry was armed with the India Pattern and New Land Pattern flintlock muskets; the cavalry had the flintlock Paget carbine and Rifle Regiments were issued with Baker Rifles.[1] With the advent of the percussion system, the Board of Ordnance began questioning the reliability of existing arms and by the mid-1830s, the transition from flintlock to percussion ignition was in progress. George Lovell, Inspector of Small Arms at the Royal Small Arms Factory, Enfield, oversaw the development of the percussion lock for military use. This advanced system was superior to the flintlock and far more reliable, particularly in wet conditions.

The old British Army flintlock muskets could also be converted to the percussion system. The Pattern 1839 Musket, manufactured from New Land Pattern flintlock musket barrels, was the first percussion arm produced for the British infantry. It was followed soon after by the Pattern 1842 Musket, which was to see service in the Crimea. Although there is currently no evidence that any Pattern 1839 Muskets were carried in the Crimea, it is feasible that British infantry regiments serving abroad may still have had them when they were sent to the Crimea. The .753in. calibre Pattern 1842 Smoothbore Percussion Musket, which fired a spherical musket ball with a charge contained within a paper cartridge, remained the weapon of several infantry regiments of the 4th Division throughout much of the Crimean War. They were replaced with new Pattern 1853 Enfield Rifle Muskets during 1855.

The percussion system involved a copper percussion cap (1) containing an explosive substance, which was placed over the nipple (2), integral in the weapon's lock. When the percussion cap is struck, a flame from the exploding charge travels through a hole in the nipple and enters the firing chamber (3), igniting a charge of powder and propelling the Minié bullet (4) down the barrel.

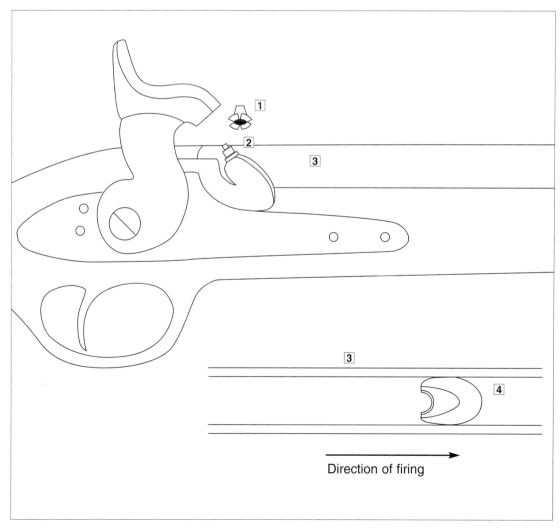

Direction of firing

Although it was only effective to about 200 yards (182m.),[2] it was reported that at the Battle of Inkerman, soldiers of the 20th (The East Devonshire) Regiment of Foot armed with Pattern 1842 Muskets were able to give more rapid fire than those with Miniés, which on this occasion proved more difficult to load quickly.[3]

In France in the 1820s a new rifle musket was under development and in 1849 the 'Minié' was created. Named after its designer, Captain Claude Etienne Minié (1814-79), it used an expanding bullet patented by Henri-Gustave Delvigne.[4]

The Delvigne-Minié system was a major advance in the development of small arms. It incorporated an elongated conical-shaped bullet with a hollow base, fitted with an iron cup. It expanded on firing to grip the rifling in the barrel. The design allowed easy loading and greater range and accuracy. In the spring of 1851 a series of trials set up by the Committee on Small Arms tested the Delvigne-Minié system for the first time in Britain.

Before all the results of the trials were known, in 1852 Field Marshal Henry William Paget, Marquess of Anglesey (1768-1854), Master-General of the Ordnance, and the Board of Ordnance, arranged contracts for 28,000 Miniés to be manufactured.[5] The haste in adopting the Minié was influenced by the shortage of arms in store at the time. It did, however, ensure that many infantry regiments were issued with Miniés at the beginning of the Crimean War.

The results of the Minié trials found the new rifle musket to be as durable as its smoothbore predecessor. The Minié proved in the trials to be easy to load due to the revolutionary expanding bullet, which distinguished it from all its official predecessors. But in spite of the positive feedback, problems were identified which led to further experimentation. The graduation on the back sight was found to be inaccurate and the slider would not stay at the desired elevation. Complaints concerning the poorly adjusted sights grew as the Minié became more widely used. There was also a problem with the ball drawer, which was screwed onto the ramrod and used to clear bullets from the barrel after misfires. It was found to be unsatisfactory and in February 1854 the Board of Ordnance, under pressure from the Commander-in-Chief, Lieutenant-General

Captain Claude Etienne Minié (1814-79), inventor of the Minié rifling system. NAM. Negative 98124

Lord Hardinge (1785-1856), replaced the Minié ball drawer with one taken from the obsolete Brunswick Rifle.[6]

Although Wellington ordered 500 of the new Minié rifle muskets to be sent to South Africa,[7] no further muskets were sent abroad until the Crimean War, when the Minié was really put to the test. Many infantry regiments had been issued with Miniés in exchange for their smoothbore muskets when they arrived in Turkey and Bulgaria. The 60th (The Kings Royal Rifle Corps) were the first to be completely re-issued with the Minié as a replacement for their old Brunswick Rifles.[8] General James B Bucknall Estcourt (1802-55), who was Adjutant General of the Army of the East, stated in June 1854 that the regiments already in Bulgaria were deficient about 600 Miniés.[9] A month later, although he does not state that they had been issued, Estcourt reported that they were 'fully complete with Miniés and some over.'[10] The 4th Division arrived subsequently, and even by the Battle of Inkerman in November 1854 all but one of its regiments still had the Pattern 1842 Musket.

The Minié, although short-lived, played a decisive role in the early battles of the war. *The Times* newspaper reported, 'The Minié is the king of weapons – Inkerman proved it'.[11] The Russians soon realised whether they were facing Minié or smoothbore fire as the Minié's range and penetration was far superior.[12] The Minié was effective to about 800 yards (731m.). Its inventor, Captain Minié, claimed from personal experience that it was still reasonably effective at about 1,800 yards (1,645m.).[13] It was popular with the British infantry and Estcourt expressed in a letter of December 1854 how it raised the men's spirits, 'The fact is these Miniés fire so well that men get great confidence. It improves the "morale".'[14]

Even before the Minié was adopted in 1851 it was appreciated that an 'improved' Minié of smaller calibre would better suit the British infantry. Lord Anglesey was aware that the Commander-in-Chief, the Duke of Wellington, would not agree to this and experiments to explore the concept of a smaller calibre weapon were only able to progress after Wellington's death in September 1852. Lord Hardinge, who succeeded Wellington as Commander-in-Chief two months later, was also in favour of a lighter, smaller calibre arm to replace the .702in. calibre Pattern 1851 Minié. Hardinge was a 'reformer', who set up the School of Musketry at Hythe in 1853 to train infantry in the effective use of the Minié and Enfield Rifle Muskets.[15]

The Minié provided a stop-gap for the British infantry while trials were being carried out to develop a reduced bore, lighter service arm, which would also address the Minié's problems. By the time of the Crimean War, the Minié was in fact officially obsolete. Its successor, the Pattern 1853 Enfield Rifle Musket had already been introduced.

Infantry sergeants carried the Pattern 1842 Short Musket throughout the Crimean War. It was identical in many aspects to the Pattern 1842 Musket, but with a shorter barrel and smaller .733in. bore. It took the same ammunition, and had the same bayonet and Lovell bayonet catch as the Pattern 1842 Musket. The Pattern 1856 Short Musket, a shorter-barrelled version of the Pattern 1853 Enfield, was later manufactured for sergeants and rifle regiments. It replaced the Pattern 1842 Short Musket, but was not produced in time for use in the Crimea.[16]

Although firearms were not the principal weapon of the cavalry, the Victoria Percussion Carbine, introduced in 1837, was issued to dragoon and hussar regiments in the Crimea. The .733in. calibre Victoria Carbine fired the standard smoothbore infantry musket ball. It was replaced in 1856 by a .577in. rifled carbine, a shorter-barrelled version of the Enfield Rifle Musket.[17]

Apart from the Royal Horse Artillery, which may have still had the Victoria Carbine in the Crimea, the remainder of the artillery carried the Pattern 1842 Smoothbore Musket or its later replacement, the new Pattern 1853 Rifled Artillery Carbine.[18]

It was not considered a priority for the Royal Engineers to carry arms; indeed it was often discouraged. They did not receive rifled firearms until after the Crimean War. During the campaign they were issued with the smoothbore Royal Sappers and Miners Carbine of 1842, which had a long socket bayonet. Like the Victoria Carbine, it also had a reduced bore of .733in. calibre and fired the infantry musket ball. After 1856 it was replaced with the Lancaster Oval Bore Carbine.[19]

Pistols and Revolvers
At the Great Exhibition of 1851 new types of revolver were exhibited for the first time. Prior to this, revolvers were unreliable, frequently misfired and the British Army did not regard them as an essential weapon. Although the Army remained unconvinced about the revolver, 5,000 Colts were purchased for use in the Crimea and distributed to officers and infantry sergeant majors.[20] A larger number was purchased for issue to the Royal Navy, which had more advanced ideas on revolvers. During the Crimean War Field Marshal Fitzroy James Henry Somerset, Lord Raglan (1788-1855) stated that he felt revolvers were of little use and was against having them as a standard arm for officers.[21]

With the wider selection of revolvers available in the early 1850s, many officers privately purchased their own. Their choice depended on personal taste, with the most popular being the five chamber British Adams or the six chamber American Colt muzzle-loading revolvers. Unlike the Colt, which had to be manually cocked, the Adams could fire five shots rapidly which made it more popular among officers in the Crimean War.

In 1838, except for lancers, trumpeters and sergeant majors, pistols had been largely withdrawn from cavalry service. A new design of percussion, single shot pistol was introduced for lancers in 1842, which was used during the Crimean War, whilst dragoons and hussars had carbines.

The Sword and Lance

The primary weapon of the British cavalry in the Crimea remained the sword. The Crimean War took place in the midst of a long-running debate about the function of the sword blade; whether it should be designed to cut, thrust, or do both, which would inevitably prove a compromise.

Light cavalry carried the Pattern 1821 Sword, which was intended to both cut and thrust. Heavy cavalry also had a Pattern 1821 Sword, which had a similar blade to the light cavalry sword but with a bowl hilt, which gave better protection to the hand. In 1853 the first universal pattern sword for all cavalry was introduced. It had a cut and thrust blade and a new grip, which unfortunately tended to twist in the hand. The 11th (or Prince Albert's Own) Regiment of Hussars received the Pattern 1853 in March 1854 before they sailed to the Crimea and complained about the blade bending too easily.[22] The 11th Hussars and the 2nd (Royal North British) Regiment of Dragoons were at least partially issued with Pattern 1853 Swords at the Battle of Balaklava and it may be that as many as half of all British cavalry involved in the battle were armed with this new sword.[23] After Balaklava, Lieutenant-Colonel Henry Darby Griffith, who commanded the 2nd Dragoons, wrote to the War Office about the problems he had encountered with the swords; 'Our swords are very defective – when our men made a thrust with the sword they all bent and would not go into a man's body.' He described the swords as 'quite unfit for active service.'[24]

The cavalry lance was introduced into the British Army in 1816. Its effectiveness relied on the momentum of the horse. Before the Crimean War three new patterns of lance were introduced, in 1820, 1840 and 1846; the Pattern 1846 Lance was the type in use at the time of the Crimean War. The lance was 9ft long (2.74m.), with an ash staff and a spear-shaped pointed steel lance head, which was attached to the staff by rivets. A red and white pennant was attached to the lance and the base of the staff was fitted with a steel shoe.[25] The 17th Regiment of

Light Dragoons (Lancers) were the only lancer regiment involved in the Charge of the Light Brigade at the Battle of Balaklava. The 12th (Prince of Wales's) Royal Regiment of Lancers came from India to join them in the Crimea in the spring of 1855.

The only weapon that cavalry officers were required to carry was the sword. The *Dress Regulations* of 1822 described the new Pattern 1821 Swords for both heavy and light cavalry officers. The Light Cavalry Officers' Pattern 1821 Sword had a three-bar hilt, and a pipe-backed blade, designed for cutting and thrusting, although it was ineffective at both. The Heavy Cavalry Officer's Pattern 1821 Sword was similar to the light cavalry sword with a steel basket hilt.[26]

Infantry officers in the Crimean War carried the Pattern 1822 Sword. This was altered in 1845 to take an improved blade, although officers were expected to keep using the earlier pattern until the swords wore out.[27] Officers of the Royal Engineers and the Royal Artillery, other than the Royal Horse Artillery, who had the Pattern 1821 Light Cavalry Officer's Sword, also carried this weapon. It had a 'Gothic' style hilt and although it remained in service until the 1890s, it was more ornate than functional.

Rifle regiment officers carried the steel-hilted Pattern 1827 Sword and staff sergeants and sergeants were issued with a plainer version of the same weapon. Officers of Highland regiments carried the broadsword and dirk. Infantry sergeant-majors, staff sergeants, sergeants of the Foot Guards, drummers, buglers and bandsmen all either carried swords similar to officers, or a specific regimental pattern. Royal Sappers and Miners' staff sergeants carried an infantry sword and the equivalent rank in Highland regiments had the broadsword, whilst Pipers carried a broadsword and dirk.

Artillery

Before the Minié Rifle Musket was introduced in 1851, artillery easily outranged small arms and there had been no incentive to improve the capability of artillery pieces. Technically, cannons had changed little in over 200 years.

In the years between Waterloo and the Crimean War artillery was in decline and in desperate need of modernisation. It was viewed as having a support role rather than as a powerful weapon in its own right. After Waterloo, the Royal Artillery was reduced from 25,000 to 6,000 men.[28] Artillery detachments to colonial garrisons and the reserve at home in Woolwich became insufficient. During the 1840s, Wellington's concerns centred on the potential threat of French invasion against Britain and he was compelled to raise the total strength of the artillery.

began to be employed in an attacking role, not solely in defensive positions.[29]

At the beginning of the war the British artillery in the Crimea comprised two troops of horse artillery, eight field batteries and a siege train. Various field, position and siege guns, howitzers and mortars were employed in the Crimea, each designed to complement one another. The 32-pounder (pdr.) gun and 8 inch howitzer were the most utilised during the campaign.

British artillery pieces fired a variety of projectiles. Round shot, in the form of a solid ball, had the density to achieve maximum range. Canister or case had a short range and low velocity and comprised a cylinder filled with small iron balls, which sprayed out when fired. Common shell consisted of a hollow spherical case with a time fuse; the case exploded into shell fragments. Shrapnel or spherical case held small solid balls in a spherical hollow case and had greater range than canister or case. In 1854, and in time for the Crimean War, the Boxer time fuse, invented by

Major Adolphus William Desart Burton, 5th (The Princess Charlotte of Wales's) Regiment of Dragoon Guards, photographed by Fenton in the Crimea carrying the Heavy Cavalry Officer's Pattern 1821 Sword. NAM. 1968-10-73-15

Lord Hardinge, when Master-General of the Ordnance in 1852, saw the potential for developing the artillery. He was involved in its modernisation before the Crimean War, but was unable to complete his reforms before the campaign commenced. Under Hardinge the numbers of men, guns and horses increased significantly and it is largely due to his attempt to transform the peacetime artillery that enabled the Royal Artillery to field a respectable force in the Crimea.

After the success at Gujerat in the final battle of the Second Sikh War (1849), it was realised that artillery could help prevent British casualties and reduce the length of a battle. This influenced tactics and artillery

Colonel Edward Mounier Boxer (1823-98), Superintendent of the Royal Laboratory, was adopted for the shrapnel shell.[30] It helped prevent the premature explosion of the shell in the barrel. Grape shot, made from a cluster of iron balls attached to a central rod inside a case, could only be used in heavy iron barrelled artillery – 18-pdr. guns or larger - to prevent it from damaging the brass barrels of the field guns.

Field guns used in the Crimea included the 6-pdr. and the 9-pdr; the 12-pdr. and 24-pdr. howitzer were also employed and the latter reportedly achieved good results at the Battle of Balaklava at ranges of about 700 to 800yards (640 to 730 metres).[31] During the campaign the 18-pdr. and 32-pdr. guns, equivalent calibre howitzers and the 8 inch howitzer were used as position guns. At Inkerman two 18-pdr. guns helped the British force the Russian retreat.[32] Under siege conditions, the 8 inch and 10 inch guns and the heavy 32-pdr. gun, 68-pdr. gun and Lancaster rifled oval bore gun, which had a tendency to jam, were used.

The British siege train in the Crimea was strong in mortars of all kinds, including 5.5 inch, 8 inch, 10 inch and 13 inch mortars. With a high trajectory, a small charge and exploding shells, they were used for clearing walls rather than penetrating them.

6-pdr. and 12-pdr. rockets were also used in the Crimea. Fired from a tube, they were intended to be useful as a light, portable weapon to support the infantry and cavalry. At a time when artillery was becoming heavier, however, rockets tended to be unstable and inaccurate.

Equipment

The early years of the nineteenth century marked a move towards standardisation of equipment in the British Army and the first universal patterns were authorised by Horse Guards. Otherwise, with peace in Europe for almost four decades, there had been little development in accoutrements and British troops arrived in the Crimea in attire similar to that worn at Waterloo. The reality of active service meant that much variation and alteration of equipment would occur.

It has always been a struggle to achieve a balance between what the British soldier needs to carry on his person and the load that he can physically bear. The knapsack, worn by infantry, was intended for carrying personal items, spare clothing and boots and cleaning equipment, and was worn on the back. The 'box' type knapsack, which was worn in the Crimea, originated in the early nineteenth century and has often been referred to as the 'Trotter' type. The Trotter family were

Nine pounder guns of the Royal Artillery attached to the 3rd Division (photograph: James Robertson).
NAM. 1978-06-26-2

less than scrupulous suppliers of knapsacks, tents and associated equipment to the Army from c1780 to 1807. There is no evidence that the Trotters invented the box knapsack, but their name somehow became associated with it. The first framed or box style knapsacks had wooden panels in the sides but not along the top or base. Later the knapsack was modified to have a four-sided frame. Regulation knapsacks of Crimean vintage are box-shaped, with a four-sided frame and buff leather straps.

On first landing in the Crimea, soldiers' knapsacks were ordered to be left aboard ship and, until they were brought ashore six weeks later, blankets were used instead by soldiers to carry their kit. However, the blankets tended not to stay in position and often came apart, which resulted in the loss of equipment.[33]

A greatcoat or blanket was usually carried on top of the knapsack with the mess tin strapped to either its top or back. The 'D'-shaped mess tin, carried in a black canvas or oilskin case, was introduced in 1814. It came in three parts, with a section for drinking, a plate, and a section to be used as a container or cooking pot. A light-coloured linen haversack for carrying rations and a blue painted, round, wooden water bottle with a brown leather strap were also worn.

Some of the infantry soldiers wore two buff leather cross belts: one ran over the left shoulder and held the cartridge pouch; the other, which held the triangular socket bayonet in a buff leather frog, ran over the right shoulder. They crossed over the chest and were held in place with a regimental belt plate. The two cross belts were superseded by the introduction of a waist belt in about 1850, which took away the discomfort caused by the underarm straps of the cross belts. As many as two-thirds of the infantry regiments may have been issued with the new waist belts before the Crimean War began.[34]

In 1854 the soldier carried his ammunition in a black leather cartridge pouch. The pouch was either attached to one of the buff leather cross belts (as previously described) with the pouch resting behind the right hip, or, if worn with the new waist belt, the ammunition pouch was attached to a separate buff leather pouch belt. The design of the ammunition pouch was subject to change at this time and there were variations for the Foot Guards and infantry, for sergeants and other ranks. The pouches may also have been modified to accommodate the ammunition for different types of firearms.

Externally the infantry pouches for the Pattern 1842 Smoothbore Musket, and the Pattern 1851 Minié and Pattern 1853 Enfield Rifle Muskets are likely to have been similar. For the Pattern 1842 Musket 60

Private of the 28th (The North Gloucestershire) Regiment of Foot in full marching order. He carries his waterbottle, ammunition pouch, knapsack, rolled blanket, haversack and Minié Rifle Musket. Note that he is wearing the waistbelt and separate ammunition pouch belt, not cross belts.
NAM. 1964-12-151-6-15

rounds were carried, and for the Minié 50 rounds, wrapped in paper packets of ten.[35]

Before the Crimean War different ways of carrying percussion caps for sporting rifles had been tried, including a magazine for caps that hung around the neck.[36] Various methods for carrying caps were employed throughout the Crimean War. Caps could be kept in a compartment, either open or with a hinged lid, which formed part of the tin tray lining the inside of the ammunition pouch. A buff leather percussion cap pouch, which was attached to the belt on which the main ammunition pouch was held, was also introduced.[37] The ammunition pouch belt passed through a loop in the back of the percussion cap pouch, holding it in place on the chest. A small supply of caps for immediate use was carried in a small leather pouch, which fitted into a pocket cut into the coatee at waist level. It was also known to have been attached to the front of the waist belt on the right hand side. In the Crimea Major-General (later General Sir) William Codrington (1804-84) gave an order to his troops to 'put the small leather pockets for the copper caps on the waist belts … in order to make sure that men in hurry of falling in at night, should never be without them.'[38] Codrington considered this a practical measure, and one that would cause only a slight change in the soldiers' appearance. However, on an inspection in April 1855, Lieutenant-General Sir George Brown (1790-1865) found fault with it, or rather with Codrington taking matters into his own hands and altering the way in which the equipment was worn.[39]

Rifle regiments were equipped similarly to the infantry. All of the belts they wore were of black leather, rather than buff, including a waist belt, which fastened at the front with a brass 'snake' buckle. The belt held a sword bayonet attached by a frog and a small black leather pouch or ball bag, which carried a percussion cap pouch and some ammunition for immediate use.

The cavalry's equipment changed very little between 1815 and the Crimean War. The haversack, waterbottle and mess tin carried was akin to that of the infantry, but the cavalry wore a valise instead of a knapsack. Sabretaches were worn only by hussars. A buff leather sword belt went around the waist and had a set of slings attached for the sword; the hussars had a further set for the sabretache. The cavalry also wore a separate pouch belt of buff leather, to which an ammunition pouch containing 20 rounds for the pistol or carbine was attached. Saddlery was a significant part of the equipment used by the cavalry. From 1805 onwards a saddle known as the 'Hussar' or 'Hungarian' saddle was issued to light dragoon regiments converted to hussars and to all the light cavalry from 1812.[40] The heavy cavalry in the Crimea had a saddle similar to the type introduced for all heavy cavalry in 1796.[41]

Soldiers of the 68th (The Durham) Regiment of Foot (Light Infantry) were still wearing the uncomfortable cross belts when photographed by Fenton in 1855. NAM. 1964-12-151-6-25

There were different patterns of bridle for the light and heavy cavalry, which were modified versions of those worn at Waterloo.

Officers' equipment was similar to that of other ranks, but as they purchased their own, it was generally of higher quality. The Royal Horse Artillery generally had the same equipment as the cavalry; field batteries conformed to their infantry counterparts.

Notes

1   D W Bailey, *British Military Longarms 1815-1865*, London (1972) p8.

2   C Robins 'Muskets and Rifles' *The War Correspondent* Vol 12, No 1, Apr 1994 p19.

3   NAM. 1968-07-264 Account of Battle of Inkerman by Capt George Carmichael, 95th Regiment.

4   C H Roads, *The British Soldier's Firearm, 1850-1864*, London (1964) p24.

5   Parliamentary Papers 1854-5, IX, part III, 4th report, p322.

6   For details of problems found with the Minié rifle musket after trials, see Roads, *op. cit.* pp38-9.

7   Roads, *op. cit.* p37.

8   *Ibid.* p39.

9   NAM. 1962-10-97 Letters of Gen Estcourt, Adjutant General of the Army of the East, to Gen Wetherall, from camp Varna, 29 June 1854.

10   *Ibid.* letter of 18 July 1854.

11   Quoted in Roads, *op. cit.* p40.

12   NAM. 1962-10-97 Estcourt to Wetherall, camp before Sevastopol, 8 Jan 1855.

13   H Strachan, *From Waterloo to Balaclava, Tactics, Technology, and the British Army, 1815-1854*, Cambridge (1985), p41.

14   NAM. 1962-10-97 Estcourt to Wetherall, camp before Sevastopol, 3 Dec 1854.

15   Strachan, *op. cit.* p50.

16   W S Curtis 'Shoulder Arms of the Crimean War, Part Twenty – Great Britain, Sergeants of Line Infantry Short Musket of 1842' *The War Correspondent* Vol 18, No 3, Oct 2000 p17.

17   W S Curtis 'Shoulder Arms of the Crimean War, Part Nineteen – Great Britain, Victoria Carbine (Pattern 1843), for   the Cavalry and the Royal Horse Artillery' *The War Correspondent* Vol 18, No 2, July 2000 p5.

18   W S Curtis 'British Crimean Rifle Notes' *The War Correspondent* Vol 15, No 4, Jan 1998 p31.

19   W S Curtis "Shoulder Arms of the Crimean War, Part Eighteen – Great Britain, Carbine of the Sappers and Miners' *The War Correspondent* Vol 18, No 1, Apr 2000 p13.

20   W H J Chamberlain & A W F Taylerson, *Revolvers of the British Services, 1854-1954,* Ontario & New York (1989) p2.

21   NAM. 1962-10-97 Estcourt to Wetherall, camp before Sevastopol, 18 Dec 1854 & 15 Jan 1855.

22   The National Archives: Public Record Office WO 44/701, cited in B Robson, *Swords of the British Army,* London (1996) p30.

23   Robson, *op. cit.* p31.

24   PRO WO 44/701; in Robson, *op. cit.* p30.

25   C Ffoulkes & E C Hopkinson, *Sword, Lance & Bayonet*, London (1938) pp102-5l, and information supplied by Capt J M Holtby, The Queen's Royal Lancers Regimental Museum.

26   Robson, *op. cit.* p87.

27   *Ibid.* p161.

28   Strachan, *op. cit.* p100.

29   *Ibid.* p125-6.

30   *Ibid.* p116.

31   F A Whinyates, *From Coruña to Sevastopol*, London (1884) p137.

32   B P Hughes, *British Smoothbore Artillery,* London (1969) p93.

33   J L Summers, Tangled Web, *Canadian Infantry Accoutrements 1855-1985*, Ontario & New York (1992) p17.

34   *Ibid.* pp3-4.

35   N Bentley (Ed.) *Russell's Despatches from the Crimea 1854-56*, London (1966) p65.

36   H L Blackmore, *British Military Firearms 1650-1850*, London (1969) p210.

37   Summers, *op. cit.* p12, and information supplied by Mr D F Harding.

38   NAM. 1978-08-90-1, Letter from Codrington to his wife, 3 April 1855.

39   *Ibid.*

40   G Tylden, *Horses and Saddlery*, London (1965) p132.

41   *Ibid.* p128.

The Army of the East

The Crimean War had its origins in the celebrated Eastern Question: what was to be done about the Ottoman Empire, 'the sick man of Europe'? Its territorial integrity had been under threat ever since the Greek War of Liberation (1821–30) when a Russian army advanced nearly as far as Constantinople. In 1840 Britain took action to prevent an insurgent Mehemet Ali, Pasha of Egypt, destabilising the Empire further. Thereafter, Russia and France jockeyed for predominance at Constantinople. In 1852 the new French dictator, Louis Napoleon, championed the rights of Roman Catholic monks as guardians of the Holy Places in Ottoman-occupied Palestine. The Tsar, Nicholas I, asserted the primacy of the monks of the Orthodox Church. A mission was sent to Constantinople under Prince A S Menshikov to enforce his claim. This was followed in July 1853 by a Russian invasion of the Ottoman Empire's Danubian principalities. On 4 October the Ottoman Empire declared war. The subsequent destruction by the Russians of a Turkish fleet at Sinope in the Black Sea ended Anglo-French efforts to restore peace. Britain and France declared war on Russia on 28 March 1854. A fleet sailed for the Baltic. Both sent an 'Army of the East' to confront the Russians on the Danube. But the Turks had already driven the Russians back. It was decided instead to send the British and French armies to the Crimea to capture the naval base of Sevastopol and neutralise the Russian Black Sea fleet. The Crimean War had begun.

'View from my tent, Aledyn, looking down the river joining the two lakes of Devina – 11th June 1854'

Watercolour, signed lower left 'G. H. W.' by Major (later Colonel) George Harry Smith Willis, 77th (The East Middlesex) Regiment of Foot, from an album of watercolour and pen and ink drawings mostly by the same hand, c1854-56, 18.3cm. h x 26.6cm. w

Presented by the Trustees of the Middlesex Regimental Museum

NAM. 1994-01-1-417-31

Private Manasseh Dennison of the 7th Regiment of Foot (Royal Fusiliers) considered the encampment a true idyll:

> I never saw such a beautiful place in my life as Alidyu [*sic*]. We were encamped on the top of a hill with a wood on each side of us & the scenery is past description. Talk of the ornamental waters of Chatsworth, & the beautiful parks of London & then they are nothing to be compared to what nature alone has done here. We wanted nothing to render the place a perfect Paradise but good & *proper* food & a little society.

Unfortunately, Paradise was lost almost as soon as it was gained. A month later, cholera broke out in the camp and the death toll mounted rapidly.

'In the Cavalry Camp at Devna (Young Cornet) "I say Charley, do you think now that in the event of our being sent to Sebastopol, the Infantry will be required to accompany us?"', c1854 (right)

Pen and ink and watercolour by Second Lieutenant William Thomas Markham (1830-86), 2nd Battalion, The Rifle Brigade, from an album of paintings and sketches by Colonel William Markham and Second Lieutenant W T Markham, c1854, 13cm. h x 17.4cm. w

Purchased with the generous assistance of the Society of Friends of the National Army Museum

NAM. 1999-02-105-45

A satire on the naive young cavalry officer who imagines that the mounted arm can accomplish everything by itself. By the late summer of 1854, after *The Times* had editorialised on the need to extirpate Russian naval power in the Black Sea by attacking Sevastopol, it was generally understood in the Army that the port would be its objective.

Sinope, 18 October 1853 (left)

Woodcut by Efita Luvleva after artist unknown, publisher unknown, published in Russia, 5 April 1854, 42.7cm. h x 55.3cm. w

NAM. 1969-07-27-23

On 30 November 1853 a Turkish fleet was destroyed by the Russian Navy at the Black Sea port of Sinope. Seven frigates, a sloop and some transports were sunk with about 4,000 men killed, leaving just one steamer and 400 survivors. The destruction of the Turkish fleet, attributed largely to the effect of explosive shells, hastened the introduction of iron-clad men-of-war to replace the vulnerable wooden warships.

The Russian Navy's ships can be distinguished by the Imperial eagle on their sterns, whereas the Turkish Navy's ships have two stars. In the background, the town of Sinope is shown under bombardment.

Lord Raglan

Photograph by Roger Fenton (1819-69)

NAM. Negative 46760

General (later Field Marshal) Fitzroy James Henry Somerset, 1st Baron Raglan (1788-1855) served on the Duke of Wellington's staff throughout the Peninsular War (1808-14), and was with him at Waterloo, where he lost an arm. He was Military Secretary at Horse Guards 1827-52, and although he had hopes of succeeding Wellington as commander-in-chief on his longstanding patron's death, the post went to Lord Hardinge instead. As consolation he was raised to the peerage as Baron Raglan and appointed Master-General of the Ordnance. In 1854 he was given command of the Army of the East, led it to victory at the battles of Alma and Inkerman but during the winter of 1854-55 was heavily criticised both by the press and in officers' letters home for the breakdown of supply and the sufferings of the troops. He died on 28 June 1855, shortly after the failure of the first attack on the Redan.

The Duke of Cambridge

Photograph by Roger Fenton

NAM. Negative 46759

Lieutenant-General (later Field Marshal) George William Frederick Charles, 2nd Duke of Cambridge (1819-1904), commanded the 1st Division of the Army of the East at the battles of the Alma and Inkerman, but the experience left him with shattered nerves and he was invalided home in December 1854. In 1856, upon the resignation of Lord Hardinge, he was appointed commander-in-chief of the Army, a post that he held until 1895.

Sir George de Lacy Evans

Photograph by Roger Fenton

NAM. Negative 46930

Promoted lieutenant-general on being given command of the 2nd Division of the Army of the East in 1854, Sir George de Lacy Evans (1787-1870) was a soldier of great experience who had seen service in India, Spain and America during the Napoleonic Wars. A member of parliament well-known for his politically radical views, he commanded the British Auxiliary Legion during the Carlist Wars in Spain 1835-37. He led his division in person during the Battle of the Alma but was absent sick for much of the Battle of Inkerman. He returned home for health reasons shortly afterwards. In 1861 he was promoted general.

Sir Richard England

Photograph by Roger Fenton

NAM. Negative 46928

Major-General (later General) Sir Richard England (1793-1883) was given command of the 3rd Division of the Army of the East. He had previously served in the Walcheren Expedition (1809), the Cape of Good Hope during the 1830s, and the 1st Afghan War in 1842. In the Crimea he was widely regarded as an ineffective commander and criticism in the press of his generalship during the Afghan War resurfaced. In July 1855, after Lord Raglan's death, the Secretary of State for War, Lord Panmure, wrote to General Sir James Simpson how the 'risk of letting the command of the Army fall into Sir R England's hands stares me in the face, and .. I am quite resolved to prevent this as far as I can..' The following month England returned home on health grounds.

'General Georg [*sic*] Cathcart'

Chromolithograph, artist unknown, probably published in Germany, *c*1855, 24.2cm. h x 16.5cm. w

NAM. 1991-04-108-1

Major-General The Honourable George Cathcart (1794-1854) had been a surprise choice to succeed Sir Harry Smith as governor and commander-in-chief at the Cape in 1851 as he had previously enjoyed little public profile. He acquitted himself well, however, was knighted and appointed, pending his return home, the Army's adjutant-general. Once back in England, he discovered that he had been given command of the 4th Division of the Army of the East; he received in addition a dormant commission which gave him command of the entire expeditionary force in the event of an accident befalling Lord Raglan. He was killed at the Battle of Inkerman on 5 November 1854.

Sir George Brown

Photograph by Roger Fenton

NAM. Negative 46917

Lieutenant-General (later General) Sir George Brown (1790-1865) had given distinguished service in the Peninsula and North America during the Napoleonic Wars, and in the post-war years he held a number of staff posts, culminating in his appointment as the Army's adjutant-general in 1850. His reactionary outlook was typified by his resignation of office in December 1853: he believed that the new commander-in-chief, Lord Hardinge, had betrayed the Army's Wellingtonian legacy. Unsurprisingly, Hardinge applied a veto to Brown serving with the Army of the East as Raglan's second in command and he was confined to command of the Light Division. Wounded at Inkerman, Brown was tough enough to recover. In May 1855 he led the expedition to Kerch and the following month was given tactical control of the assault on the Redan. The attack failed and at the end of June 1855 he was invalided home. His men breathed a sigh of relief: Brown's harsh discipline and strict adherence to dress regulations had made him deeply unpopular.

Lord Lucan

Mezzotint after Sir Francis Grant (1803-78), publisher unknown, *c*1855, 75.1cm. h x 48.2cm. w

NAM. 1972-01-7

Lieutenant-General (later Field Marshal) George Charles Bingham, 3rd Earl of Lucan (1800-88) first joined the Army in 1816 and rose rapidly through the purchase of his commissions to command the 17th Regiment of (Light) Dragoons (Lancers) within ten years. He remained in post until 1837 when he went onto half pay; the only active service he had seen was in the Balkans in 1828 as an observer on the Russian staff. Upon the outbreak of the Crimean War he nevertheless applied for a command and was given the Cavalry Division. His unfamiliarity with new tactics and general rustiness soon became manifest, a situation made worse by his bad relations with his brother-in-law Lord Cardigan, who commanded the Light Brigade of cavalry under him. His caution moreover earned him the sobriquet 'Lord Look-On'. At the Battle of Balaklava he was a leading player in the chain of events which sent the Light Brigade to its doom, and his subsequent determination to justify himself at the expense of his working relationship with Lord Raglan led to his recall from the Crimea in January 1855.

'Parade of the Scots Fusilier Guards at Buckingham Palace, (before Her Majesty the Queen, & His Royal Highness the Prince.) on the morning of their departure for the Seat of War, March 2nd 1854.'

Coloured tinted lithograph by E Walker after George Housman Thomas (1824-69), published by Paul and Dominic Colnaghi, 21 June 1854, 41cm. h x 51.8cm. w

NAM. 1952-01-68

Lieutenant The Honourable Hugh Annesley described the scene thus:

When we got in front of Buckingham Palace the Regiment halted in line, the officers came to the front, the colours were lowered, and the whole presented arms. Her Majesty, the Prince, and the Royal children, appeared on the balcony and acknowledged the salute, then the Colonel turned to the men, waved his sword, and a thousand voices gave three hearty hurrahs for their Majesties, waving their bearskin caps in the air and by every gesture manifesting the most intense enthusiasm and loyalty. Her Majesty appeared much affected, and bowed and smiled most graciously on her gallant third Regiment of Guards.

'Embarkation of the 93rd Highlanders at Plymouth, March 1st 1854, in the Great Steam Ship "Himalaya."'

Coloured lithograph, after artist unknown, number four in the series 'Going to the War', published by Read and Co, London, 1854, 24.2cm. h x 31.7cm. w

NAM. 1973-11-21

The 93rd (Highland) Regiment of Foot are shown being rowed out in small boats to the modern steamship *Himalaya*, commandeered from the Orient & India Line by the government. Larger and faster than many of the ships used to transport the expeditionary force, the *Himalaya* conveyed the entire regiment to the Bosphorus in under two weeks.

'Scene in the Café du Commerce Valetta. "Mourir pour la patrie" Malta 1854 Entente Cordiale'

Watercolour and pencil, signed lower right 'H.J.W.', by Lieutenant (later Colonel) Henry John Wilkinson (1829-1911), 1st Battalion, 9th (The East Norfolk) Regiment of Foot, 1854, 25.1cm. h x 35.2cm. w

Generously donated by the Royal United Service Institution

NAM. 1972-07-6-50

French and British officers toasting the prospect of success of their joint expedition to the east. During the nineteenth century, the British possession of Malta was an important staging-point for British forces in the Mediterranean. On this occasion, French troops were allowed to land on the island before trans-shipping to steam vessels for the remainder of their voyage to Turkey.

'Landing of the R. Horse Artillery on the Bosphorus - 3rd May 1854'

Pencil and wash, artist unknown, 1854, 38 cm. h x 52.2 cm. w

NAM. 1990-05-34

The artist, an unnamed artillery officer, shows the disembarkation from transport ship No 2, the *Mercia,* of the left division of 'C' Troop Royal Horse Artillery, commanded by Captain G C R Levinge. At the foot of the hills to the right is Kulali Barracks, vacated by a regiment of Turkish lancers in favour of the Royal Artillery. An engraving after this sketch was published in *The Illustrated London News* on 3 June 1854.

'Main Guard Grenadier Guards, Haider Pasha'

Photograph by James Robertson (1813-88), 20cm. h x 29cm. w

NAM. 1979-10-79

The 3rd Battalion of The Grenadier Guards arrived at its encampment at Scutari (on the eastern or Asiatic side of the Bosphorus, opposite Constantinople) at the end of April 1854. The remainder of the Grenadier Guards' camp is situated behind the photographer; on the slopes in the distance are the tents of the Light Division. Scutari Barracks is silhouetted on the horizon with part of Scutari Hospital just visible to the left of the picture.

Artillery park on the shores of the Bosphorus

Photograph by James Robertson, 26.2cm. h x 26.4cm. w

NAM. 1966-05-55-1

James Robertson (1813-88) was a coin engraver who in 1841 took up the position of chief engraver to the Imperial Mint in Constantinople. In the early 1850s he opened a photographic studio with his brother-in-law Felice Beato and in 1853 an album of his photographic views of Constantinople was published in London. In this photograph c1855 he shows the Turkish capital geared up for war, with a row of artillery pieces set against the evocative backdrop of a mosque on the shores of the Bosphorus. Robertson would later visit the Crimea and take photographs of Sevastopol after its capture.

'Siege of Silistria', 1854

Turkish Troops storming the Russian Guns.

Steel engraving by W Ridgway after Harden Sidney Melville (*fl.* 1837-82), a plate from Edward Henry Nolan's *The History of the War against Russia*, London (1857), 16cm. h x 25.5cm. w

Generously donated by Mr McFarlane Brennan

NAM. 1964-04-58-6

If the Russians were to make a success of their campaign on the Danube, they needed to capture the stronghold of Silistria; but the successful resistance mounted by the Turks during the course of a two month siege (April-June 1854) proved a revelation. The British imagination was captured by the part played in the defence by two volunteers, Captain James Butler and Lieutenant Charles Nasmyth, and this print, showing one of them in the forefront of the action, reflects the fact.

'The Guards and Highlanders received by Omar Pasha and Marshal St Arnaud commanded by the Duke of Cambridge at Aladyn, 6 July 1854'

Watercolour, signed lower right 'F A Grant fecit', by Lieutenant Francis Augustus Grant (1829-54), 79th (Cameron Highlanders) Regiment of Foot, 1854, 17.8cm. h x 25.3cm. w

NAM. 1964-04-19-12

The title inscribed in pencil verso continues, 'St Arnaud's escort of Spahis on the right of the picture/ Names of the figures in the foreground -/ On the left St Arnaud on a white horse/ Next Omar Pasha on a chestnut horse/ Duke of Cambridge with his hand on his side/ Fourth figure Col Mc Donald ADC to ditto.'

The Turkish and French Commanders are shown reviewing the British troops at Aladyn near Varna. *The Illustrated London News* published an account of the Review on 22 July 1854,

> Omer Pacha left Varna early, and on arriving at Aladyn he found the Duke of Cambridge's division ready to receive him. He expressed in the most lively way his admiration at the magnificent appearance of the Guards and Highlanders; and, after the review, he remained for some time, and partook of some refreshment.

According to the monthly returns the artist died on 1 October 1854, in the 'Camp Balaclava Heights'. Since he is not recorded as either killed in action or dying as a result of wounds, it is presumed that Lieutenant Grant succumbed to disease.

'Marching order - July - 1854'

Pen and ink and watercolour by Captain (later Colonel) The Honourable William James Colville (1827-1903), Rifle Brigade, *c*1854, 17.8cm. h x 11.9cm. w

NAM. 1974-02-131-1

On 17 April 1854, while advanced elements of the British Army were still at Gallipoli, Lord Raglan had been notified that white calico shako covers were being sent from England. Lord Hardinge was anxious that they should be used and on 22 June the deputy adjutant-general wrote to Raglan from Horse Guards that:

> The General Commanding in Chief being deeply impressed, from his own experience in India, .. of the importance of keeping the head well protected from the sun, has directed me to bring to your Lordship's notice the expediency of ordering the troops under your command, to wear during the hot weather, on all occasions, the white linen cap covers which have been provided, on the recommendation of the General Commanding in Chief, at the Expence of the Public.

53

'The new Summer uniform or tickling the Cossacks', 1854

Coloured lithograph by and after Edward Morin (1824-82), number seven in the series 'Lloyd's Incidents from the War in the Crimea. I', published by Lloyd Brothers and Co, London, November 1854, 26.1cm. h x 35.7cm. w

NAM. 1979-03-33

Hearing that the British troops in Bulgaria had been issued with white cloth covers for their shakos as a means of warding off sun-stroke, the artist has imagined what would be the effect of the Guards Regiments being issued with cloth covers for their bearskins. The effect, he has clearly decided, would be risible, and he has depicted the Russians collapsing in fits of laughter at the British uniform. Note also the open-neck collars, reflecting the success of the campaign in the newspapers to rid the soldier's throat of the uncomfortable leather stock.

Other Rank's Shako, 1844-55 pattern

49th (Princess Charlotte of Wales's or Hertfordshire) Regiment of Foot

Black felt and leather, brass shako plate

NAM. 1969-07-33

The 1844-55 pattern shako is usually referred to as the 'Albert' shako after the Prince Consort who, as with so many things, is believed to have influenced its design. With its peaks both fore and aft the style is Austrian. One of the ugliest headdresses ever inflicted on the British Army, it was also unpopular for practical reasons, as Colonel George Bell of the 1st (The Royal) Regiment of Foot explained when writing from Scutari in June 1854: 'The next thing I want to pitch aside is the abominable Albert as it is called, whereon a man may fry his ration beef at mid-day in this climate, the top being patent leather to attract a 10 fold more portion of the sun's rays to madden his brain.'

Officer's Shako and Ball Tuft, c1844-55

9th (The East Norfolk) Regiment of Foot

Black beaver and patented leather, gilt metal chin chain, gilt metal and silver shako plate, gilt metal ball fitting, white over red tufted wool

NAM. 1993-05-228, -1, -2

Officers' shakos were of higher quality than those of the men, being made of black beaver mounted on felt, possessing a gilt chin chain rather than a plain leather chin strap, and a having a ball-tuft on top. A white over red tuft, as opposed to an all white or all green one, denoted a field officer or battalion company officer.

Major-General (later General Sir) William John Codrington (1804-84)

Photograph by Roger Fenton

NAM. Negative 46764

Although largely unheralded, Codrington's career was perhaps the most remarkable of any general officer during the Crimean War. Eager to be involved, the then Colonel Codrington went out with the Army of the East as a supernumerary major hoping for a permanent appointment. Promoted major-general in the brevet of 20 June 1854, Codrington feared that as a consequence of his new rank he would have to return home. Shortly afterwards, however, a vacancy arose to command the 1st Brigade in the Light Division, in which capacity Codrington went to the Crimea in September 1854, distinguishing himself at the Battle of the Alma. He succeeded to the command of the Light Division upon the invaliding home of Sir George Brown in June 1855, and in November 1855, following the resignation of Sir James Simpson, became General Commanding-in-Chief of the Army of the East. Codrington's meteoric rise reflected the dearth of alternative military talent; his appointment took place even after he had been heavily criticised for his mismanagement of the attack on the Redan, 8 September 1855.

Tent, 1854

Linen, 2.12m. h x 1.82m. w x 2.12m. l

NAM. 1980-02-75

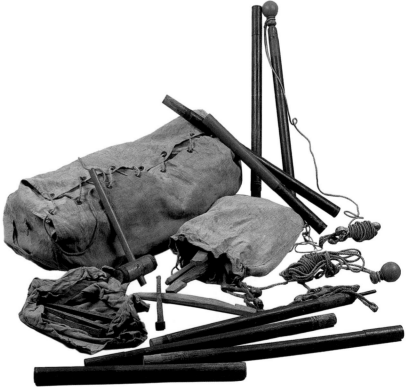

General Codrington believed that the official issue bell tent – which weighed 75 pounds (34 kg.) – would to be too much for his baggage animals, so when he moved with the Brigade of Guards from Scutari to Bulgaria in June 1854, he took with him instead this lighter-weight linen tent, purchased privately. On 11 July he wrote to his wife: 'My tent is about 6 ft wide, by about 7 ft long – and 7 ft high in the ridge – a small house indeed – but it has proved itself a sound one.'

Orders and Medals awarded to Major-General William Fergusson Beatson, 1837-56

Crimea War Medal 1854-56, with clasps: Balaklava, Inkermann, Sebastopol; Order of St Ferdinand, Spain, Stars 2nd Class 1837; Order of the Mejidie, Turkey, 3rd Class, 1855; Turkish General Service Medal 1854, in gold; Turkish Crimean War Medal 1855, Sardinian issue *(top to bottom, left to right)*

Generously donated by the Royal United Service Institution

NAM. 1963-11-31

Lieutenant-Colonel (later Major-General) William Fergusson Beatson (1804-72) had long experience of commanding native troops in India and, the skill being considered transferable, in 1854 he was given charge of the Bashi Bazouks, Turkish irregulars in British pay. He took part in the Charge of the Heavy Brigade during the Battle of Balaklava as a member of Brigadier-General James Yorke Scarlett's staff. His award of the Spanish Order of St Ferdinand was for service with the British Auxiliary Legion during the Carlist War, 1835-36.

'Bashi Bazouk of Circassia, & others at exercise in the background', *c*1854

Watercolour and pencil by Second Lieutenant William Thomas Markham (1830-86), 2nd Battalion, The Rifle Brigade, from an album of paintings and sketches by Colonel William Markham and Second Lieutenant W T Markham, *c*1854, 10.8cm. h x 21.1cm. w

Purchased with the generous assistance of the Society of Friends of the National Army Museum

NAM. 1999-02-105-52

The Bashi Bazouks had earned an unsavoury reputation for pillage and indiscipline during the fighting around Silistria. In spite of the subsequent attempt of Beatson to instil order amongst the 4,000 Bashi Bazouks taken into British pay, his efforts were undermined by the refusal of Lord Raglan to make use of them. 'They will do us great discredit,' Raglan wrote, 'and all the crimes and horrors they may commit will be attributed to the English Army.'

Commemorative jug, 1855

Earthenware Staffordshire jug, cast in three pieces, impressed with the maker's mark for E Ridgeway and Abingdon, Hanley, 1 August 1855, 21.2cm. h x 13cm. w x 16cm. d

NAM. 1962-11-181-1

Although the British alliance with the French and the Ottoman Empire had come about somewhat unexpectedly, it was nevertheless hailed with enthusiasm. Commemorative items were produced, such as this jug, decorated in relief with three figures representing the British, French and Turkish Armies bayoneting and trampling the Russian Imperial two-headed eagle underfoot.

Medal commemorating the Alliance of Britain and France, 1854

Bronze, designed by 'Punch', produced by Allen and Moore, 44mm. diam

NAM. 1981-11-50

This medal commemorates the previously unlikely alliance between Britain and France against Russia. Its obverse depicts a Grenadier Guardsman greeting a French rifleman, with French and British flags, a drum and cannon in the background. It is inscribed in English and French: THE HOLY ALLIANCE and LA SAINTE ALLIANCE. The reverse bears the words: ENGLAND AND FRANCE UNITED TO DEFEND THE OPPRESSED AND AVENGE INSULTED EUROPE.

Obverse   Reverse

'Kadikoi near Scutari from 23rd Camp 5th May 54', 1854

The town and harbour of Kadikoi

Pencil sketch by 'Henry', 23rd (Royal Welsh Fusiliers) Regiment of Foot, 1854, 12.6cm. h x 35.5cm. w

Generously donated by Brigadier Peter Young

NAM. 1960-05-199-5

Upon arrival at Constantinople the 23rd (Royal Welsh Fusiliers) Regiment of Foot was encamped with the 7th and 88th Regiments on open ground behind Scutari Barracks. The conditions were surprisingly cold and damp and Major Daniel Lysons complained that 'in wet weather our camp is one mass of clay-mud that sticks to everything'.

It is unfortunately impossible to identify the artist of this sketchbook, as in 1854 there were six officers with Henry as part of their name serving in the 23rd Royal Welsh Fusiliers. From the dates on some of the drawings, the artist must have survived the Battle of the Alma, during which many officers of the regiment were killed. However, none of the Henrys was amongst the dead, whilst four of them are still in the *Army List* for 1855.

'1st Camp at Aladdyn. from my tent by moonlight', *c*1854

Watercolour and pencil by Second Lieutenant William Thomas Markham (1830-86), 2nd Battalion, The Rifle Brigade, from an album of paintings and sketches by Colonel William Markham and Second Lieutenant W T Markham, *c*1854, 8.6cm. h x 12.5cm. w

Purchased with the generous assistance of the Society of Friends of the National Army Museum

NAM. 1999-02-105-38

'My packhorse, "the black slave", loaded for the march _' *c*1854

Watercolour and pencil by Second Lieutenant William Thomas Markham (1830-86), 2nd Battalion, The Rifle Brigade, from an album of paintings and sketches by Colonel William Markham and Second Lieutenant W T Markham, c1854, 12.6cm. h x 17.5cm. w

Purchased with the generous assistance of the Society of Friends of the National Army Museum

NAM. 1999-02-105-39

Much to the chagrin of the Army's officers, who purchased their baggage animals privately, there was not space aboard the transport vessels to carry packhorses from Bulgaria to the Crimea. When the Army set sail in September 1854, the animals had to be set loose and left to fend for themselves.

Map of the Baltic theatre of operations

'Landing of the French Troops near Bomarsund in the Aland Islands, Augst. 1854. Sketched from on board H.M.S. "Vulture"'

Tinted lithograph by L Huard after Edwin Thomas Dolby *(fl.* 1849-70), reproduced as plate nine in 'Dolby's Sketches on the Baltic', published by Paul and Dominic Colnaghi, 1854, 38.1cm. h x 51.3cm. w

NAM. 1976-07-55

A British fleet had sailed for the Baltic upon the outbreak of war but finding the fortress of Kronstadt, which protected the Russian capital of St Petersburg, too strong, had accomplished little apart from some coastal raiding. On 28 June 1854 the British Cabinet agreed to attack the Russian fortress of Bomarsund on the Aland Islands. French troops were disembarked and on 13 August a bombardment was commenced from the landward side. Three days later the Russians surrendered. After destroying Bomarsund's fortifications, the Allies sailed away.

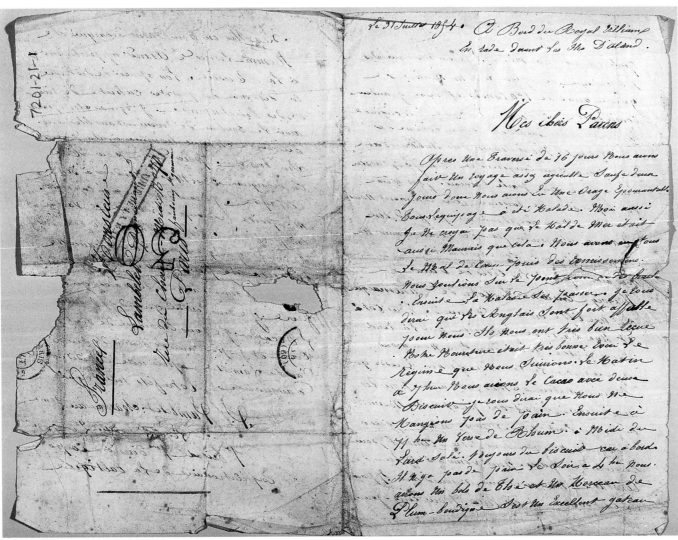

Letter of *Chasseur* François Lambelet, 1854

Manuscript, HMS *Royal William*, 31 July 1854, 20 cm. h x 26.6cm. w

Generously donated by M. Guilbert Martial

NAM. 1972-01-21-1

For the expedition to the Aland Islands in the Gulf of Finland, the French provided 9000 troops and the British supplied transportation. The French embarked at Calais and *Chasseur* François Lambelet of the 2nd *Léger* found himself aboard the *Royal William*, a sailing 120 gun three decker. He writes to his parents that the voyage to the Aland Islands had been pleasant, apart from two stormy days, and that his English hosts had been most friendly, although not one of them - not even the ship's captain - could speak French.

Russian Copy of Brunswick Rifle, .70in., captured at Bomarsund, 1854

118cm. l

Generously donated by Lieutenant-Colonel A R Close

NAM. 1962-06-28

During the Crimean War the Russian Army employed both smoothbore firearms and rifles. The Russians arranged for the manufacture of rifles that were almost exact copies of the British Army percussion Brunswick Rifle, which had been used by British rifle regiments prior to the introduction of the Minié. It had a range of about 300 yards (274m.).

The brass patch box on the butt, stamped with the Russian Imperial eagle, has been engraved to reveal that this Russian Brunswick rifle was taken at the capture at Bomarsund in 1854 by Lieutenant F A Close of HMS *Blenheim*. The weapon is undated but the lock was made in Liege, Belgium by gunmaker P J Malherle.

Belted Lead Rifle Ball, for Brunswick Rifle, 1837-*c*1850

NAM. 2003-07-99

The Brunswick Rifle was rifled with two grooves and originally fired a belted lead ball of .64in. (1.63cm.) diameter (.766in. (1.95cm.) diameter at the widest point), weighing 555 grains (36g.). The Russians developed a conical bullet for the Brunswick which gave it an enhanced range of 600 yards (546m.); it was this type of bullet that killed Brigadier-General Goldie at Inkerman (see p138).

Baltic Medal 1854

Specimen. Silver. The obverse designed by William Wyon shows the sovereign's head as on the Crimea War Medal. The reverse by Leonard Wyon, depicts Britannia holding a trident in her right hand and looking over her left shoulder; in the background are the fortresses of Bomarsund and Sveaborg, with the word BALTIC above and the dates 1854-1855 below. The medal was sanctioned on 23 April 1856 as an award for service in the Baltic and was mainly issued to the Royal Navy and Royal Marines. A small number of officers and men of the Royal Engineers and the Royal Sappers and Miners were entitled to the medal.

Generously donated by the Ministry of Defence

NAM. 1958-11-96-9

Medals awarded to Commander Berkeley Belson, 1854-65

Baltic Medal 1854-55; Crimea War Medal 1854-56, with clasp: Sebastopol; 2nd China War Medal 1857-60; New Zealand Campaigns Medal 1845-66, reverse dated 1863-1865; Turkish Crimean War Medal, British issue

Generously donated by Colonel P C E Belson and Mr D B E Belson

NAM. 1992-02-7

Berkeley George Albert Belson (1840-1918) was born into a distinguished naval and military family, the nephew of Major-General Sir Charles Philip Belson who had commanded the 28th Regiment in the Peninsula and at Waterloo. He joined the Royal Navy in 1853 and served as a Cadet and Midshipman in the Baltic and Crimea, for which he was awarded the Baltic Medal and Crimea War Medal with two clasps. He went on to serve in the Second China War 1857-60 and as a Lieutenant aboard HMS *Eclipse* in the New Zealand Campaign 1863-65. He retired in 1873 with the rank of commander, dying at Portsmouth in 1918.

Baltic Medal 1854, awarded to Sapper Alexander Wallace

NAM. 2002-04-845

Alexander Wallace was a miner by trade who enlisted in the Royal Sappers and Miners in 1845, aged 18. Much of his military career was spent abroad, including nearly six years spent in the West Indies, as well as in the Baltic and the Crimea. In addition to his medal, he was also entitled to the Crimea War Medal, with clasp: Sebastopol and the Turkish Crimea War Medal. His career was unfortunately a chequered one, as the report of the Discharge Board at Chatham, dated 7 January 1863, reveals. 'His conduct has been indifferent', it stated, he having 'been six times tried by Court Martial' and guilty of '39 Regimental Offences'; these were mostly for absence without leave, but also for 'habitual drunkenness' and 'sleeping on his post'. He was discharged at the age of 36 years, four months, because of 'lameness of [the] left thigh', the result of an injury 'caused by falling down steps in the New Palace Barracks'. Ironically, his mishap was not one 'aggravated … by vice or misconduct'.

'Russian prisoners from Bomarsund/ Devonshire Hulk Sep 30th/ 1854/ Shaving'

Pencil sketch attributed to Robert Thomas Landells (1833-77), special artist for *The Illustrated London News*, 1854, 13.7cm. h x 21cm. w

NAM. 1976-10-2-1

Russian prisoners from Bomarsund, on board the 831 ton prison ship *Devonshire*, moored on the River Medway, Sheerness. *The Illustrated London News* recorded on 23 September 1854, 'There are now 1140 Russian prisoners on board the Devonshire and Benbow, at Sheerness…

The Emperor of Russia does not grant them any pay while they are prisoners of war, nor allow them to return home on parole of honour not to serve…. Lewes gaol and Milbay prison, at Stonehouse, are to be their future abodes.'

The Army of the Ottoman Empire

Simon Moody

The role of the Ottoman Army in the Crimean War has frequently been overlooked by historians, perhaps because there are genuine difficulties in studying the contribution of the Ottoman Empire's army to the war. Contemporary first-hand Turkish sources are almost non-existent outside the Turkish archives (save for at the highest level of command) and there are no equivalents to the numerous journals and letters published in Britain, France and Russia after the war had ended. Consequently, any assessment of the Ottoman forces in the Crimean war is forced to rely heavily on highly partisan and occasionally xenophobic commentaries by their allies and enemies. Most of these commentators had little knowledge of the history, culture and customs of the Ottoman Empire and thus were motivated by suspicion and, frequently, religious and ideological intolerance.[1]

When Tsar Nicholas I made his now famous comment on the Ottoman Empire 'We have on our hands a sick man, a very sick man', he was in effect referring to its military power. The Ottoman Army at the time of the Crimean War was not the force it had once been. During the fifteenth and sixteenth centuries, combining well-armed and motivated light infantry and irregular cavalry, it had been greatly feared by both western and near-eastern opponents. Compared to the small mercenary armies of Europe, the sheer size of the Ottoman forces was a serious threat. By the middle of the eighteenth century, however, the balance had changed and it became clear that the Ottomans were being increasingly outclassed by more modern western armies, particularly that of Russia. Successive sultans attempted military reforms, introducing modern artillery and more rigid tactics.[2] Among the most drastic of the changes for the army had been the suppression in 1826, during the Sultanate of Makmud II, of the Janissaries. These once fearsome (and politically influential) warriors, originally drawn from Christian hostages who had converted to Islam, were discarded in favour of a more highly trained western-style of infantry. In 1850, in a further measure of change, the Ottoman Empire's Christians (who had previously paid a poll tax instead of performing military service) were required to serve alongside their Moslem counterparts. Latterly, the military reforms were based on the Prussian model and observed and implemented by Helmuth von Moltke and other Prussian officers. Corps, division and regimental structures were introduced and nominal establishments devised.

By the time of the Crimean War, the regular Ottoman Army (or *Nizam*) was conscripted and theoretically consisted of six army corps (or *Ordu*). These corps garrisoned particular areas of the empire. Each corps consisted of two divisions of two brigades, totalling six infantry and four cavalry regiments, together with supporting artillery. In support was the *Redif* (or reserve) to which a soldier passed after serving in the regular

army for five years. These men then served in the *Redif* for a further seven years. In reality, this level of organisation was rarely attained and the total regular army never numbered more than 150,000 men.[3] In terms of ethnic makeup, although significant proportions of the reformed army were Anatolian Turks, the Ottoman Empire could also call upon forces from its vassal states. The rulers of Tunisia and Egypt both supplied contingents to the Crimea, the latter performing well on a number of occasions.

Ultimately, the effects of the reform programme are difficult to gauge. Giving his opinion of the Turkish Army in 1877, the Russian, General Bogdanovich wrote:

> The Turkish infantry is not well suited to action on the open field but nevertheless stubbornly maintains itself in fortifications. This character of the Turkish forces, evidenced in all the wars, was unchanged in 1854 regardless of Turkey's introduction of a regular organisation.[4]

He also went on to suggest that this characteristic prompted Turkish commanders to prefer static defence rather than meet the Russians in open battle. Certainly, the introduction of a regular organisation fundamentally changed the nature of the Ottoman Army; but, in a sense, with the Westernising of drill and equipment, perhaps many of the more admirable irregular qualities of the Ottoman forces were lost, or at least suppressed.

The Danube campaign, 1853-54

Following the declaration of war by Turkey on 4 October 1853, initial operations on the Danube proved unexpectedly successful for the Turkish forces. Early victories at Oltenitza (4 November 1853), and Citate (5 January 1854) enabled the Turks to maintain the integrity of the Danube as a frontier. In the Black Sea, however, a Turkish fleet was annihilated by the Russian fleet at Sinope on 30 November 1853. This defeat led to the strengthening of pro-Turkish sentiment in Britain and France.

The investment of the Bulgarian city of Silistria by the Russians on 14 April 1854 was a serious cause for concern, given its strategic position, blocking the route south into European Turkey. The siege was prosecuted with considerable ferocity but the city refused to fall, despite increasing numbers of Russian troops and the lack of action taken to raise the siege by the overall Turkish commander, Omar Pasha, encamped at Shumla. A number of British officers were serving with the Turkish defenders and were shocked at the conduct of some of the

Turkish Infantry, 1855. Their headdresses are without peaks so as not to impede the faithful from touching the ground with their foreheads in prayer. NAM. 1968-06-331-6

townspeople of Silistria and the indifference towards it of the Turkish defenders, as Captain James Butler noted on 29 May 1854:

> One ruffian, whilst we were sitting with Moussa [Pasha], came and threw down a pair of ears which he had cut from a Russian soldier. Another boasted that a wounded Russian officer having begged for mercy in the name of the prophet, he deliberately drew his knife & in cold blood cut his throat![5]

With the arrival of the French and British forces at Varna, the Russians, almost at the hour of victory, on 20 June 1854 withdrew. Psychologically, Silistria was a great boost to Turkish morale and a further Turkish victory at Giurgevo on 7 July 1854 and the subsequent withdrawal of the

Russians north of the Danube on 28 July 1854 effectively ended the campaign. Its successful conclusion was less of a surprise to the British than it might once have been. When he arrived at Constantinople in April, Captain Nigel Kingscote, one of Lord Raglan's aides de camp, had observed:

> The little I have seen of the Turks makes me think they are very poor Allies and of this I am certain they are the greatest liars on the face of the earth. If they say they have 150,000 men you will find that on enquiry there are only 30,000. Everything in the same proportion, and from all I hear, I cannot make out why the Russians have not walked over them.[6]

However, after travelling with Raglan to Shumla the following month and seeing Omar Pasha's army, Kingscote revised his opinion:

> We were very much surprised at the Turkish troops. They are strong built men and move very quickly, which we did not expect and I believe there is hardly such a thing as crime among them. There are 45,000 Infantry and 5,000 Cavalry and Artillery with more Cavalry in the neighbourhood. Omar Pasha is a fine looking fellow, unlike the Turks, dresses in a plain grey frock coat with Jack boots, and sits well on his horse with an English seat. He does everything himself and must see it done or it is not done, the staff of every kind being the worst part of the Turkish Army.[7]

It was also during the Danube campaign that the British and French first encountered the irregular troops of the Ottoman Empire. Most notorious of these were the Bashi-Bazouks, a species of light cavalry who both fascinated and frustrated their western allies. "The most irregular of

**Omar Pasha and his British liaison officer, Colonel (later Field Marshal Sir) Lintorn Simmons (1821-1903), Royal Engineers.
NAM. 1968-10-73-9**

**Turkish irregulars: a group of Bashi-Bazouks, Zabeks and Kurdish Arabs, painted by Second Lieutenant W T Markham of The Rifle Brigade, Shumla 1854.
NAM. 1999-02-105-52**

irregular horse,"[8] as one British officer described them, their traditional role was skirmishing, pursuit and plunder. The depredations of these irregulars made their subsequent use less attractive to the western allies, despite efforts to convert them into more reliable troops.

The Crimea, 1854-55

Buoyed by success in Bulgaria, Turkish troops embarked for the Crimea on 5 September 1854 with their British and French allies. The force, some 7000 strong under the command of Omar Pasha, landed with their allies at Kalamita Bay on the 14 September and were efficiently and fully encamped by the following day.[9] Nevertheless, the logistical shortcomings of the Turks came quickly to the fore. An almost complete lack of a commissariat for supplying their troops ensured that the provision of ammunition and food was at best haphazard and frequently non-existent. Turkish troops on the Crimean Peninsula rapidly went hungry. Medical services were also primitive. While this was a problem for all the allies in the Crimea, the Turkish sick and wounded suffered perhaps most of all. The result was a very high death rate. The special correspondent of the *Morning Herald*, N A Woods, visited a Turkish hospital (previously used as a cholera hospital) in the Crimea in late 1854 and was horrified by the sight of one young Turkish surgeon, working ankle deep in filth with patients dying of malnutrition and dysentery all about him. The English-trained surgeon was unable to save a single man.[10] Admiral Sir Adolphus Slade, writing later, described the condition of 400 Turks in the Turkish hospital at Balaklava in November 1854:

> They lay dressed as brought in from camp, without beds, covering or attendance. The doctor, an Armenian, had no means of alleviating their sufferings: he had not even utensils to heat sufficient water for drink, far less purification. Many were dying every day, and the deaths rapidly augmented in the course of the winter, through over-toil in the British lines as night working parties.[11]

The chaotic medical and administrative situation makes an estimate of the total of Ottoman dead in the Crimean War very difficult. It is likely to have been at least 100,000 in all theatres and was probably considerably higher. The proportionate losses were also staggering. In the Tunisian contingent alone, of 10,000 troops provided, some 7000 perished during the conflict.[12]

The suffering of the Turks was virtually ignored by the French commissariat, but the British at least tried to assist. Unfortunately, British Army rations proved unsuitable, as the Moslem Turks could not touch the rum and pork rations, and an extra biscuit as compensation

proved inadequate.[13] With the deterioration of the weather, the poor quality uniforms and lack of greatcoats caused additional misery, many Turks wrapping themselves in thin blankets.[14] Sadly, the British and French soldiers possessed little sympathy for their allies and could act brutally towards them. Captain Henry Clifford, in a letter of 16 December 1854, described the aftermath of a beating administered on one unfortunate Turk:

> He crawls away and tries to make off and escape more ill-treatment and hard words, hard words, though he can't understand them, but he knows since he ran away in front of Balaklava, every English and French soldier detests and despises him, and treats him like a dog.[15]

The Turks had been spectators in the Battle of the Alma on 20 September 1854 but as Clifford suggests, the reputation of Johnny Turk (as the British troops called him)[16] had taken a severe blow at the Battle of Balaklava on 25 October 1854. Some 4000 reinforcements, mostly militia[17] (a mixture of Anatolian Turkish and Tunisian troops) had arrived in the Crimea and were assigned to British command at Balaklava. They were ordered to garrison a series of redoubts along the Causeway Heights overlooking the town. The defence of No.1 Redoubt on the Heights during the early morning attacks by General Liprandi's Russian forces was one of the heroic acts of the war. About 500 Turks held off superior forces for over an hour before being overwhelmed. Unfortunately, the subsequent flight of the remaining garrisons back to the port and the collapse of the Tunisians acting in support of Sir Colin Campbell and the 93rd (Highland) Regiment of Foot, did little to suggest that the Turks were reliable. In fact, most of those who were critical of the Turks' conduct (including Lord Raglan and William Howard Russell, *The Times* journalist) were actually ignorant of the brave defence of Redoubt No.1, having only arrived on the battlefield at about 8.00am.

Thereafter, Turkish troops saw little action in conjunction with their French and British allies, taking no part at Inkerman or in the trenches before Sevastopol. Turkish troops did participate in the expedition to and garrisoning of Kerch in May 1855 and a small Turkish force arrived just too late to participate in the Battle of the Chernaya River on 16 August 1855.

Following Balaklava, the allied high command's attitude towards Turkish troops was reflected in its relegation of much of them to labour and supply duties. The British Government, however, desperate for auxiliary manpower, realised that the Turkish troops could still prove useful. It was therefore agreed with the Sultan, in a convention signed on the 3

February 1855, that a force would be placed under British command and effectively hired from the Ottoman Empire. Principally officered by British officers, this force became known as the Turkish Contingent and eventually amounted to sixteen infantry and eight cavalry regiments, six battalions of artillery as well as engineer and land transport units. The contingent was consigned primarily to garrison duties, most noticeably at Kerch under the command of Lieutenant-General Robert Vivian during 1855-56. Conflicting opinions as to their value persisted amongst British observers. One officer serving with the Contingent at Kerch noted that conditions for the Turks were much improved under British command:

Being naturally a very steady race of men, they are contented to sitting at their own firesides nightly, and listening to the recital of oriental tales. They all appear well contented with the discipline, etc, established by the English officers who command them and their wants being supplied in food, pay and clothing, they have no cause of complaint.[18]

Lieutenant Alfred Howell, an officer of the Land Transport Corps, was less complimentary towards his charges, commenting in a letter from Kerch dated 24 November 1855 that:

A French print of the Battle of the Windmills.
NAM. 1968-06-315-1

The Turk fatigue party or building corps who erect the huts, dig trenches etc etc are a rather dilatory lot. In digging trenches the beggars stop devilish often and stick their spade or axe before them, their arms across their breasts and say their prayers kneeling, this is whenever they feel tired, which is very often but we have positive orders not to interfere with their religion so we let them do as they like in this respect, but one of my men stopped 9 times in $2^3/_4$ hours. Now though I do not dispute his devotions I thought this was too much of a good thing and as I knew Mahomet would not come to help him dig and do his work, I do not think Mahomet ought to have any more of his time so I laid my whip across his back which seemed to waken him a bit.[19]

With the Turks serving the British chiefly employed in this way, it was only in the north, around the strategic port of Eupatoria, that any sort of Turkish field force was maintained. Under Omar Pasha's command, they were successful in repulsing a major Russian attack on 17 January 1855. Little attention has been paid to the so-called 'Battle of the Windmills', the only one in the Crimea that the Turks fought largely unsupported. From behind defensive earthworks, some 20,000 Turks repelled 33,000 Russians, killing over 500 of them for the loss of about a hundred men.[20] However, Omar Pasha's troops were never able to act independently other than in a static role because of a lack of cavalry, and in July 1855 Omar Pasha requested French and British permission to withdraw the bulk of his forces from the Crimea in order to try to relieve the city of Kars in Asia Minor, which was under Russian siege. Although the allies were reluctant, the Turks were released following the fall of Sevastopol in September 1855.

The Caucasus

In Asia Minor, Russian and Turkish forces confronted one another on the borders of Anatolia. Initial encounters in November 1853 had proved disastrous for the Turks. The small army of Zarif Mustapha Pasha had been forced to retire before a larger Russian force under Prince Bebutov after crushing defeats at Bayezid and Ongulsi in Armenia. Further Turkish troops were swept aside on 14 November by Prince Andronikov at Akhaltsike. Only the activities of Islamic rebels under Shamyl (now supporting his former Ottoman enemies against the Russian infidel) prevented a complete collapse in Asia Minor.

The remaining Turkish defences now hinged on the strategic city of Kars. It was to here that Colonel Fenwick Williams was sent as British liaison officer to Zarif Pasha, arriving on 24 September 1854. Williams and his fellow British officers were appalled at the poor defensive preparations and therefore took over responsibility for them. His initial

impressions of the Turkish soldiery did nothing to improve his confidence, writing of a cavalry trooper:

> He wore no helmet, a light fez being the only protection of his skull from the unfriendly contact of Russian sabres. His garments were in tatters, what was left of them, gaudy and filthy in the extreme. The arms of this wretchedly apparelled man were in keeping with his accoutrements and horse furniture. He had a carbine of the old flintlock order, which would not always go off and by which no enemy was ever shot, except by chance.[21]

The city was besieged by the Russians under General Muraviev in June 1855 in what became (with Plevna in 1877) one of the great set piece sieges of the nineteenth century. A probing attack on 16 June 1855 by the Russians was the first of many throughout the summer. If Williams had been disillusioned with the defensive preparations and condition of the Turkish army on his arrival, the conduct of the common Turkish soldier now impressed him thoroughly, as he wrote on 21 July 1855:

> The Turkish Infantry are now so many battalions of sappers, and work, not only with cheerfulness, but also with surprising tact and intelligence; this and defending positions are their best qualities and depend upon it I will not throw them away.[22]

With great fortitude the defenders held out in desperate circumstances. Food quickly became scarce; half rations were introduced on 1 September 1855. The weakened defenders resorted to eating cats and dogs. They also suffered terribly from disease, mainly dysentery, in spite of the best efforts of Dr Humphry Sandwith, Williams' chief medical officer. The fighting too took its toll. On 29 September, a strong attack on the north of the town was again beaten back by the exhausted Turks, over 6000 Russians and 1000 defenders becoming casualties.

Two separate efforts were made by Turkish forces to relieve the city. After leaving the Crimea, Omar Pasha landed on 3 October 1855 at Suchum Kaleh and advanced on the city. Despite driving off a Russian force at the River Ingur on 6 November 1855, his advance was too slow and, hampered by bad roads and weather, he failed to reach Kars in time. On 22 October 1855, Selim Pasha [23] had landed at Trebizond and advanced to Erzerum. From here, inexplicably, he moved no further.

By late November 1855, it became clear that Kars was unable to hold out any longer and would not be relieved. Humphry Sandwith recorded

Colonel (later General Sir) Robert Cadell (1825-97), an East India Company officer, commanded the Turkish artillery at the Battle of the Windmills and distinguished himself at the River Ingur (overpainted photograph, 1856). NAM. 1962-10-20

Ismail Pasha (1813-65), a Hungarian patriot born György Kmety, fled his homeland after the insurrection of 1848-49 and became the Turkish hero of the defence of Kars. NAM. 1964-12-151-6-46

the following lines in his diary on 20 November:

> We have about 2000 men in hospital, and more than 100 deaths per Diem: we have only seven days' provision left. We have no artillery horses or cavalry; moreover our troops, though admirable for patient endurance and courage, are not to be depended upon for manoeuvres on the plain; besides which most of them are too weak for an hour's march, the ground is covered with snow, and the nights are intensely cold. A retreat would seem hopeless.[24]

Williams capitulated on 26 November 1855. So impressed by the defence were the Russians that Williams and his regulars were offered the honours of war and allowed to ride out of the city. Ultimately, however, the fall of Kars proved the final expression of allied indecision and rivalry, which came to typify the conduct of the Crimean War. The delay by the

French and British in releasing Omar Pasha's force from the Crimea, and the inability (or unwillingness) of Selim Pasha to relieve the city, sealed the fate of Williams and his gallant Turkish forces.

Aftermath

The over-riding impression of the Ottoman Army in the Crimean War is one of suffering, neglect, failure and prejudice. Yet the negative conclusions reached by many western observers of the Ottoman Army contrasts with the obvious courage, on many occasions, of the ordinary Turkish soldier. Even as the Turks streamed out of the redoubts at Balaklava, Private Mitchell of the 13th Regiment of Light Dragoons saw one soldier display bravery and a cool head:

> Two Cossacks came over the ridge together. One of them lanced a Turk in the back, who uttered a loud scream and fell. Another Turk being a short distance ahead, they both

made for him, but before they could reach him, Johnny, who had his piece loaded and bayonet fixed, turned and suddenly fired at the foremost, knocking him off his horse. The other coming up made a point, but whether it touched the Turk I cannot say; but in an instant he had bayoneted the Cossack in the body, and he also fell from his horse. Johnny resumed his journey at a walk.[25]

Moreover, for the Turks the Crimean War was, in the short term, a success. Notwithstanding heavy casualties, the Ottoman Empire had survived. Yet the halo soon slipped. Political instability persisted. Conflict with Russia in 1877-78, the war against Italy of 1911-12 and the Balkan Wars of 1912-13 each cost the Ottoman Empire territory and sapped its strength. Nevertheless, during the First World War, the under-rated Turkish Army (assisted by German advice and equipment) would severely embarrass the over-confident British at Gallipoli and Kut-al-Amara. Here, the ordinary Turkish soldier once again showed his tenacity and endurance. In spite of its military failures, the so-called 'sick man of Europe' endured, just as its soldiers had proved they could during the Crimean War. Ultimately, Nicholas I's observation proved wrong and it is perhaps ironic that the Sultanate would come to outlast their rivals, the Russian Romanov dynasty, by a year.

Notes

1 For a more detailed analysis of the psychology of and cultural relationships between the Turks and their allies, see R B Egerton, *The Legacy of the Crimean War*, Oxford (1999), pp165-86.

2 Specific aspects and an assessment of these reforms are discussed in V Askan 'Breaking the spell of Baron de Tott: Reframing the question of military reform in the Ottoman Empire' *The International History Review*, Vol XXIV, June 2002, pp 253-77. More general themes are discussed in M Yapp 'The modernisation of Middle Eastern armies in the nineteenth century: a comparative view' in *War technology and society in the Middle East*, V J Parry and M Yapp (eds), London, 1975, pp330-66.

3 C Farmer, 'The Organisation and Uniforms of the Ottoman Army during the Crimean War', Crimean War Research Society Special Publication SP22, 1999, pp1-5.

4 Lt-Gen M I Bogdanovich, 'The Organisation of the Turkish Army' from *Vostochaya Voina 1853-65 godov*, St Petersburg, 2nd Ed. (1877), translated by M Conrad and reproduced in *The War Correspondent*, Vol VIII, Jan.1991, pp12-17.

5 NAM. 1968-03-45 Copy manuscript journal of Captain James Armar Butler, Ceylon Rifle Regiment, who was killed serving with the Turkish Army at the Siege of Silistria, June 1854.

6 NAM. 1973-11-170-1 Kingscote to his father, 29 April 1854.

7 *Ibid.* 25 May 1854.

8 W S Curtis 'Major Henry Astbury Leveson of the Turkish light cavalry' *The War Correspondent*, Vol XIV, No 3, Oct. 1996, p13.

9 A W Kinglake, *The Invasion of the Crimea*, (6th Edition) Vol II Ch XXII, London (1885), p349.

10 N W Woods, *The Past Campaign: a sketch of the war in the east.* Vol II, London (1855), pp227-232.

11 A Slade, *Turkey and the Crimean War*, London, (1867), p331.

12 Slade, *op.cit.* p273.

13 Slade, *op.cit.* p335.

14 For detailed further information on Turkish uniforms and equipment see Farmer, *op.cit.* pp6-30.

15 H Clifford, *Henry Clifford VC. His letters and sketches from the Crimea*, Toronto (1956), pp126-7. Quoted by kind permission of Nicholas Fitzherbert Esq.

16 This was a nickname still in use during the First World War.

17 Known in Turkish as *Esnan*.

18 E H Nolan, *The History of the War against Russia*, Chapter CXX, London, (1857), p669.

19 NAM 1972-08-51 Letter from Howell to his brother Stephen dated Kerch, Crimea, 24 Nov 1855.

20 Slade, *op.cit.* p375-77.

21 Nolan, *op.cit.* Chapter LV, p764.

22 A Lake, *Kars and our captivity in Russia*, London (1856), p165.

23 This general should not be confused with the leader of the Egyptian contingent killed at Eupatoria.

24 H Sandwith, *A Narrative of the Siege of Kars*, London (1856), p300.

25 A Mitchell, *Recollections from one of the Light Brigade*, Canterbury, (1885), p81.

**Advance of the Allies from Kalamita Bay to Balaklava,
19-26 September 1854**

Eupatoria

Crimea

Kalamita
Bay

R. Bulganak

R. Alma

R. Kacha

R. Belbek

Sevastopol

R. Chernaya

Balaklava

Black Sea

The Landing in the Crimea and the Battle of the Alma

The Allies landed at Kalamita Bay, fifty kilometres north of their objective, Sevastopol, on 14 September 1854. They numbered 27,000 British, 30,000 French and 7000 Turks. On 19 September the Allied armies began their advance and, the following day, encountered 40,000 Russians under Prince Menshikov strongly posted on the heights south of the River Alma. In the battle that ensued the brunt of the fighting fell on the British, commanded by Lord Raglan. Leading the assault was Lieutenant-General de Lacy Evans' 2nd Division and the Light Division under Lieutenant-General Sir George Brown. They met stiff resistance and the Light Division was repulsed from the Great Redoubt, which threw into confusion elements of the Duke of Cambridge's 1st Division following behind. The Brigade of Guards soon rallied, however, and with Major-General Sir Colin Campbell's Highland Brigade executing a decisive flanking attack, and further to the west the 2nd Division and the French also making progress, the Russians were defeated. The British suffered 2000 casualties, the French a reported 1300, and the Russians over 5000.

'Alma "Forward Forty Second!"', 20 September 1854

Colour photolithograph after Robert Gibb (1845-1932), 1888, published as a supplement to the Christmas number of *Black and White*, 1898, 52cm. h x 74.5cm. w

Generously donated by Mr C C P Lawson

NAM. 1965-03-44-74

The 42nd (The Royal Highland) Regiment of Foot was one of the three battalions of the Highland Brigade, commanded by Major-General Sir Colin Campbell. The Highland Brigade's irresistible advance at the Battle of the Alma was of crucial importance in securing victory.

'A descriptive plan and explanatory key to the view of the sailing of the British portion of the Allied Expedition from Baljik to the Crimea, on the morning of the 7th of September, 1854 … by Captain James Rawstorne, RN, late in command of the First Division of the transports of the expedition.'

Hand coloured lithograph by Hullmandel & Walton, after a drawing by Captain Rawstorne, printed by James Wakeham, 4 Bedford Terrace, Church Street, Kensington (W), 1859, 25cm. h x 86.8cm. w

Generously donated by Mr R Codrington

NAM. 1978-08-90-9

The assembly of the British armada in Baljik Bay, Bulgaria, was to some a source of pride. Captain William Pollexfen Radcliffe of the 20th (The East Devonshire) Regiment of Foot wrote home from aboard the steamship *Colombo*:

> The French are greatly astonished at the magnificent vessels our Troops are conveyed in, & well they may be, for their own are nothing more than coasting vessels .. Let the Papers say what they will, "Old England" is superior to every nation, & I don't wonder at Englishmen being prejudiced; the more I see of Foreign countries, the more I am assured of her superiority in everything essential.

Note how the majority of steamships take in tow two sailing vessels each.

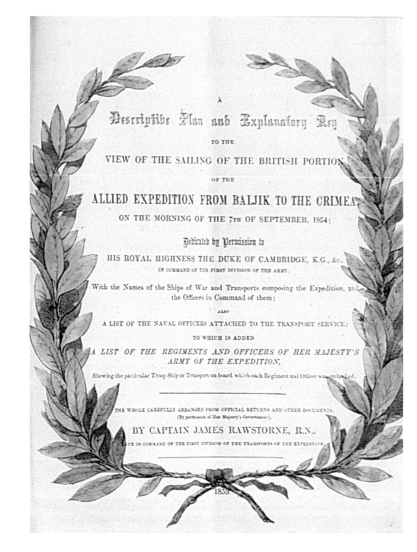

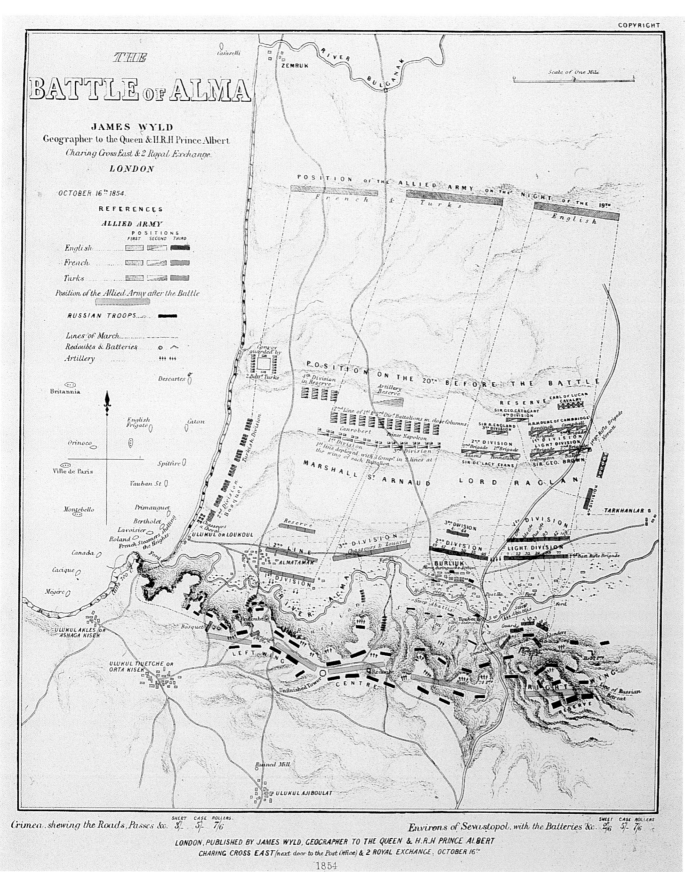

The Battle of Alma

Published by James Wyld Charing Cross East & 2 Royal Exchange, London, 16 October 1854, 34.3cm. h x 29cm. w

Generously donated by Mr G Boynton Williams

NAM. 1975-03-7-94

A substantially accurate representation of the Battle of the Alma, 20 September 1854, published in London within a month of the battle taking place.

**'Expedition in the Crimea landing of the Allied troops
14 September 1854'**

Coloured lithograph by Max Beeger and A Faure after 'Lieutenant R.',
published by Bulla Freres in Paris, Ferd. Ebner in Berlin, E Gambart and
Co in London and Emile Seitz in New York, 1854, 41cm. h x 86.8cm. w

NAM. 1979-07-145-1

The Allied expedition had left for the Crimea still uncertain of where it was
to land, and only after Lord Raglan had undertaken a personal
reconnaissance of the coastline aboard the *Caradoc* was it determined to
disembark at Kalamita Bay, a long sandy beach 50 kilometres north of
Sevastopol. It took five days for the disembarkation to be completed; the
British, unlike the French and Turks, had sailed with a brigade of light
cavalry aboard, and landing horses over an open beach was a time-
consuming process.

'The position on the Alma in seven sketches from the field on the day after the battle', 1854

Coloured lithograph after a panorama by Major Edward Bruce Hamley, Royal Artillery, published by William Blackwood and Sons, Edinburgh and London, 1855, 14.5cm. h x 171.1cm. w

NAM. 1963-05-4

This panorama reveals the extent of the battlefield of the Alma. The left-hand plate shows the plain across which the Light and First Divisions advanced towards the heights. The second plate shows the hill on the left that formed the right of the Russian position; their line extended along the upper and lower range of heights. The Russians also occupied all the lower range of heights shown in the third plate; Hamley depicts the funeral of Lieutenant Robert Horsley Cockerell, Royal Artillery, in the foreground. Plate four shows where the main British battery was ranged, directing its fire towards the Russian heavy guns on the knoll to the right; and plate five shows where Lord Raglan ordered two guns to be brought up to silence these Russian guns. The French advanced across the valley seen in plate six and up Telegraph Hill, while the Turks crossed the river near the sea in plate seven and advanced up a hill-path.

'September. 1854 On the March'

Pen and ink and watercolour, signed lower right 'WJC', by Captain (later Colonel) The Honourable William James Colville (1827-1903), Rifle Brigade, c1854, 17.8cm. h x 11.9cm. w

NAM. 1974-02-131-2

The march from Kalamita Bay to Sevastopol proved a testing one for the British soldier. Men died in their hundreds from cholera. The landscape was parched and water scarce. As Colville's drawing shows, it did not take long for the soldier to adapt his dress to the conditions. The hated leather stock was discarded. Cast aside too was the Albert shako, to be replaced by the Kilmarnock bonnet, a soft forage cap.

Waterbottle

Royal Artillery

Wood, 17.5cm. w x 10cm. d

NAM. 1975-03-31

This round wooden cask waterbottle is a modified version of the type carried in the Crimean War; the only difference is that with the earlier version the wooden panels on the curved edge protrude marginally over the front face. Although waterbottles carried in the Crimean War were usually painted blue, this example has been re-painted black and marked to the Royal Artillery, although in places some blue paint can still be seen.

Never was the waterbottle a more essential piece of equipment than during the advance from Kalamita Bay to the River Bulganak on 19 September. Short of water and wracked by cholera, the British soldier suffered agonies of thirst.

Infantry Other Rank's Knapsack, *c*1829-54

43cm. w x 33cm. h x 10cm. d

NAM. 1998-06-173

The 'box' style knapsack originated in the early nineteenth century and, by the beginning of the Crimean War, had developed a four-sided frame. Intended to hold clothing and boots, cleaning equipment and personal items, it was worn on the back and held in place by buff leather straps. Upon landing in the Crimea, soldiers' knapsacks were ordered to be left onboard ship: Lord Raglan believed that his troops, debilitated by disease, were incapable of carrying 'full marching order'. Instead, rolled blankets were used – ineffectively - to carry the soldiers' kit until the knapsacks could be brought ashore. This did not happen until November.

There were many complaints about the ill-fitting knapsack. General James B Bucknall Estcourt, Adjutant General of the Army of the East, was among its critics: 'The knapsack is not good. In order to keep it high and small people have made it wide. I believe it would be better deeper down the back and narrower.'

Ammunition Pouch, pre-1856

Grenadier Guards

23.5cm. l x 13cm. w x 9.5cm. d

Generously donated by the Royal United Service Institution

NAM. 1963-10-332

Dating from the time of the Crimean War, this black leather Grenadier Guards ammunition pouch bears the regimental badge on the front and is stamped inside with the Board of Ordnance mark, 'BO', which was replaced by the War Department's 'WD' mark after 1855. The pouch is lined with a tin tray, divided into three open compartments, which would have held either loose cartridges or the packets of ten in which cartridges were issued.

Soldiers wore the pouch resting on the right hip. It was either attached to a cross belt, or, after the new waist belt replaced the uncomfortable cross belts, attached to a separate pouch belt.

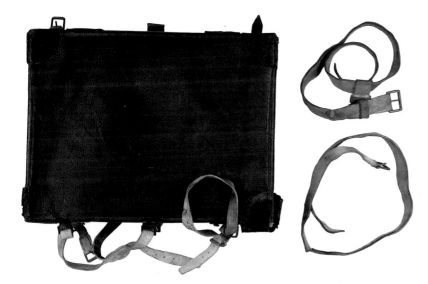

Ammunition Pouch, post-1855

Sergeants of Foot Guards

Leather, 21.5cm. l x 12.5cm. w x 8.5cm. d

Generously donated by the Royal United Service Institution

NAM. 1963-10-330

Externally this ammunition pouch is similar to the Grenadier Guards example, but the badge on the front is missing; there are two holes indicating where it would have been attached. Although it is stamped inside with the War Department mark, 'WD', which dates it after 1855, the basic design and dimensions are very similar to the Grenadier Guards pouch.

The interior of the pouch is fitted with a tin tray, divided into three compartments. Two remain open while the third possesses a hinged lid, possibly for percussion caps.

Crimean War diary of Major Edward Wellesley, 1855

Manuscript, leatherbound, 18.5cm. h x 23.7cm. w

Generously donated by Miss A M Bray

NAM. 1970-06-8

Major Edward Wellesley (1823-54), a great nephew of the 1st Duke of Wellington, was first commissioned in 1839, transferring to the 73rd Regiment of Foot in 1844. When in 1854 Lord Raglan appointed him Assistant Quartermaster-General to the Army of the East, he had already seen active service at the Cape. Wellesley died of cholera on 20 September 1854 and his diary, having been left with his baggage aboard ship when the Army disembarked at Kalamita Bay, was - evidently inadvertently - sold in the auction of his effects held at Raglan's headquarters before Sevastopol in December. Ironically, when the late Field Marshal Lord Carver edited his great grandfather Edward Wellesley's South African and Crimean War letters for publication in 1995, he was unaware of the diary's existence.

Lord Raglan's Telescope

56.5cm. l x 12.5cm. w x 8.5cm. h

Generously donated by the Royal United Service Institution

NAM. 1963-10-214

The telescope is mounted on a skeleton rifle stock, which enabled Lord Raglan to use it one handed. His right arm had been amputated as a result of a wound received at the Battle of Waterloo in 1815.

The historian Alexander Kinglake, who was an eye-witness of the Battle of the Alma, recalled seeing Raglan demonstrate the use of the telescope beforehand to the French commander, Marshal Jacques Leroy de St Arnaud.

Officer's Coatee, *c*1831-55

42nd (Royal Highland) Regiment of Foot

Wool cloth, and gilt metal buttons

NAM. 1982-10-99

The coatee worn by the Highland regiments differed slightly from those worn by other foot regiments in that the skirts were a little shorter. The skirts of the officer's coatee were decorated with buttons and button loops of gold lace or embroidery with skirt ornaments and a triangle of lace between the two waist buttons.

At the Alma the 42nd Highlanders or Black Watch were part of Sir Colin Campbell's Highland Brigade which, advancing in line, drove back no fewer than twelve Russian infantry battalions.

Officer's Shell Jacket, *c*1854

23rd (Royal Welsh Fusiliers) Regiment of Foot

Wool cloth, gilt metal buttons, gold wire cord

Generously donated by Captain S V Jephson and Mrs D Holmes

NAM. 1960-04-39

Shell jackets, reminiscent of Eton College jackets, were adopted in place of the undress coat by infantry officers *c*1830 and continued to be worn until 1856. This example belonged to Lieutenant-Colonel Harry George Chester who joined the 23rd (Royal Welsh Fusiliers) as an ensign on 26 October 1830 and was killed leading his regiment at the Alma. 'The army & his Country,' Sir George Brown wrote afterwards, '.. did not contain a more gallant soldier or more accomplished gentleman.'

'The grand charge of the Guards on the Heights of the Alma. Septr. 20th. 1854'

Colour lithograph by and after L Huard (d. 1874) 'from a Sketch taken on the Spot by an English Officer', published by E Gambart & Co, London, 1 November 1854, 50.3cm. h x 68.2cm. w

Crookshank Collection, transferred from the British Museum

NAM. 1971-02-33-26

The Duke of Cambridge had not handled the Brigade of Guards well and when the Light Division was forced back from the Great Redoubt, the Guards were not in close enough support. The Scots Fusilier Guards crossed the River Alma slightly before the Grenadier and the Coldstream Guards but, having had their ranks disordered by men of the Light Division retreating through them, were thrown back from the Great Redoubt in turn. The situation was retrieved by the approach of the Grenadiers and Coldstreams, who dispersed the Russians with accurate Minié fire.

'Battle of Alma', 20 September 1854

Watercolour, signed lower right 'Orlando Norie', by Orlando Norie (1832-1901), *c*1854, 32.3cm. h x 48.3cm. w

Generously donated by the Royal United Service Institution

NAM. 1968-06-321-2

The Coldstream Guards are shown exchanging fire with Russian Infantry.

Orlando Norie's uncle, Frederick Norie, is believed to have accompanied the Sardinian Army in the Crimea, painting a number of military scenes there in 1854-55. Although Orlando painted a number of Crimean battle scenes, it is thought that he did not travel to the seat of war in the East, but rather based his watercolours on his uncle's sketches. This may account for the 'staged' quality of the picture.

The Battle of the Alma, 20 September 1854

Oil on canvas, by E[dmund ?] Walker (*fl.* 1836-62), 1854, 35.3cm. h x 50.8cm. w

NAM. 1962-07-1

In this representation of the Battle of the Alma, the artist has compressed the action by showing the Guards Brigade, Highland Brigade and men of Brigadier-General H W Adams' Brigade of the 2nd Division storming the Great Redoubt simultaneously. In reality the Highlanders carried out an outflanking move to the left, Adams' Brigade was engaged to the right and the only one of these brigades actually to close with the Redoubt was that of the Guards.

Officer's Undress Overalls, *c*1851

95th (The Derbyshire) Regiment of Foot

Wool cloth and brown composition buttons

Generously donated by Captain P Baty

NAM. 1979-12-84-3

Worn by Lieutenant Robert Graham Polhill, who joined the 95th in June 1848 and was promoted lieutenant in April 1852. The legs of the overalls are cut straight and without creases. While the *Dress Regulations* of 1846 state that a scarlet stripe was to be worn on the outside leg, it was quite common for undress trousers to be made without the stripe.

Lieutenant Polhill fell at the Alma, having been, as Kinglake wrote, 'torn and slain with grape'.

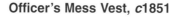

Officer's Mess Vest, *c*1851

95th (The Derbyshire) Regiment of Foot

Wool Cloth, silk, fine woollen twill weave lining, and gilt metal stud buttons

Generously donated by Captain P Baty

NAM. 1979-12-84-4

When the shell jacket was first introduced for officer use, it was popularly employed as a mess jacket. This was increasingly worn open, allowing a fancy regimental waistcoat – as in this example belonging to Lieutenant Polhill - to be worn underneath. Many regiments had their own pattern: this has sixty gilt metal stud buttons to the front of the vest, the hook and eye fastenings extending from the lower edge to half way up the front so that the upper part of the centre front resembles a V-neck. The upper, front and lower edges and the pockets are trimmed with 'Russia' braid, a narrow braid of double weave.

Prince Menshikov's Boots

Black leather, E.G. Müller, St Petersburg

Generously donated by the Trustees of the Middlesex Regimental Museum

NAM. 1992-10-7-1

Worn by Prince Alexander Sergeievich Menshikov, Commander of the Russian Forces at the Battle of Alma, 20 September 1854. They were presumably recovered from his coach, which was captured after the battle.

The toe fronts are squared off and the inside of the leather is coloured fawn. At the front of the leg section is the maker's stamp 'E G MÜLLER ST PETERSBURG' (repeated in cyrillic) and down the inside of each side seam is a 125 mm wide strip of red Russian leather. The front section of each turnover is coloured faded blue and the rear half has faded to pink. On the right boot turnover, at the rear and in manuscript, an inscription (barely legible) reads:
'BOOTS OF MENSCHIKOFF WON BY NASMYTH [?] FROM/ HIS…/…./…GCO/ …SCUTARI'.

Side Drum, 1854

Russian Infantry

37cm. w x 34.5cm. h

Generously donated by the Royal United Service Institution

NAM. 1951-12-35-1

Russian infantry side drum, captured by Corporal John Larking of the 88th Regiment of Foot (Connaught Rangers) at the Battle of the Alma.

Russian Percussion Musket, Model 1845, .709 in., 1847

147 cm. l

Generously donated by the Ministry of Defence, Royal Army Ordnance Corps, Weedon

NAM. 1963-12-251-111

Two types of musket were used by the Russians during the Crimean War: old flintlock muskets which had been converted to the percussion system and new Model 1845 Smoothbore Percussion Muskets. The design of this Russian Model 1845 was influenced by the French Model 1842 Musket, which it resembled; the Russian musket differed in having brass furniture and a stained Arctic birch stock, a feature typical of Russian firearms.

This weapon, picked up from the battlefield of the Alma, is engraved with the Russian Imperial Eagle and all its major components are stamped with the arsenal mark and date of manufacture. The butt has a raised cheek piece, unlike the flat cheek piece on the French musket.

The Russian muskets fired a spherical lead ball .67in. in diameter. It weighed 450 grains and was wrapped with its powder charge in a paper cartridge.

'The heights of Alma – day after the battle', 21 September 1854

Tinted lithograph after Joseph Austin Benwell (*fl*. 1856-86) after a sketch by an officer of the 95th (The Derbyshire) Regiment of Foot (erroneously referred to on the print as the 95th Highland Regiment), published by Read and Co, London, and H Mandeville, Paris, 27 October 1854, 37.9 cm. h x 52.7 cm. w

NAM. 1995-02-17

The British, short of shipping space, had brought none of their ambulances with them from Bulgaria to the Crimea and the process of clearing the battlefield of dead and wounded took two days. Marshal St Arnaud, whose army had suffered fewer casualties and possessed an efficient ambulance corps, chafed at the delay.

Lieutenant-Colonel Harry Chester's body is shown being carried away on a stretcher in the foreground; Prince Menshikov's coach can be seen behind.

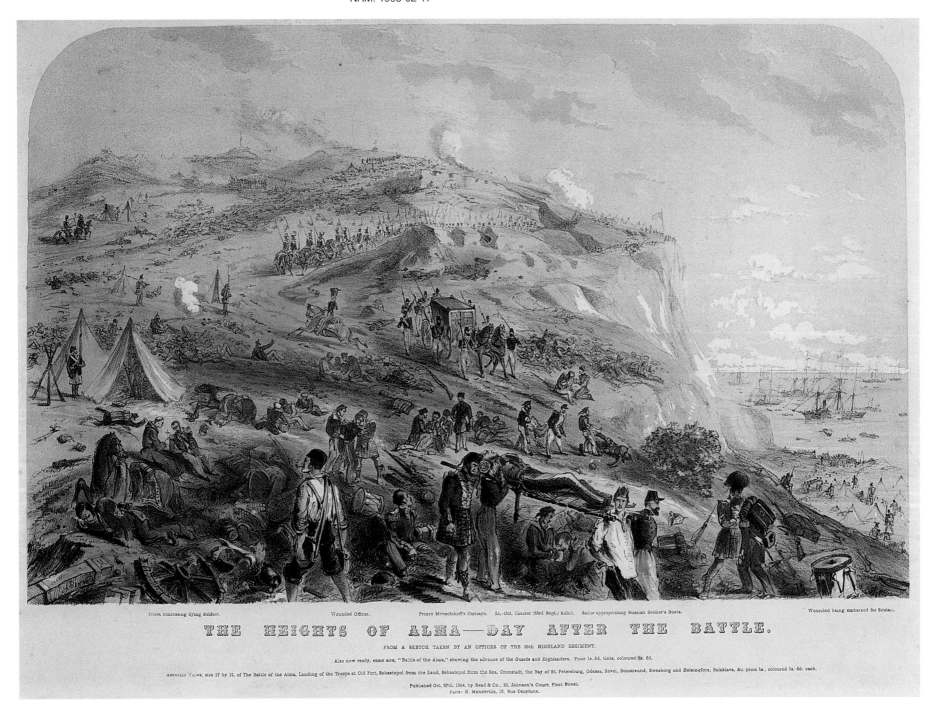

Lieutenant-General Sir George de Lacy Evans' report on the Battle of the Alma, 1854

Manuscript, dated 22 September 1854, 22.8cm. h x 18.5cm. w

Generously donated by the Royal United Service Institution

NAM. 1968-07-288-1

Lord Raglan required his divisional generals to submit reports after each battle detailing the part played by their commands in the action. The information supplied was then incorporated in Raglan's official dispatch. Sir George de Lacy Evans was not backward in promoting the contribution to victory made by the 2nd Division, concluding his report:

> ... I beg to state that there were no troops in front of the 2d Divn. during any part of the Battle, except those of the Enemy - that the Lt Divn. and 1st Divn attacked the Enemy's line and redoubt after passing the river, simultaneously with the 2d Divn. which was on their right - & that the 3rd Divn. was in reserve to the 2d Divn. - And I believe the 2d Divn. was the first engaged with the Enemy.

'High mountain road from McKenzie's farm. There ought to be plenty of figures of troops marching down the roads', 1854

Watercolour and pencil, signed indistinctly by the artist verso 'J F Baddeley', by Second Captain (later Major) John Fraser Lodington Baddeley (d. 1862), Royal Artillery, 1854, 26cm. h x 36.4cm. w

NAM. 1999-12-6

Lord Raglan and Marshal St Arnaud's decision not to attack Sevastopol on its northern side but to march around the town and attack from the south has been heavily criticised. Instead of seizing Sevastopol by *coup de main* (which, given the demoralised state of the Russian defenders after their defeat at the Alma, was perfectly feasible), the Allies settled down to a protracted siege for which the British, at least, were ill-prepared. True, by attacking from the south, the British gained the use of the port of Balaklava (and the French of Kamiesch); but they also surrendered to the Russians the commanding Mackenzie Heights to the north of Sevastopol. This is the moment that the artist captures, as the British artillery descends from MacKenzie's Farm on its march towards Balaklava, 25 September 1854.

Fragment of Regimental Colour carried in the Crimea, 1854-56

57th (The West Middlesex) Regiment of Foot

Generously donated by the Trustees of the
Middlesex Regimental Museum

NAM. 1992-12-14

The traditional role of the regimental colours was to act as a rallying point during battle, and as such they took on totemic significance. It was not unknown for pieces to be cut from regimental colours - as in this instance - when they were replaced by new ones, and some were even laid up in churches in a mutilated condition.

Sir George Cathcart's 4th Division had not fully assembled at the time of the landing in the Crimea, and the 57th (The West Middlesex) Regiment only reached Raglan's Army on 23 September, three days after the Battle of the Alma.

Crimea War Medal 1854-56, with clasp: Alma

Awarded to Lieutenant-Colonel Augustus Cox

Generously donated by Miss I V Cox

NAM. 1966-12-24

Augustus Cox was commissioned Lieutenant in the Grenadier Guards on 27 July 1832, rising to Captain and Lieutenant-Colonel in February 1847. He died of cholera at Balaklava on 27 September 1854. Having lost his horse, his death was undoubtedly hastened by exhaustion suffered during the rigours of the long approach march. A fellow officer, Captain (later General Sir) George Higginson described how:

> Universally popular, not only with us, but with a large circle of friends at home, he had borne the privations and fatigues of the last ten days with admirable fortitude, though already well advanced in years. A battery of artillery was passing by our flank, and our poor comrade was lifted on to a gun limber after a hasty and sad farewell to us all. He was thus carried in to Balaklava, and died that night on board the *Caradoc*.

Medals commemorating the Battle of the Alma, 20 September 1854

Bronze, John Pinches Ltd, 41mm. diam

Generously donated by the Royal United Service Institution

NAM. 1963-05-23-1

White metal, John Pinches Ltd, 41mm. diam

Generously donated by Mr J C Crisp

NAM. 1960-12-100-1

Bronze and white metal versions of the same medal, showing obverse and reverse. The obverse in bronze depicts British soldiers climbing the heights of Alma, led by an officer carrying the colour, with the word: ALMA impressed into a rock below and the date of the battle above. The reverse carries a list of all the divisions and regiments that were present.

The medal is one of a set of three, struck in silver, bronze and white metal, by Pinches, with two other similar medals, commemorating the battles of Balaklava, and Inkerman.

A relish pot or jar entitled 'The Battle of Alma', 1854

Earthenware, with transfer-printed decoration, possibly made by T J and J Mayer at the Furlong Works and Dale Hall Pottery, Burslem, c1854, 9.4cm. h x 7.3cm. w x 7.3cm. d

NAM. 1960-12-10

The design shows the Highland Brigade crossing the River Alma and storming the heights, watched by staff officers. James Thomas Brudenell, 7th Earl of Cardigan (1797-1868), appears among the mounted officers in his elegant uniform of the 11th (or Prince Albert's Own) Regiment of Hussars. In the background the Allied ships ride at anchor in the bay.

The Opening of the Siege of Sevastopol and the Battle of Balaklava

With Menshikov's army demoralised by defeat, and the defences of Sevastopol on the landward side negligible, the capture of the town by the Allies appeared certain. Fatally, it was decided to besiege Sevastopol rather than risk an assault. This gave time to the Russian engineering genius, Colonel Todleben, to construct defences so formidable that even after the Allies commenced their bombardment on 17 October 1854, they still dared not attempt a storming. Menshikov's field army, meanwhile, had been reinforced, and on 25 October a detachment 25,000 strong under General Liprandi attacked the port of Balaklava, through which the British outside Sevastopol drew all of their supplies. Liprandi enjoyed initial success and he captured some redoubts garrisoned by the Turks, along with seven British cannon. His cavalry, however, was turned back from Balaklava itself by the 93rd Highlanders, the 'Thin Red Line', and roughly handled by the Heavy Brigade of British cavalry. By now reinforcements were arriving from the British siegeworks before Sevastopol and Lord Raglan ordered his Light Brigade of cavalry to advance and retake the guns captured earlier by the Russians. Disastrously, his orders were misunderstood, and the 673 horsemen of the Light Brigade charged in the wrong direction straight towards the entire Russian army. The Light Brigade, despite prodigies of valour, was cut to pieces.

Lieutenant-Colonel (later Lieutenant-General) James Thomas Brudenell, 7th Earl of Cardigan (1797-1868), 11th (or Prince Albert's Own) Hussars, *c*1854

Oil on millboard by Alfred Frank de Prades (*fl.* 1844-83), *c*1854, 60.3cm. h x 47.6 cm. w

NAM. 1967-02-19

Lord Cardigan is shown mounted on his thoroughbred chestnut horse 'Ronald', which he rode in the Charge of the Light Brigade. Ronald's distinctive two white 'stockings', both reaching high up the leg, served to mark Cardigan out when controversy later arose concerning what he did or did not do in the course of the Charge.

'The Thin Red Line', 25 October 1854

Coloured photogravure after Robert Gibb (1845-1932), published by Archibald Ramsden, London, 1 September 1883, 56.7cm. h x 87.5cm. w

Generously donated by the Argyll and Sutherland Highlanders

NAM. 1956-02-721

At a crucial moment of the Battle of Balaklava, a strong body of Russian cavalry swept towards the British-held port. All that stood between them and the British base were six companies of the 93rd (Highland) Regiment of Foot under Sir Colin Campbell. Drawn up in ranks two deep – a 'thin red streak' as the journalist William Howard Russell described them - the Highlanders fired two volleys which turned the Russians back. The artist has depicted the Russians approaching too close: in reality, the range and accuracy of the Minié rifle sent them into retreat at a distance of 230 metres.

Letter to Lord Raglan from Sir George Cathcart, 4 October 1854

Manuscript, 18 cm. h x 11.2 cm. w

Generously donated by the Royal United Service Institution

NAM. 1968-07-292-7

Sir George Cathcart had advised that Sevastopol be assaulted immediately the Allies arrived at the south side of the town. His advice was rejected. Cathcart's *amour propre* was further affronted when, aware that he held a secret commission to succeed as commander-in-chief in the event of Raglan's incapacitation, he found that Lieutenant-General Sir George Brown and the Quartermaster-General, Brigadier-General Richard Airey had assumed the role of Raglan's chief lieutenants. Cathcart therefore wrote to Raglan demanding an immediate interview. To the satisfaction of both parties, Cathcart's secret commission was withdrawn by the Government at the end of October.

'Camp Sebastl Siege train - covering gun - wheels - with sheep skins - to prevent noise. Preparations to go out to trenches. Oct 1854'

Watercolour, signed and dated lower left 'Oct 1854 J A Crowe', by Joseph Archer Crowe (1825-96), 'special' artist for *The Illustrated London News*, 1854, the original for a print entitled 'Siege of Sebastopol – preparing a train for the trenches', published in *The Illustrated London News*, 4 November 1854, 23.8cm. h x 34.cm. w

Generously donated by Mrs Aldred Brown

NAM. 1963-10-18-3

Once the Allies had decided to subject Sevastopol to bombardment before commencing their assault, the siege train had to be unshipped and transported (in the case of the British) from Balaklava, a distance of ten kilometres. The British landed 73 heavy guns, many of them naval pieces which had to be conveyed on spare travelling carriages (with larger wheels). In this scene the artist shows a trenching party preparing for a night's work: the wheels of the covering guns are covered with sheepskins to prevent creaking and avoid the Russians being guided to where the trenching-party was to begin digging.

'Life in camp before Sebastopol. No. 4 The midnight alarm', *c*1854

Coloured lithograph after artist unknown, number four in the series of six prints of life in camp before Sebastopol, published by Read & Co, London, 22 November 1854, 21.9 cm. h x 27.2 cm. w

NAM. 1981-10-110-2

The Cavalry Division was posted near Balaklava, guarding the British army's lines of communication. During October 1854, false alarms were numerous, as Lieutenant Edward Seager of the 8th (The King's Royal Irish) Regiment of (Light) Dragoons (Hussars) complained:

> The cavalry have been worked very much, as we do all the outpost duty, night and day. We cover Balaklava, being encamped in the valley leading to the town and we have to find patrols, pickets, and vedettes for all the country around our position. We are protecting the rear of our position from attack, and what annoys us the most is there is scarcely a day passes that it does not sound turn out the whole, and away we have to go to look at a few cossacks; perhaps to remain there for many hours.

'By a sudden spring the 33rd man seized the Russians firelock, and, on the speculation of its being loaded discharged it at its owner, who rolled over dead, and his companion was immediately clubbed. Calmly picking up his own Minnie, our friend returned to his regiment', 1854

Coloured tinted lithograph by M & N Hanhart after Michael Angelo Hayes (1820-77), number eight in the second series of Lloyd's 'Incidents From The War in the Crimea', published by Lloyd Brothers & Co, 26 December 1854, 33.6cm. h x 31cm. w

Generously donated by Mrs W M Watson

NAM. 1964-12-41

On 31 October 1854, after the First Bombardment of Sevastopol, Major George Mundy, in temporary command of the 33rd (The Duke of Wellington's) Regiment of Foot, wrote the following to his mother:

I had to call out one of our men Private Pat McGuire and present to him from Ld Raglan a gratuity of £5 for "Gallant conduct of the Field". The facts of the case are these. Several volunteers from different Reg[imen]ts are daily selected as sharpshooters to advance as near as possible to the enemy's guns & shoot the gunners & to prevent the approach of their sharpshooters. On the 18th P McGuire was one of these. Somehow or another he and another man were surrounded & taken prisoner. Two of the Russians walked him off, one of these carrying his gun as well as his own. He was marching a little way behind them when he noticed that the man on his right was carrying his firelock very clumsily & the one on his left looking the other way he took the opportunity, sprang forward, wrested the firelock from him & shot him dead, then swung the firelock round hitting the other man in the stomach, *regained* his own firelock! and rejoined the men. This was seen by several persons & reported immediately.

Patrick McGuire (1837-62) was later recommended for the Victoria Cross, but was turned down because his deed was considered of doubtful morality and it was feared that it might encourage the enemy to execute prisoners. His exploit nevertheless captured the public imagination and was the subject of three different prints.

Medals awarded to Sergeant-Major John Motion, 1854-66

Crimea War Medal 1854-56, with clasps: Alma, Balaklava, Sebastopol; Indian Mutiny Medal 1857-58, with clasps: Relief of Lucknow, Lucknow; Army Long Service and Good Conduct Medal c1866; Turkish Crimean War Medal 1855, British issue

NAM. 1990-12-21

John Motion (1830-1911) was born near Pitlessie in Fife and attested for the 93rd (Highland) Regiment of Foot at Perth in August 1849. He served with the 93rd for 21 years, reaching the rank of colour-sergeant. He was in the Crimea for 29 months, being engaged in the Battles of the Alma and Balaklava, the Siege of Sevastopol and the expeditions to Kerch and Yenikale. One of the 'thin red line' at Balaklava, he served as a deputy provost martial in 1855-56, and afterwards accompanied the regiment to India, seeing action at the Relief of Lucknow and the Capture of Lucknow during the suppression of the mutiny in the Bengal Army. After leaving the Army he served for 20 years as a drill instructor on the Clyde Training Ship *Empress*.

Major-General James Scarlett

Photograph by Roger Fenton

NAM. Negative 46921

Major-General The Honourable (later General Sir) James Yorke Scarlett (1799-1871) was first commissioned in 1818. By 1854, having served with the 5th (Princess Charlotte of Wales's) Dragoon Guards since 1830 (and commanded them since 1840), he was on the point of retiring when he was given command of the Army of the East's Heavy Brigade of Cavalry. At the Battle of Balaklava on 25 October 1854 he led his 800 men of the Heavy Brigade against 3000 Russian cavalry and forced them to withdraw. He succeeded Lord Lucan in command of the Cavalry Division in 1855.

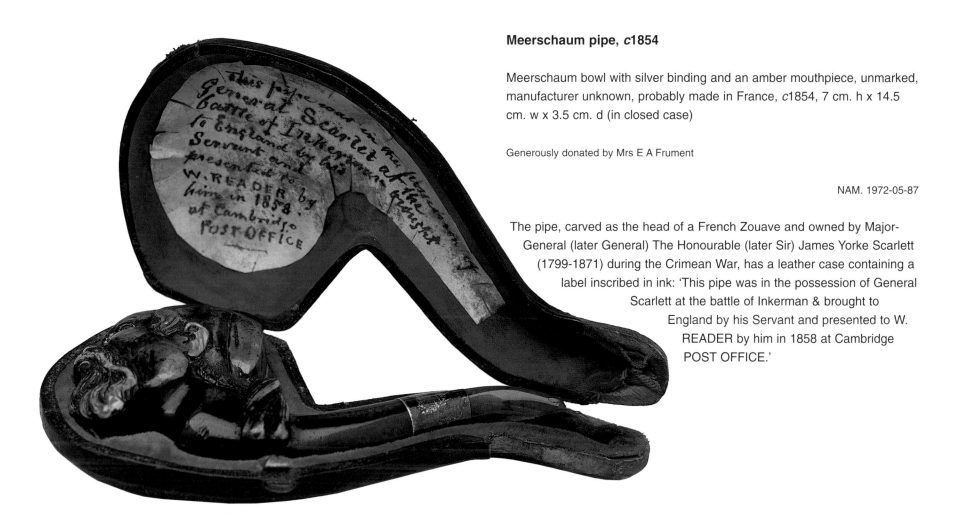

Meerschaum pipe, *c*1854

Meerschaum bowl with silver binding and an amber mouthpiece, unmarked, manufacturer unknown, probably made in France, *c*1854, 7 cm. h x 14.5 cm. w x 3.5 cm. d (in closed case)

Generously donated by Mrs E A Frument

NAM. 1972-05-87

The pipe, carved as the head of a French Zouave and owned by Major-General (later General) The Honourable (later Sir) James Yorke Scarlett (1799-1871) during the Crimean War, has a leather case containing a label inscribed in ink: 'This pipe was in the possession of General Scarlett at the battle of Inkerman & brought to England by his Servant and presented to W. READER by him in 1858 at Cambridge POST OFFICE.'

Percussion Pistol, *c*1850

Parker Field & Sons, High Holborn, London

34cm. l

Generously donated by Miss E C Twist

NAM. 1959-11-224

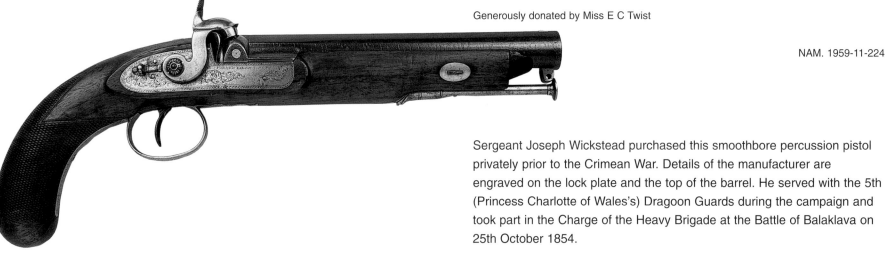

Sergeant Joseph Wickstead purchased this smoothbore percussion pistol privately prior to the Crimean War. Details of the manufacturer are engraved on the lock plate and the top of the barrel. He served with the 5th (Princess Charlotte of Wales's) Dragoon Guards during the campaign and took part in the Charge of the Heavy Brigade at the Battle of Balaklava on 25th October 1854.

Pattern 1821 Heavy Cavalry Officer's Sword

105cm. l.

NAM 1988-02-12

Colonel (later General Sir) Edward Cooper Hodge (1810-94) was first commissioned in the 4th (Royal Irish) Dragoon Guards in 1826. He probably acquired this sword when the 4th Dragoon Guards introduced a regimental variant of the Pattern 1821 Heavy Cavalry Sword with a pronounced and lengthened pommel. As with the Light Cavalry Sword, the Heavy Cavalry type initially had a pipe-back blade which only began to be replaced by the stronger Wilkinson flat-back type in the late 1840s. The new pommel was similar to that of an existing sword of the 2nd Life Guards and seems to have been influenced by French styles.

Hodge commanded the 4th Dragoon Guards throughout the Crimean campaign and led it in the Charge of the Heavy Brigade at Balaklava. He also commanded the Heavy Brigade itself briefly in 1855 and 1856.

Pattern 1821 Heavy Cavalry Officer's Sword, *c*1845

105cm. l.

Bequeathed by Mr H J J Warr

NAM 2002-11-747

Lieutenant-Colonel (later General Sir) Henry Dalrymple White (1820-86), carried the sword whilst leading the 6th (Inniskilling) Dragoons in the Charge of the Heavy Brigade, during which his helmet was stove in by a Russian sabre. The historian Kinglake, to whom White passed information, remarked of him that during the Charge:

> He saw a fair-haired Russian lad of seventeen, enwrapped like the rest in the coarse heavy over-coat which was common to officers and men; and what seems to have interested him – for he looked with the eyes of a man who cares much for questions of race – was the powerlessness of a levelling costume to disguise the true breed, and the certainty with which, as he thought, he could detect gentle blood under the common grey cloth of a trooper. 'He looked', says Colonel White, - 'he looked like an Eton boy.' The boy fought with great bravery; but it was well if he had no mother, for before the fight ended he fell, his youthful head cloven in two.

Although technically a heavy cavalry officer's sword, White's is quite different to that owned by Colonel Hodge. A particularly light sword, it has a blade more akin to the light cavalry pattern. It was presented to White by his fellow-officer, Captain Charles Cameron Shute.

Orders and Medals of General William Charles Forrest, 1856-75

Order of the Bath, Companion badge (CB) 1875; Crimea War Medal 1854-56, with clasps: Balaklava, Inkermann, Sebastopol; Order of the Mejidie, Turkey, Badge of the 5th Class *c*1856; Sardinian War Medal *c*1856; Turkish Crimean War Medal 1855, Sardinian issue

Generously donated by Lieutenant-Colonel A G F Monro

NAM. 1959-02-53

Captain Forrest had escaped Lord Cardigan by exchanging out of the 11th Hussars into the 4th (Royal Irish) Dragoon Guards in 1844. He received his majority in 1848. During the Crimean War he served as second-in-command of the 4th Dragoon Guards to Colonel Hodge. In his correspondence Forrest rather slightingly referred to his commanding officer as 'Little Hodge' (at sixteen Hodge had been only 5' 1" tall). Hodge, for his part, could not abide Forrest's wife (she joined her husband in the Crimea in 1855). In 1863 Forrest received command of the 7th Dragoon Guards; he was appointed CB in 1875 while Honorary Colonel of the 11th Hussars. He died in 1902.

Helmet and Plume, *c*1854-63

7th (Princess Royal's) Dragoon Guards, formerly of the 4th (Royal Irish) Dragoon Guards

Gilt metal, black leather lining, horse hair plume

Generously donated by Lieutenant Colonel A G F Monro

NAM. 1959-02-56, -1, -2

This helmet was worn by Major William Charles Forrest of the 4th (Royal Irish) Dragoon Guards during the Charge of the Heavy Brigade. 'I got a crack on the head in one charge but the brass pot stood well, & my head is only slightly bruised', he reported. Forrest was obviously attached to the helmet for when he assumed command of the 7th Dragoon Guards in 1863 he kept it, merely changing the badge and plume for that of his new regiment.

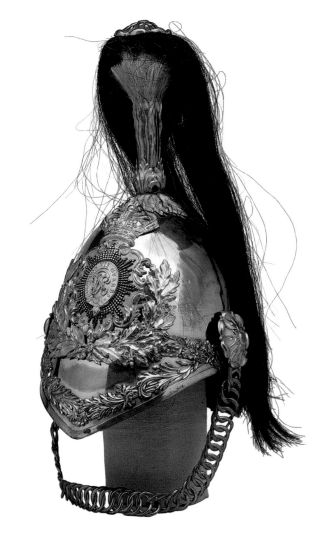

Officer's Coatee, short tailed, *c*1854

5th (Princess Charlotte of Wales's) Dragoon Guards

Wool cloth, gold wire and spangle embroidered ornament, gilt metal buttons

NAM. 1955-02-1

The coatee, meaning a small coat, is a nineteenth century body garment closed in front and cut across the waist leaving only small skirts behind. In 1847 the coatee of the heavy cavalry had been shortened still further to a jacket style. The coatee of the dragoon guards was single breasted, with round cuffs and velvet regimental facings. The turnbacks at the rear of the coatee were in the regimental facing colours and edged in gold lace for officers and yellow for the men and bore a regimental pattern skirt ornament. Shoulder scales, lacking from this coatee, were not worn in the Crimea.

Other Rank's Sabretache, *c*1854

12th Hussars, Ingermanlandski Regiment

Black leather, drab canvas lining, blue wool cloth

Generously donated by Mr E Mollo

NAM. 1977-12-66

The Ingermanlandski Regiment was one of the Russian cavalry units defeated in the Charge of the Heavy Brigade and this sabretache was reputedly retrieved from the battlefield. Made of black leather, to the centre of the front flap is an appliquéd piece of blue woollen cloth, leaving a border of yellow fabric. The blue cloth is cut away in the form of a Russian numeral.

Other Rank's Helmet and Plume, *c*1855

4th (Royal Irish) Dragoon Guards

Gilt metal, white horse hair plume

Generously donated by Mrs D Bowen

NAM. 1963-09-599, -1, -2

Medals awarded to Sergeant-Major Timothy Marks, 1854-56

Crimea War Medal 1854-56, with clasps: Balaklava, Inkermann, Sebastopol; Turkish Crimean War Medal 1855, Sardinian issue

Generously donated by Mrs D Bowen

NAM. 1963-09-599, -3, -4

Worn by Sergeant-Major Timothy Marks during the Crimean War. The 'Albert' style helmet introduced for heavy cavalry in 1849 was similar to that worn by the Household Cavalry since 1842, and superseded the earlier 'Roman helmet'. The new helmet was the first of the *pickelhaube* style – then favoured by the Germans and Russians – and later prevalent in the British Army. The plume issuing out of the leaf-shaped socket on top of the helmet was not worn in the Crimea.

Timothy Marks was born in 1831 at Roscrea, County Tipperary. In June 1849 he attested at Dublin to serve in the 47th (The Lancashire) Regiment of Foot, transferring to the 6th Regiment of Dragoon Guards (Carabineers) in January 1850, and the 4th (Royal Irish) Dragoon Guards in March 1852 – remaining in that regiment until his discharge in October 1870. His only overseas service was the 25 months he spent in Turkey and the Crimea, during which he was promoted corporal in August 1855 and sergeant in December 1855. He achieved the rank of troop-sergeant-major in January 1867. At the time of his discharge he was suffering from dyspepsia and an enlarged liver. His health had been affected by 'climatic influence and severe military duty to which he was necessarily exposed during the Crimean campaign'. After he left the regular army his served for 13 years as a troop-sergeant-major on the Permanent Staff of the Nottinghamshire Yeomanry Cavalry, for which his pension was increased to 2/9d per day in July 1884.

One of Marks' medals is the Turkish Crimean War Medal. It had been the intention of the Turkish Sultan to award all survivors of the Crimean Army

with a silver medal, which he instituted in 1855. It was struck in three slightly different versions for British, French and Sardinian troops, the arrangement of the flags depicted on the medal denoting the country concerned. Approximately 75,000 medals were claimed by Britain. However not all these reached their destination, owing to a shortfall in production and the loss of a consignment of some 22,000 medals when the SS *Pomona* was shipwrecked near Malta on 22 February 1860. The shortage in British medals was made up to a great extent by issuing British soldiers with Sardinian or French versions.

The Charge of the Heavy Brigade, Balaklava, 1854

Watercolour and pen and ink, signed lower right 'Orlando Norie', by
Orlando Norie (1832-1901), c1854, 31cm. h x 48.1cm. w

Bequeathed by Dr B L Steele

NAM. 1992-07-268

The 4th (Royal Irish) Regiment of Dragoon Guards and the 2nd (Royal
North British) Regiment of Dragoons are depicted charging the enemy.

The Charge of the Heavy Brigade at the Battle of Balaklava, 25 October, 1854

Oil on canvas, signed and dated lower right 'G D Giles 1897', by Godfrey Douglas Giles (1857-1941), 1897, 122.2cm. h x 213.4cm. w

NAM. 1994-05-57

On the 25 October 1854, Russian forces mounted an attack on the British position at Balaklava, and a body of some 3,000 Russian cavalry threatened the road to the harbour of Balaklava itself.

The British Heavy Brigade, about 800 strong, consisted of ten squadrons of heavy cavalry, commanded by Major-General (later General) The Honourable (later Sir) James Yorke Scarlett (1799-1871). Seeing the

Russian horsemen halted, and thus vulnerable to attack, Scarlett immediately charged uphill with three of his squadrons, being successively reinforced by the remaining seven squadrons of his Brigade. Reeling from this series of attacks, the Russian cavalry was forced to give ground and retreated.

The painting shows the action as the first line of the Heavy Brigade crashes into the Russian cavalry. In the foreground is the 2nd squadron of the 6th (Inniskilling) Dragoons, while in the background are two squadrons of the 2nd (Royal North British) Dragoons (later Royal Scots Greys). In reality, because of the difficulties of the ground, the Heavy Brigade's attack was delivered at a rather gentler pace than the painting suggests.

'The Late Captain Lewis [*sic*] Edward Nolan, 15th Hussars'

Wood engraving 'from a picture painted in India', artist unknown, published in *The Illustrated London News*, 25 November 1854, 15.6cm. w x 11.2cm. w

NAM. Books 18561

Captain Louis Edward Nolan (1818-54) was raised in Italy from the age of eleven and served in the Austrian cavalry before gaining a commission in the 15th (The King's) Regiment of (Light) Dragoons (Hussars) in 1839. He served with his regiment in India for much of the 1840s before returning to England and writing two well-received books, *The Training of Cavalry Remount Horses: A New System,* and *Cavalry: Its History and Tactics.* These brought him to the attention of the military authorities and in 1854 he was given a staff appointment in the Army of the East. His Crimean campaign journal, and the testimony of his friend, *The Times* journalist William Howard Russell, make plain the frustration that he felt at the timid handling of the cavalry by Lord Lucan, and he has long been held at least partly responsible for sending the Light Brigade charging in the wrong direction at the Battle of Balaklava on 25 October, 1854. Whether his dashing out in front of Lord Cardigan at the beginning of the Charge was done in an attempt to re-direct the Brigade will forever remain unknown: he was killed by the first Russian shot fired.

Cavalry Officer's cloak, *c*1854

Worn by Captain L E Nolan

Generously donated by The Royal United Service Institution

NAM. 1963-10-314

Captain Louis Edward Nolan lent his cloak to *The Times* journalist William Howard Russell who was still in possession of it when Nolan was killed in the Charge of the Light Brigade. Russell bought the cloak at the auction of Nolan's effects and in later years donated it to the Royal United Service Institution.

Campaign Journal of Captain Louis Edward Nolan, 1854

Manuscript, 18cm. h x 23cm. w

NAM. 1989-06-41

Nolan began to keep a campaign journal as soon as he landed in the Crimea on 14 September. In lay-out his narrative occupies the right-hand page and his commentary the left-hand. The failure of the cavalry to mount a pursuit of the defeated Russians after the Battle of the Alma on 20 September left Nolan severely critical of the caution of the Cavalry Division's commander, Lord Lucan:

At no time sh[oul]d Cavalry stand fast to count the opposing squadrons. Frederick the Great gave an order that any Cav[a]l[r]y Officer meeting the Enemy & not charging sh[oul]d be cashiered! When a routed army was in full retreat what excuse can any one find for those horsemen who did not do their duty & whose chief replied to an order to advance that the Russians were very numerous!!

Nolan's strictures upon Lord Lucan help explain his state of mind when, a month later, he delivered the fateful order that launched the Charge of the Light Brigade.

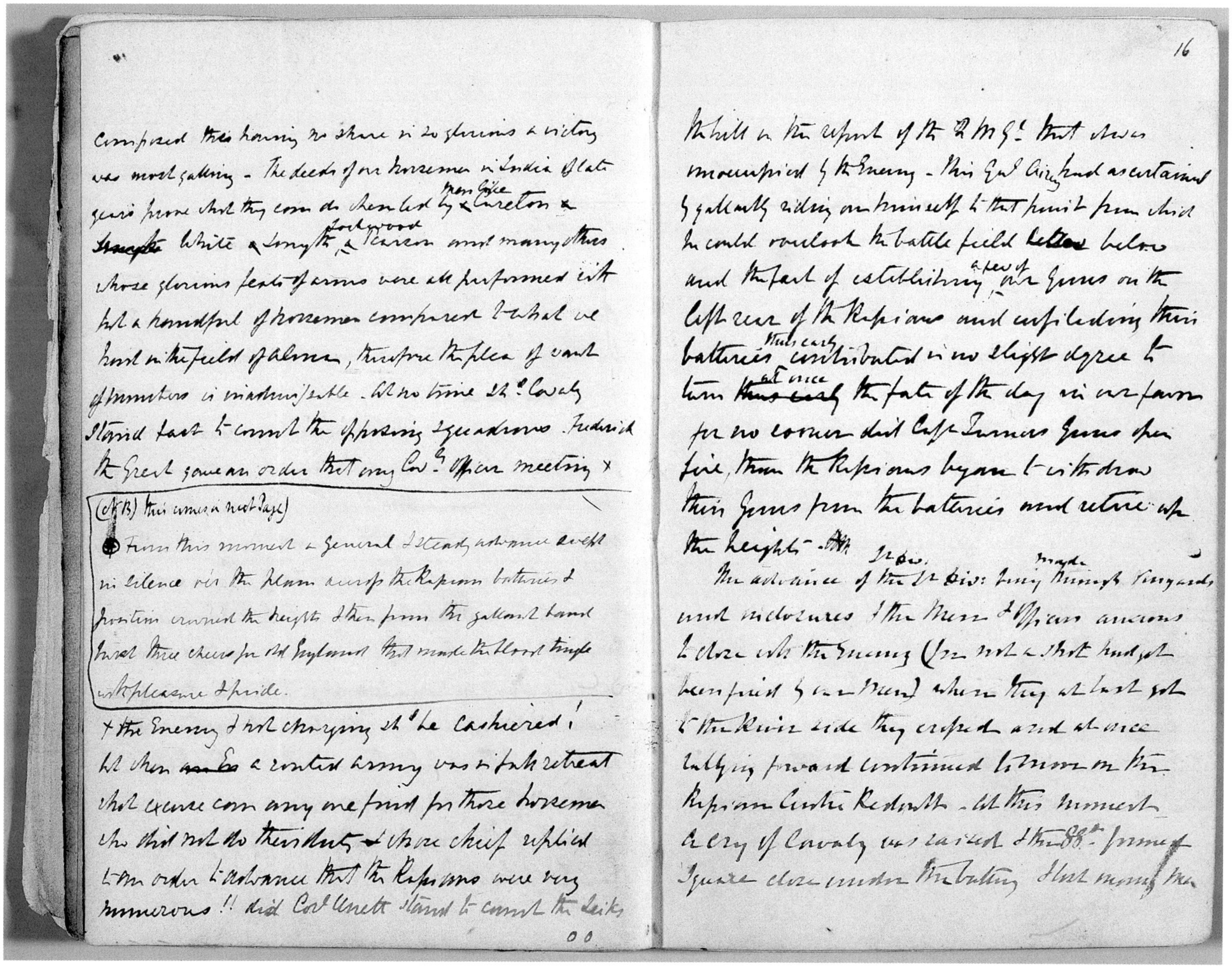

The Order that launched the Charge of the Light Brigade, 1854

Manuscript, 11cm. h x 18.2cm. w

Loan

NAM. 1962-11-4-3

After the defeat of the Russian cavalry by the Heavy Brigade, Lord Raglan – observing the battlefield from 182m. above on the Sapoune Height - wished to exploit his success by recapturing the redoubts on the Causeway Heights. One order had already been sent 45 minutes earlier for Lord Lucan to advance with the Cavalry Division but, misunderstanding its content, Lucan failed to act. Matters took on a greater urgency when it became evident to Raglan that the Russians were removing the British cannon from the redoubts. A further order, dictated by Raglan and written down by the Quartermaster-General, Richard Airey, renewed the instruction to Lucan to attack. It was conveyed – fatefully - by Captain Nolan. Lucan, who from where he stood could see very little of what was apparent to Raglan, reported his exchange of words with Nolan:

Captain Nolan, the aide de camp of the Quartermaster-General, came up to me at speed, and placed in my hands this written instruction:- 'Lord Raglan wishes the cavalry to advance rapidly to the front, follow the enemy & try to prevent the enemy carrying away the guns. Troop Horse Artillery may accompany. French cavalry is on your left. Immediate. R Airey'. After reading this order I hesitated, and urged the uselessness of such an attack, and the dangers attending it; the aide de camp, in a most authoritative tone, stated that they were Lord Raglan's orders that the cavalry should attack immediately. I asked him where? and what to do? as neither enemy nor guns were within sight. He replied in a most disrespectful but significant manner, pointing to the further end of //the valley, 'There, my lord, is your enemy; there are your guns.'

Nolan's impatient gesture, rather than pointing towards the Causeway Heights, indicated a battery of twelve Russian cannon a mile distant, behind which had regrouped their defeated cavalry. On either side of the North Valley, on the Causeway Heights to the south and the Fedioukine Heights to the north, the Russians had further batteries as well as riflemen. Attacking in that direction was surely suicidal. Yet Lucan felt he had no choice but to obey.

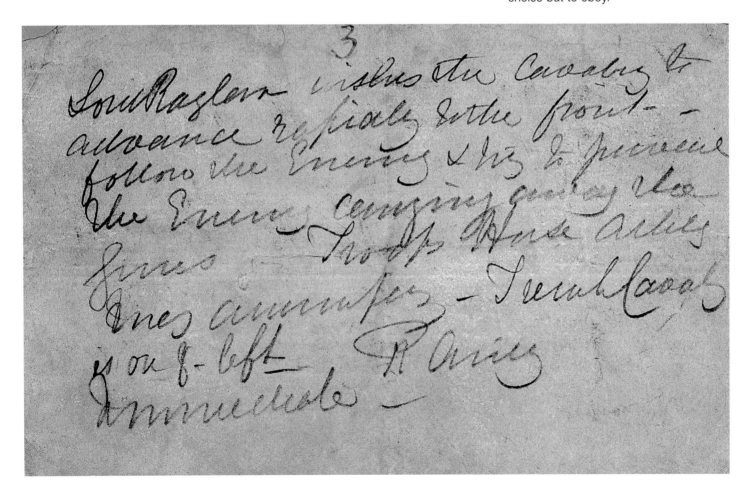

Lord Cardigan's Memorandum on the Charge of the Light Brigade, 1854

Manuscript, 23.5cm. h x 37.4cm. w

Generously donated by the Royal United Service Institution

NAM. 1968-07-288-2

Cardigan delivered his memorandum to Lord Raglan on 27 October, two days after the Charge. The section reproduced reads as follows:

> [A] few minutes afterwards the Lt General [Lucan] came in front of the Brigade, ordered the 11th Hussars to fall back in support and told me to attack the Russians in the Valley, about 3/4 of mile distant with the 13th Lt Dragoons & 17th Lancers. I answered "certainly but allow me to point out to you that the hills on each side are covered with Artillery & Riflemen. The Lt General replied "I cannot help it, you must attack, Lord Raglan desires the Lt Brigade immediately to attack the enemy. A few minutes afterwards whilst advancing Capt. Nolan came in front of the Brigade with a view as it appeared of hurrying it on. A shell burst between him & me which was the cause of his death. I led the Brigade down the [?hill] in front of the Russian battery of heavy guns firing shells, grape shot [& round shot].

Relief of the Light Brigade, 25 October 1854

Oil on canvas, signed and dated lower left 'R Caton Woodville/ 1897', by Richard Caton Woodville (1856-1927), 1897, 76.2cm. h x 114.3cm. w

Purchased with the assistance of a benefaction from The Headley Trust

NAM. 1989-01-1

Of all British military engagements during the nineteenth century, the Charge of the Light Brigade at the Battle of Balaklava remains the most notorious. One of the most spectacular of military disasters, surrounded by controversy as to its cause, the tragic charge of the British light cavalry regiments along the 'valley of death' under murderous fire from the Russian guns was genuinely heroic. The legend of the 'gallant 600' remains deeply rooted in the public mind today, some 150 years later.

Not surprisingly, contemporary pictures of the Charge are few and they fail to convey more than a distant 'bird's-eye view' of the action. It was left to the most dramatic exponent of military art in the late-Victorian era, Richard Caton Woodville, to capture the supreme moment of the Charge, when the British troopers, depleted by the murderous fire of Russian artillery overlooking their route, finally arrived at the far end of the valley to cross swords with the enemy. Widely reproduced, this is still the most popular image of the event today. It was originally reproduced as a chromolithograph Supplement to *Holly Leaves*, *The Illustrated Sporting and Dramatic News* Christmas Number 1897, entitled 'The Relief of the Light Brigade'.

Letter of Private Edward John Firkins, 13th Regiment of (Light) Dragoons

Manuscript, dated 27 December 1854, Camp before Sebastopol, 18cm. h x 22.8cm. w

Generously donated by Mr L E Allen

NAM. 1986-02-75

In his letter Firkins, having here described the loss of the redoubts by the Turks, goes on to describe his part in the Charge of the Light Brigade. At one point he was attacked by two Russian lancers, one of whom he killed before being saved by the intervention of a British lancer. It is indicative of the difficulty of determining who actually rode in the Charge that for a long time it was thought Firkins had been absent but, as he explains, he returned from Scutari just in time to participate. The late Canon William Lummis, co-author of *Honour the Light Brigade,* the chief work on the subject, saw this letter in 1985 and as a result revised his earlier opinion that Firkins had not been a 'Charger'.

Medals awarded to Private William Sewell, 1854-56

Crimea War Medal 1854-56, with clasps: Balaklava, Sebastopol; Turkish Crimean War Medal 1855, British issue. The latter has a privately made silver suspender.

Generously donated by the Royal United Service Institution

NAM. 1963-10-68

Private William Sewell (*c*1830-1910) enlisted in the Army in 1851/52 and was badly wounded at Balaklava during the Charge of the Light Brigade. The injury to his head was so severe that for the remainder of his life a plate was fixed over the wound. He left the Army as a sergeant and became a coachman, dying in Liverpool.

Other Rank's Coatee, Forage Cap, Spurs, *c*1855

13th Regiment of (Light) Dragoons

Wool cloth, brass buttons, cloth cap, leather chin strap, steel spurs

NAM. 1963-11-20, -1, -3, -4

The short-tailed coatee worn by Private William Sewell has a brass screw-button on each shoulder for attaching shoulder scales. His forage cap was originally a small cap worn by the men of cavalry regiments whilst out collecting forage for the horses. Later the term was applied to the undress caps worn by cavalrymen when the full dress headdress was to be preserved. It was generally round and stiffened, with or without a peak, with a cloth band in the regimental facing colour and a black leather chin-strap with adjustable buckle. The straight necked, box pattern, steel spurs have a spike fitting and screw bar for attaching to the boots.

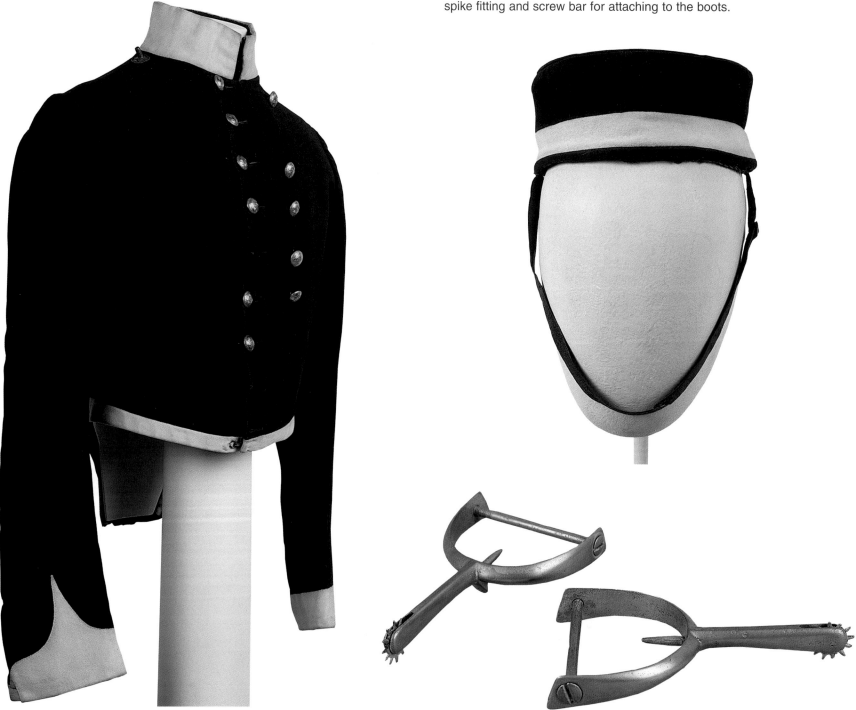

Medals awarded to Sergeant Frederick Peake, 1854-56

Crimea War Medal 1854-56, with clasps: Alma, Balaklava, Sebastopol; Turkish Crimean War Medal 1855, British issue. Each medal has a privately made silver brooch fitting with foliate decoration.

Generously donated by Mrs E Peake

NAM. 1956-10-45

Frederick Peake was born in Dublin where he enlisted into the 13th (Light) Dragoons aged eighteen in November 1846. After service in the United Kingdom he embarked with the Army of the East in 1854 and was promoted sergeant during the voyage. His arm was broken by a canister shot during the Charge of the Light Brigade. Evacuated first to Scutari, he was invalided home on 20 December 1854 and remained throughout 1855 at the Invalid Depot at Chatham. He was discharged from the Army as a result of his wound in January 1856 with a pension of 1/3d per day. Because he could read and write, Peake secured a post as a military stores clerk with an increased pension. He nonetheless encountered financial difficulties and before his death in 1906 had sought relief from the Light Brigade Survivors' Fund and the Royal Patriotic Fund.

Other Rank's Coatee, c.1854

13th Regiment of (Light) Dragoons

Wool cloth, brass regimental buttons

Generously donated by Mrs E Peake

NAM. 1956-10-44-1

Worn by Sergeant Frederick Peake, the damage to the coatee is believed to have occurred during the Charge of the Light Brigade. The lower right sleeve where Peake was wounded has been cut away and the upper sleeve cut and fastened with two white tapes. The upper left sleeve is also damaged. The coatee has been let-out at the sides, lengthened, and the buttons moved, probably to ensure that it fitted Sergeant Peake in later life when he attended dinners of the Balaklava Commemoration Society.

Frederick Peake

Cabinet photograph, 13.2 cm. h x 10.5cm. w

Generously donated by Mrs E Peake

NAM. 1956-10-47-7

Frederick Peake in old age, dressed in the coatee that he wore during the Charge of the Light Brigade.

Medals awarded to Sergeant John Taylor, 1848-66

Punjab Campaign Medal 1848-49, with clasps: Goojerat, Chilianwala; Crimea War Medal 1854-56, with clasps: Alma, Balaklava, Sebastopol; Army Long Service and Good Conduct Medal c1866; Turkish Crimean War Medal 1855, Sardinian issue

Generously donated by Mr P Taylor

NAM. 1979-09-27

John Taylor served in India with the 3rd (King's Own Light) Dragoons, transferring to the 13th (Light) Dragoons on 1 July 1853. He was invalided to England on 15 April 1855. Although Taylor legitimately possesses a Balaklava clasp to his Crimea War Medal he is not believed to have participated in the Charge of the Light Brigade.

'Col. Doherty Officers & Men 13th Light Dragoons'

Photograph by Roger Fenton, 14.4cm. h x 19.3cm. w

Generously donated by Lieutenant-Colonel N Lovett

NAM. 1964-12-151-6-39

Photographed by Fenton in the spring of 1855. The officers wear peaked forage caps; the other ranks caps of the pillbox type. More than one of the officers wear the popular rabbit-skin 'bunny' coat.

Medals and order awarded to Major Thomas Hutton, 1854-56

Crimea War Medal 1854-56, with clasps: Alma, Balaklava, Sebastopol, and Turkish Order of the Mejidie, 5th Class.

Generously donated by Lady Violet Graham

NAM. 1967-06-31-20

Captain Thomas Everard Hutton (1821-96) exchanged into the 4th Light Dragoons in 1847 from the 15th (Yorkshire, East Riding) Regiment of Foot and was promoted captain in 1852. He was severely wounded during the Charge of the Light Brigade, as he wrote afterwards:

> I got a disagreeable fore-runner by a ball ripping the cloth of my jacket at the elbow &, the next moment, I was struck on the right thigh, with such violence I thought my whole leg had been carried off by a cannon shot, - I charged on, however, with the regiment, in spite of pain and loss of blood …

> We returned from our charge, & singular to say, I was again struck about the same spot on the other leg.

After treatment at Scutari and Malta, Hutton returned to England in March 1855 and received his Crimea War Medal from Queen Victoria at the presentation ceremony on Horse Guards Parade, 18 May 1855. He retired from the Army as a brevet-major by sale of his commission in 1857.

Saddle, c1847-54

55cm. l x 50cm. w x 62cm. h

Generously donated by Lady Violet Graham

NAM. 1967-06-31-1

Captain Thomas Hutton used this saddle during the Charge of the Light Brigade when he was severely wounded in both thighs. On his return, according to the historian Kinglake, Hutton 'was lifted out of his saddle in a scarcely conscious state.' He himself wrote three days later: 'Altogether I consider myself most fortunate & I trust, if the cloth from my overalls and linen has in each case been forced through, & does not remain in, soon to be well enough to return to England. I took one of the balls that favoured me out of the flap of my saddle.'

This type of saddle, commonly known as the Hussar Pattern, was first issued to all hussar regiments in 1805. It latter became the pattern for all the light cavalry and continued in use until after the end of the Crimean War. The Hussar saddle was also known as the Hungarian saddle because it was first used by Hungarian cavalry regiments of the Austrian Army. It was copied and used not only by the British but also by the French, German and American armies.

Harness Bosses, 1854

4th (The Queen's Own) Light Dragoons

Hollow domed brass on brown leather backing, 5.5 cm. w

Generously donated by Lady Violet Graham

NAM. 1967-06-31-7

These bosses, owned by Captain Thomas Hutton, were worn on the horse's leather bridle or body harness. After receiving eleven wounds during the Charge of the Light Brigade, Hutton's horse had to be destroyed.

Officer's Shako, Forage Cap, Sabretache, Shabraque Badge and Spurs, *c*1854

4th (Queen's Own) Light Dragoons

Bequeathed by Mr W E Brinkley

NAM. 1967-06-31, -10, -11, -15, -16, -17

Captain Thomas Hutton's dress and equipment includes the Light Dragoon shako, introduced in 1846, which although more cylindrical in shape than its bell-topped predecessor, retained the lace band round the top and the Maltese Cross plate. In the Crimea foul weather covers were worn. His forage cap, as prescribed by *Dress Regulations*, should possess a peak, but Hutton's is of a pillbox type similar to those of other ranks, albeit made of superior material. The light dragoons, in common with all British cavalry other than the hussars, had been ordered to dispense with their sabretaches before sailing to the Crimea, and Hutton would not have taken his. Similarly, many of the cavalry regiments destined for the Crimea decided to leave behind their shabraques, the horse cloth under the saddle, and Hutton's ornate shabraque badges, worn at the fore corners, would not have seen active service. His officer's full dress spurs are made of gilt metal.

Pattern 1821 Light Cavalry Officer's Sword, 1847-54

107cm. l

Bequeathed by Mr W E Brinkley

NAM 1967-06-40-2

Thomas Hutton would have purchased this sword when he transferred to the 4th (Queen's Own) Light Dragoons in 1847. It was wielded to effect by him during the Charge of the Light Brigade, in spite of his wounds: 'He was shot through the right thigh during the advance', wrote his commanding officer, Lord George Paget,

and holloaed to his squadron leader: "Low, I am wounded, what shall I do?" to which the latter replied: "If you can sit on your horse, you had better come with us; there's no use going back now, you'll only be killed." He went on, and if report speaks truly, made good use of his powerful right arm in disabling some of the enemy. On his return he was shot through the other thigh, his horse being hit in eleven places.

Like the Infantry swords of the period, the Light Cavalry sword was criticised for its flimsy pipe-back blade. This sword has the so-called Wilkinson blade, manufacturered by Wilkinson & Co., a heavier fullered blade that made the pattern a better fighting weapon.

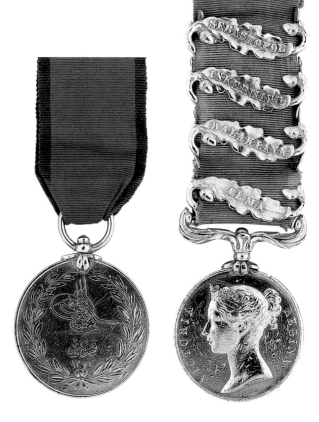

Medals awarded to Corporal Denis Flanagan, 1854-56

Crimea War Medal 1854-56, with clasps: Alma, Balaklava, Inkermann, Sebastopol; Turkish Crimean War Medal, Sardinian issue

Generously donated by Mr Flanagan

NAM. 1991-08-229

Denis Flanagan was born in County Limerick and enlisted in January 1854 at the age of 18. He served in the Crimea with the 4th (The Queen's Own Light) Dragoons from July 1854 to May 1856, received two good conduct badges and was medically discharged in Edinburgh after 12 years service in 1866 on a pension of eight pence a day. According to his records Corporal Flanagan was not entitled to the Balaklava clasp and therefore must have added it unofficially, a not uncommon practice among Crimean veterans.

'Officers of the 4th Light Dragoons', 1855

Photograph by Roger Fenton, 16 cm. h x 15.7cm. w

Generously donated by Lieutenant-Colonel N Lovett

NAM. 1964-12-151-6-35

Photographed by Fenton in 1855, most of the officers wear black-braided blue-patrol jackets and the cavalry forage cap with gold band and embroidered peak, although one sports a French képi.

Officer's Stable Jacket, Undress, *c*1854-1856

17th Light Dragoons (Lancers)

Wool cloth, cotton cloth, morocco leather waistband, gold metal lace olivette, gilt-metal buttons

Generously donated by the Royal United Service Institution

NAM. 1951-12-83-1

Lieutenant (later Lieutenant-Colonel) Sir William Gordon (1830-1906) was first commissioned in the 17th Light Dragoons (Lancers) in 1850. Although he wrote to his mother five days after the Charge of the Light Brigade that 'I only got a few cracks on the head which are of no consequence', the five sabre cuts he sustained were in fact of such severity that it was remarked at the hospital how he was the only patient 'with his head off'.

In the absence of formal campaign dress for the British Army, the stable jacket, as worn by Gordon during the Charge, was often donned by cavalry officers during service overseas in preference to the full dress uniform. Gordon's stable jacket shows the marks of battle on the left side, right rear shoulder and the centre back towards both the waist and at the neck edge; there are still bloodstains on the right collar and down the front. Gordon's arm must have been raised at the time that the slash on the left side was delivered.

The jacket is secured with sixteen hook and eye fastenings or with the braid loop and brass hook at the neck if worn open. There are 68 studs down the centre left front and domed buttons bearing the skull and cross bones (the regimental insignia) at the shoulder and cuffs.

Medals awarded to Trumpet-Major Henry Joy, 1854-57

Distinguished Conduct Medal 1855; Crimea War Medal 1854-56, with
clasps: Alma, Balaklava, Inkermann, Sebastopol; Long Service and Good
Conduct Medal, Army 1857; Turkish Crimean War Medal 1855, Sardinian
issue

Generously donated by the Royal United Service Institution

NAM. 1963-10-51

Born in Ripon, Yorkshire, Henry Joy was the son of James Joy, a Private in
the 1st Life Guards, who had served in the Peninsula and at Waterloo.
Henry entered the Royal Military Asylum at Chelsea in 1825 at the age of
six and in 1833 he enlisted in the 17th Light Dragoons as a musician in the
regimental band, becoming a trumpeter in 1838. Promoted trumpet-major in
1847, he was in charge of the Band at the funeral of the Duke of Wellington
in 1852. Appointed Orderly Trumpeter to the Earl of Lucan in the Crimea,
he rode in the Charge of the Heavy Brigade where he had two horses shot
under him and was slightly wounded. The exact circumstances of the
award of his Distinguished Conduct Medal are not recorded. He died in
1893.

Bugle, 1854

18cm l.

Generously donated by the Royal United Service Institution

NAM. 1963-10-10

As Orderly Trumpeter to Lord Lucan at Balaklava on 25 October 1854, Joy
used this bugle to sound the Charge for the Heavy Brigade. Five years
after his death his bugle was sold at auction and achieved the considerable
price of 750 guineas, largely because it was believed that it was also used
to sound the Charge of the Light Brigade. It was sold again in 1908 and
subsequently donated to the Royal United Service Institution.

Museum Token, *c*1898-1908

3.3cm. w

Generously donated by Mr I Bassingthwaighte

NAM. 2000-02-20

Private museum publicity token, issued by Mr T G Middlebrook, *c*1898-1908. It illustrates the bugle, then on display, used by Trumpet-Major Henry Joy of the 17th Light Dragoons (Lancers) reputedly to sound the Charge of the Light Brigade.

'The Charge of the Light Brigade', 1854

Coloured photogravure after Richard Caton Woodville (1856-1927), published by Henry Graves & Co, London, 1895, 59.5cm. h x 91.5cm. w

NAM. 1988-06-19

Whereas in his painting 'Relief of the Light Brigade', the artist Richard Caton Woodville had depicted the moment that the 11th Hussars reached the Russian guns, in this composition he shows the 17th Lancers at the beginning of the Charge. The central figure is the painting is Private James William Wightman, who was severely wounded and taken prisoner in the Charge.

Medals commemorating the Battle of Balaklava, 25 October 1854

Bronze, John Pinches Ltd, 41mm. diam

Generously donated by the Royal United Service Institution

NAM. 1963-05-23-2

White metal, John Pinches Ltd, 41mm. diam

Generously donated by Mrs E E Mockett

NAM. 1960-03-109

Versions of the same medal, showing obverse and reverse. The obverse depicts Lord Cardigan leading a line of lancers over the Russian cannon, with the word BALAKLAVA above. The reverse carries a list of all the regiments, corps and divisions present at the battle.

The medal is one of a set of three, struck in silver, bronze and white metal by Pinches, usually sold with two other similar medals, commemorating the battles of Alma and Inkerman. The white metal medal is contained in an original box of issue.

Plan of the Charge of the Light Brigade, 1854

Taken from A W Kinglake's *The Invasion of the Crimea* Volume V (Wm Blackwood and Sons, Edinburgh and London, 6th edn 1877)

Kinglake's nine-volume history of the Crimean War, the first volumes of which were published in 1863, remains the standard account. The maps which accompanied his history were so highly regarded that they were re-issued separately in 1899 as an *Atlas to Illustrate Kinglake's Invasion of the Crimea, Adapted for Military Students by Lieut.-Colonel Sir George Sydenham Clarke.*

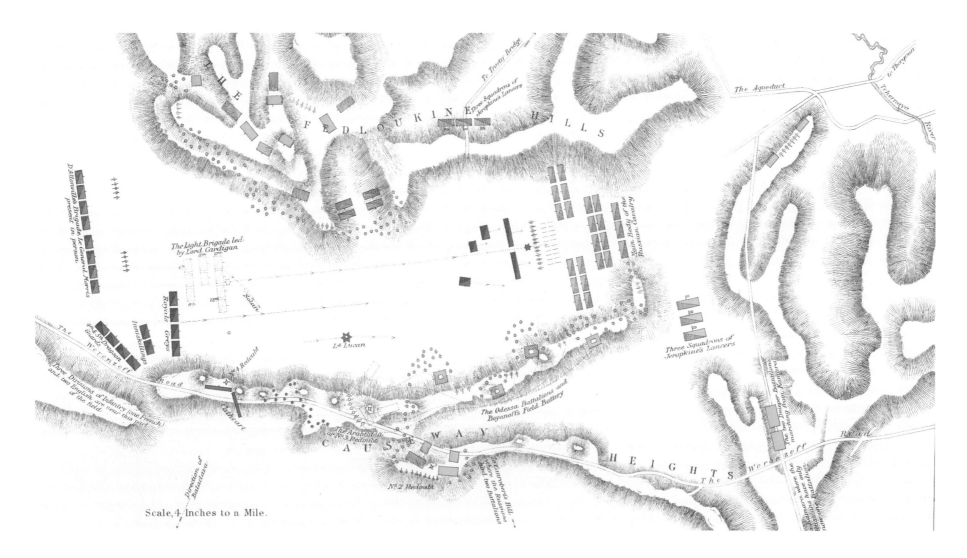

'Sir Briggs, horse of Lord Tredegar, 17th Lancers, ridden at Balaclava, 1854', in camp in the Crimea, 1854

Oil on canvas, signed and dated lower left, 'A F de Prades/ 1856', by Alfred Frank de Prades (*fl.* 1844-83), 1856, 63.5cm. h x 76.2 cm. w

Generously donated by the Viscount Tredegar

NAM. 1961-08-7

While little is known about 'Sir Briggs' beyond the evidence of this painting, it is certain that he was a survivor of the Charge of the Light Brigade at the Battle of Balaklava on 25 October 1854. His owner, Captain The Honourable Godfrey Charles Morgan (later Viscount Tredegar) (1831-1913), commanded a squadron of the 17th Regiment of Light Dragoons

(Lancers) in the famous charge. The number of horses killed in this action was far higher than the 113 human lives lost. Of the 643 animals paraded that morning, over 370 were killed in action and another 85 returned wounded.

A prominent Welsh landowner, Morgan sold his commission in January 1855 but continued to serve in the Royal Gloucestershire Yeomanry until 1875. He was Honorary Colonel of the Royal Monmouth Engineer Militia from 1885 and Member of Parliament for Breckonshire from 1858 to 1875.

The artist, de Prades, probably visited the Crimea in 1854, when he may have made the preliminary sketches for this oil. He is particularly noted both for his equestrian and sporting paintings, and for scenes from the Crimean War.

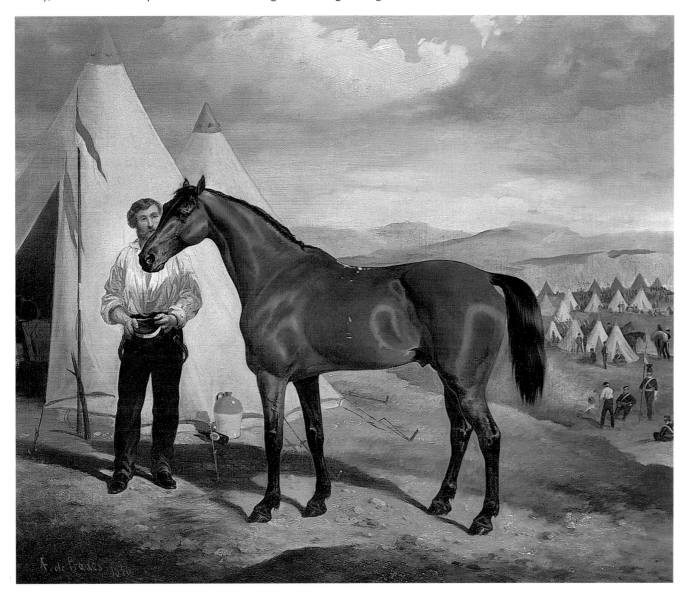

The Charge of the 17th Lancers at the Battle of Balaklava, 25 October 1854

Bronze relief in four panels, by Sir William Goscombe John (1860-1952), c1909, probably the casting which was exhibited at the Royal Academy 1910 No. 1753, 84.7cm. h x 174, 90, 171.6 & 89.6cm. w

Generously donated by Lord Tredegar

NAM. 2003-03-617

These four panels are cast from the original moulds for the frieze decorating the plinth of the equestrian statue of Lord Tredegar (1831-1913) in Cardiff. In 1854, Tredegar, then Captain The Honourable Godfrey Charles Morgan, mounted on his horse 'Sir Briggs', led a troop of 17th Regiment of Light Dragoons (Lancers) in the Charge of the Light Brigade.

A Cardiff man, Goscombe John was a prolific sculptor who produced public monuments for cities around the world. This statue of his fellow Welshman, Lord Tredegar, stands in Cardiff Civic Centre and was unveiled in 1909, on the 55th anniversary of the Battle of Balaklava. This unsigned version of the frieze may be the one exhibited at the Royal Academy a year later.

The Battle of Inkerman

Encouraged by their relative success at Balaklava, the Russians made a second attempt to force the Allies to raise the siege of Sevastopol. Once again, the British Army was their target. On the foggy morning of 5 November 1854, 35,000 Russian troops crossed the River Chernaya and attacked the British 2nd Division, 3000 strong, protecting the right flank of the Allied siegeworks. Amidst the mist and thick oak brushwood, the battle resolved itself into a series of combats in which British – and later French – troops fought in their hundreds to stay the advance of the Russian thousands. Allied reinforcements gradually arrived. The Guards distinguished themselves at the Sandbag Battery. Lieutenant-Colonel Frederick Haines of the 21st Regiment (Royal North British Fusiliers) led the stubborn resistance at the 'Barrier'. Eventually, the British cannon on Home Ridge began to subdue the fire of the Russian artillery on Shell Hill and by the early afternoon the Russians were in retreat. The British lost 2,500 killed or wounded, the French nearly a thousand and the Russians over 10,000. The Russians nevertheless had pre-empted the Allies' plan to launch an assault against Sevastopol, and thereby condemned them to endure a winter – for which the British were ill-prepared – shivering outside the walls of the town.

Private John McDermond VC (1832-68), 47th (The Lancashire) Regiment of Foot, winning the Victoria Cross by saving Colonel Haly, his Commanding Officer, at Inkerman, on 5 November 1854

Oil on paper, mounted on cardboard, by Louis William Desanges (b 1822, *fl*. 1846-87), *c*1860, 35.8cm. h x 50.8cm. w

Generously donated by Wantage Urban District Council

NAM. 1958-12-40

Private (later Corporal) John McDermond (1832-68) was awarded the Victoria Cross for saving the life of Colonel William O'Grady Haly, his commanding officer, at the Battle of Inkerman on 5 November 1854. The Colonel, who had been several times bayoneted, lay disabled on the ground surrounded by a party of Russian soldiers, when McDermond rushed to his aid and killed the Russian who had inflicted Haly's wounds.

This painting is one of a series of 55 depicting Victoria Cross actions executed between 1859 and 1862 by the British artist Louis Desanges, 46 of which were purchased by Colonel Lord Wantage 1832-1901) in 1900 and donated to the town of Wantage. Lieutenant Robert Lindsay (later first Baron Wantage of Lockinge), Scots Fusilier Guards, was awarded his Victoria Cross for acts of bravery at both the Battles of Alma (20 September 1854) and Inkerman (5 November 1854).

Stanford's New Map of Sevastopol, and the Surrounding Country

Based on new Admiralty Charts & authentic sketches by Capt [Edward] Wetherall & other officers. Published London, Edward Stanford, 6 Charing Cross, December 1854, 47.8cm. h x 62.2cm. w

Generously donated by Mr G Boynton Williams

The map shows both the course of the Battle of Inkerman and the site in the south of the Battle of Balaklava, fought in October.

NAM. 1975-03-7-98

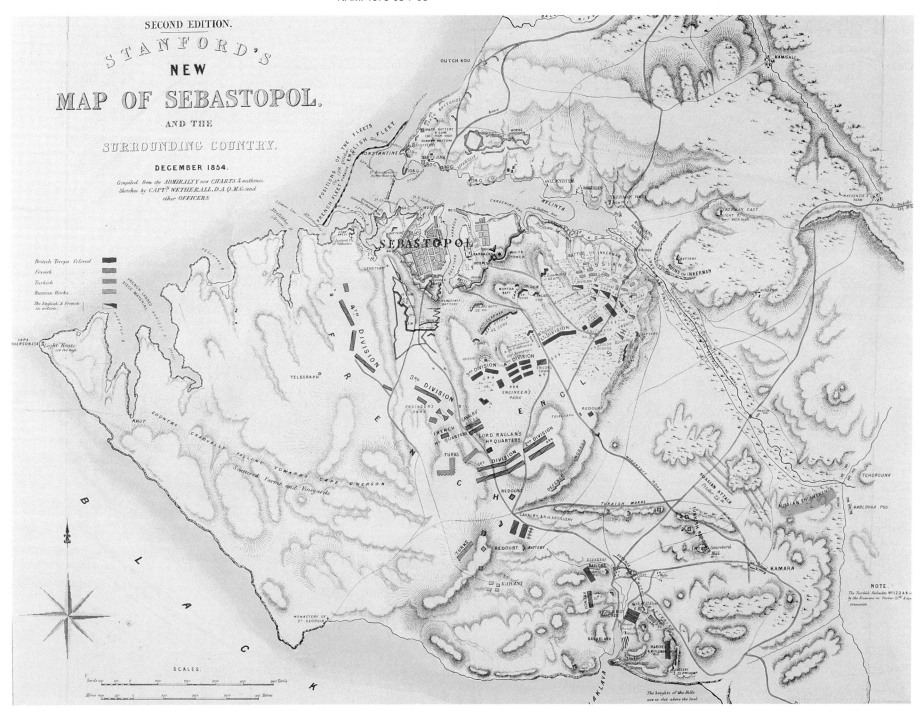

'Oct 26 1854. attack of Rus. on Heights above Sebastol'

Watercolour, signed lower centre 'J A Crowe', by Joseph Archer Crowe (1825-96), 'special' artist for *The Illustrated London News*, 1854, 25cm. h x 42.8cm. w

Generously donated by Mrs Aldred Brown

NAM. 1963-10-18-5

When a wood engraving after this watercolour of the attack of 'Little Inkerman' was published in *The Illustrated London News* on 11 November 1854, it was accompanied by an apology from the artist: 'I am sorry to be obliged to send you so little in the shape of sketches this week, but I have been in two actions, which are two days lost from writing or drawings; and today I have spent giving you an account of the battles. I shall endeavour to make up for this by next mail.'

In his autobiography Crowe noted that at the Battle of Balaklava, the day before the events shown in this drawing, he had been so close to the action that: 'Now and then a shell from the Russian field-pieces came bowling along. One of them burst under my horse's belly, and took him off his legs. I manfully held on, with my sketch-book in one hand, my reins in the other; no harm done.'

Letter of Private George Burdis, 27 October 1854

Manuscript, 22.3cm. h x 35.6cm. w

Generously donated by Miss E Appleby

NAM. 1963-11-151-2

Inspired by their partial success at the Battle of Balaklava, the following day - 26 October 1854 - the Russians in Sevastopol launched a sortie against the right flank of the British army on the Inkerman Heights. They met stiff resistance from Lieutenant-General Sir George de Lacy Evans' 2nd Division. The determination to hold their ground of the outlying pickets -

among whom was Private George Burdis of the 47th (The Lancashire) Regiment of Foot - was especially noteworthy, as Burdis related in this letter to his brother and sister a day later: 'I was on outline Piquit when they turn'd out and a very severe engagement we had 1 Man killed and 7 wounded that was on the same duty that I was on but thank God I escaped and a very narrow escape it was but I had to fight my way through sending Prince Menshikoff home with a broken head & wounded arm.'

De Lacy Evans elected not to support his pickets but to allow the Russian columns to press forward. This drew them onto his artillery, ranged along Home Ridge. The fire of eighteen guns soon dispersed the enemy.

Crimea War Medal 1854-56, with clasps: Alma; Inkermann

Awarded to Private George Burdis, 47th (The Lancashire) Regiment of Foot

Generously donated by Miss E Appleby

NAM. 1963-08-66

George Burdis had previously served as a bugler in the 68th (The Durham) Regiment of Foot (Light Infantry). He was killed in the trenches before Sevastopol on 26 November 1854.

Lieut.–Colonel Nathaniel Steevens, *The Crimean Campaign with "The Connaught Rangers," 1854 - 55 - 56*

London, Griffiths and Farran, 1878, 359pp, 23cm. h x 30.5cm. w

Generously donated by Miss P N Steevens

NAM. 8628

In this copy of his book, the author, who served in the Crimea, has interleaved letters from people either complimenting him on its publication or, as in this case, who had assisted him in its preparation. The anecdote about Captain Joshua Crosse of the 88th Connaught Rangers shooting dead four Russians at Inkerman is printed on the right hand page; the conclusion of Crosse's manuscript account of the same episode (written in 1876), upon which Steevens based his published version, is on the left.

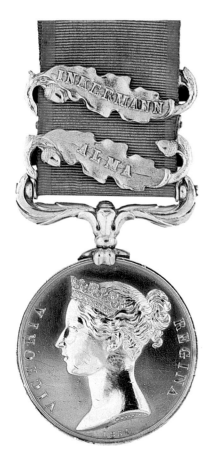

Deane Adams Percussion Revolver, .45 in., *c*1851 (below)

Manufacturer, Deane Adams & Deane, 30 King William Street, London Bridge, London

29cm. l

Generously donated by the Ministry of Defence, Royal Army Ordnance Corps, Weedon

NAM. 1963-12-251-271

Deane Adams Percussion Revolver, .50in., *c*1852 (above)

Deane Adams & Deane, 30 King William Street. London Bridge, London

35cm. l

Generously donated by the Ministry of Defence, Royal Army Ordnance Corps, Weedon

NAM. 1963-12-251-190

After the Great Exhibition of 1851, a wider selection of revolvers became available and many officers purchased their own to take with them to the Crimea. The British Adams and the American Colt revolvers were the most popular. The five chamber Adams revolver was produced in a range of calibres and as it was self-cocking it could fire five shots rapidly. The Colt revolver had to be manually cocked.

Captain Joshua Crosse of the 88th Regiment of Foot (Connaught Rangers) used the largest calibre Adams, the .50in., in the Crimea. He wrote favourably about the revolver to its inventor, Robert Adams, following the Battle of Inkerman, in which he was wounded after being surrounded by Russians:

> I then found the advantages of your pistol over that of Colonel Colt's, for had I to cock before each shot I should have lost my life; but with yours, having only to pull the trigger, I was able to shoot four Russians, and therefore save my life. I should not have had time to cock, for they were too close to me, being only a few yards from me; so close that I was bayoneted through the thigh immediately after shooting the fourth man.

Both revolvers are marked to the manufacturer, Deane Adams & Deane (makers to HRH Prince Albert), of London Bridge and the .50in. revolver is inscribed on the barrel to L A Richardson who joined the 5th (Princess Charlotte of Wales's) Regiment of Dragoon Guards as a cornet in February 1855.

Orders and Medals awarded to General Edmund Jeffreys, 1854-56

Order of the Bath, Companion Badge (CB) 1855; Crimea War Medal 1854-56, with clasps: Alma, Inkermann, Sebastopol; Order of the Mejidie, Turkey, 5th Class; Turkish Crimean War Medal, Sardinian issue

Generously donated by Mrs M E Jeffreys

NAM. 1973-09-33-6, -7, -8, -9

Commissioned an ensign in the 88th Regiment of Foot (Connaught Rangers) on 16 June 1825, Edmund Richard Jeffreys (1808-89) received a brevet lieutenant-colonelcy on 20 June 1854 and as senior major commanded the four companies of the 88th that were present at the Battle of Inkerman. He was wounded and returned home, taking command on 16 March 1855 of the Depot Battalion at Parkhurst, Isle of Wight. He retired with the rank of lieutenant-general in 1878, and in 1881 was appointed honorary general, and Colonel of the 63rd (West Suffolk) Regiment, later the Manchester Regiment.

Colonel Edmund Jeffreys, c1858

Overpainted photograph, 45.5cm. h x 38.4cm. w

NAM. 1973-09-36

Colonel Jeffreys, then commanding the Depot Battalion at Parkhurst, is shown wearing his Companion Badge of the Order of the Bath and his Crimea War Medal with three clasps, Order of the Mejidie and Turkish Crimean War Medal.

Shoulder Belt Plate, Shako, Waistbelt Clasp, *c*1844-55

88th Regiment of Foot (Connaught Rangers)

Frosted gilt metal, gilt metal; (shako) black beaver and patented leather, gilt metal chin chain, gilt metal shako plate

Generously donated by Mrs M E Jeffreys

NAM 1973-09-33, -2, -3, -5

Worn by Lieutenant-Colonel Edmund Jeffreys while serving with the Connaught Rangers. On the inside of the shako, above the front peak, is a piece of paper bearing the following inscription: 'Shako worn by Major E R Jeffreys at Inkerman on 5th Nov 1854 with hole made by a grape shot. This same discharge killed his horse and wounded him in the shoulder'. According to Nathaniel Steevens in his *The Crimean Campaign with the Connaught Rangers*, the four companies of the Regiment under Jeffreys' command spent much of the battle subjecting the Russian artillery on Shell Hill to accurate Minié fire, bringing upon themselves heavy discharges of grape in return. It was probably under these circumstances that Jeffreys sustained his wound.

3.5 oz ball of grape shot, 1854

3cm. w

Generously donated by Mrs M E Jeffreys

NAM. 1973-09-34-5

This 3.5oz (99g.) ball is part of a discharge of grape shot, so called because assemblage of similarly-sized iron balls gathered together in a bag and fired from a cannon at short range (achieving an effect like a giant shot-gun) resembles a bunch of grapes. It is believed to have caused the hole that can be seen in the shako (NAM. 1973-09-33-3) worn by Lieutenant-Colonel Edmund Jeffreys during the Crimean War.

Actual size

Russian devotional crucifix, *c*1854

Brass, made in Russia, *c*1854, 8.1cm. h x 4.9cm. w

Generously donated by Mrs M E Jeffreys

NAM. 1973-09-35-3

On the top of the cross is an image of the Mandilion, the icon created by Christ impressing his features on a cloth, that was sent to heal King Agbar of Edessa of leprosy. Below, two angels hover above a depiction of the Crucifixion. Along the upper and lower edges, an almost illegible inscription refers to a hymn sung on the feast of the Holy Cross (14 September) 'Thy cross we venerate O Master, and we glorify thy Holy Resurrection.' At the foot is the cave with the skull of Adam and traces of letters, now very worn, forming the words 'Place of the skull' and 'Was crucified'. The reverse of the icon is decorated with a floral pattern and bears a suspension loop. Trophies such as these were often taken from the bodies of Russian soldiers as souvenirs. This one belonged to Lieutenant-Colonel Edmund Jeffreys.

Russian devotional icon, *c*1854

Brass, made in Russia, *c*1854, 6.4cm. h x 9.5cm. w

Generously donated by Mrs M E Jeffreys

NAM. 1973-09-35-5

This icon is made of three plain-backed sheets of brass hinged together, which fold out to reveal a triptych. The central panel depicts the figure of a saint identified in Cyrillic as the fifteenth century monk Saint Tikon. Above this section, on a rectangular projection, is an image of the Mandilion and to the left and right, the panels each depict three pairs of saints, also identified in Cyrillic.

Although very small folding-panelled icons might be worn round the neck on a chain, larger examples such as this would probably have been carried in a bag. Such icons are regarded by Orthodox Christians as more than just religious pictures. They are visual aids for worship, following strict rules of composition, subject and technique. The contemplation of such icons is believed to bring the people of God into a direct encounter with His presence and honour paid to them is believed to transfer to the subject depicted therein. This example was acquired by Lieutenant-Colonel Edmund Jeffreys during the Crimean War.

General Pennefather

Photograph by Roger Fenton

NAM. Negative 46919

Major-General (later General Sir) John Lysaght Pennefather (1800-72) received his first commission in the Army in 1818. He commanded the 22nd (The Cheshire) Regiment of Foot with great distinction under Sir Charles Napier at the Battle of Meani in Scinde (1843) and in 1854 was given command of the 1st Brigade in the 2nd Division for the expedition to the East. Promoted major-general on 20 June 1854, in the absence ill of Lieutenant-General Sir George de Lacy Evans he commanded the 2nd Division at the Battle of Inkerman in which it bore the brunt of the fighting. Pennefather's tactic of 'feeding the pickets' amidst the fog and thick brushwood which broke up the heavy Russian columns proved the right one, and in so far as any general could claim the credit for winning what became known as 'the Soldier's Battle', it was Pennefather. He continued to serve in the Crimea until invalided home in July 1855.

'The soldiers battle, Inkerman, - Novr 5th 1854'

Coloured tinted lithograph by and after artist unknown, published by Paul and Dominic Colnaghi, London, 27 June 1855, 55cm. h x 74cm. w

Crookshank Collection, transferred from the British Museum

NAM. 1971-02-33-213

Men of the Brigade of Guards, clothed in their greatcoats but still wearing their bearskins, are depicted charging the Russians in the vicinity of the 'Sandbag Battery', an abandoned artillery emplacement. Some of the most savage fighting of the battle took place around what was in fact a useless prize as the Battery's parapet was too high to enable it to be defended by infantry. The artist, in order to allow the action to be seen, has banished most of the all-pervasive fog that shrouded the battlefield.

'The Battle of Inkermann Novr. 5th. 1854. The Gallant attack of Lieut.[*sic*] General Sir Geo. Cathcart who was killed with several officers in the engagement. His Division consisted of portions of the 20th. 21st. 46th. 57th. 63rd. and 68th Regiments of Foot.'

Coloured lithograph by Edmund Walker (*fl*. 1836-62) after Henry Martens (*fl*. 1828-54, d 1860), published by Messrs Fores, London, 11 December 1854, 38.7cm. h x 51cm. w

NAM. 1995-05-46

The print reproduces an extract from *The Times*, 23 November 1854 describing the Battle of Inkerman:

> Sir G. Cathcart at their head encouraging them, and when a cry arose that the ammunition was failing, he said coolly "HAVE YOU NOT YOUR BAYONETS." A deadly volley was poured into his scattered regiments. Sir George cheered them and led them back to the hill, but a flight of bullets passed where he rode and he fell from his horse close to the Russian Columns.

In reality, Cathcart had thrown his life away. Still indignant at the way his advice was disregarded while he had been in possession of his dormant commission to succeed Lord Raglan, he ignored an order to move the 400 men under his immediate command to fill a gap in the British line, launching them instead in a foolish attack which the historian Kinglake dubbed 'the false victory'. Brigadier-General Richard Airey, who had conveyed Raglan's order to Cathcart, found it hard to muster much sympathy: 'Poor Cathcart - so wild and inconsiderate, was always for performing some action without reflection or knowledge. What he attempted quite wrong & against the orders I had positively given him 5 minutes before - so sad!!'

Study of a Wounded Guardsman, Crimea, *c*1854

Oil on board by Elizabeth Thompson (1846-1933) (later Lady Butler), *c*1874, 21.8cm. h x 12.7cm. w

Generously donated by Lieutenant-Colonel P R Butler

NAM. 1963-11-194

This half-length portrait of a soldier with his head bandaged is a preliminary study for the key figure standing in the centre of Elizabeth Thompson's famous painting, 'The Roll Call', which was exhibited at the Royal Academy in 1874 and subsequently acquired by Queen Victoria.

The muster of soldiers depicted in 'The Roll Call' was not linked by the artist to a particular action, rather it was intended to form an archetypal image of the arduous conditions under which the Army laboured in the Crimea. Although the finished canvas conveyed with a dramatic realism the effect that the experience of war must have had on the guardsmen, the anxious, drawn face of the figure in this study was altered considerably and rendered more stoical in appearance.

Paperweight, 1854

Inscribed 'The bullet which caused the death of Brig. Genl. Goldie at the Battle of Inkerman. Nov. 5th. 1855 [*sic*]', 1854

Lead bullet mounted on a marble base, 6.3cm. h x 10.3cm. w x 6cm. d

Genrously donated by the Trustees of the
Middlesex Regimental Museum

NAM. 1994-01-1-322

Brigadier-General Thomas Leigh Goldie (1807-54) was born on the Isle of Man into a family distinguished for its military service. He joined the 66th (or The Berkshire) Regiment of Foot as an ensign in June 1825, was promoted lieutenant later that year and captain three years later. By March 1840, Goldie had attained the rank of lieutenant-colonel in the 57th (The West Middlesex) Regiment of Foot. Although it is said that this rapid promotion was attributable more to money and influence than military merit, Goldie published several works on infantry tactics and was regarded by many as the most skilful infantry officer of his rank in the army. Appointed brigadier-general in Major-General Sir George Cathcart's 4th Division, he was mortally wounded by a shot in the head at the Battle of Inkerman. The large calibre conical bullet which surmounts this paperweight would have been fired from a Russian marksman's rifle and was presumably removed from Goldie's body in an effort to save his life. Lord Raglan recorded that, 'Brigadier-General Goldie was an officer of considerable promise, and gave great satisfaction to all under whom he has served'.

Officer's Coatee, Full Dress, *c*1848-55

77th (The East Middlesex) Regiment of Foot

Wool cloth, metal thread lace, waist lined with Morocco leather, gilt-metal buttons

Generously donated by the Trustees of the
Middlesex Regimental Museum

NAM. 2003-07-199

This coatee was worn by Captain (later Lieutenant-General) Henry Kent (1825-1921) who served with the 77th (The East Middlesex) Regiment of Foot earning clasps on his Crimea War Medal for the Alma, Inkerman and the Siege of Sevastopol. He returned home on 26 March 1855. His coatee, of a pattern superseded in 1855, is well-worn, with patches on the underarm upper edge of the right sleeve, the left sleeve at the elbow and below the elbow on the right sleeve. On each shoulder is a brass stud and short brass strap for attaching epaulettes (now absent). Kent, who was first commissioned into the 77th Regiment as an ensign in 1845, clearly gained in bulk over the years: the coatee has been enlarged on the left and right side with a gusset, and the bodice has been lengthened all around at the waist.

Officer's Greatcoat, *c*1854

77th (The East Middlesex) Regiment of Foot

Milled wool cloth, velvet collar, gilt metal buttons, shalloon sleeves

Generously donated by the Trustees of the
Middlesex Regiment Museum

NAM. 1992-09-63

Most of the troops who fought at Inkerman wore their greatcoats and this example of an officer's greatcoat was worn by Lieutenant (later Colonel) William Molesworth Cole Acton (1828-1904). The feat performed by him at Inkerman was one of the most remarkable of the battle and was given due prominence by the historian Kinglake. Sent by General Pennefather with an augmented company of the 77th to reinforce the 'Barrier' across the Sevastopol post road, when the battle was nearing its close Acton was ordered to clear a Russian battery from Shell Hill. Acton could take his own company and two others that he would find up ahead. Unfortunately, when he reached the companies in front,

> Both the officers thus called upon to act refused in plain terms to do so, saying that they (the three companies) were not strong enough. Then Acton said, 'If you won't join me, I'll obey my orders and attack with the 77th;' and so saying, he ordered his men to advance; but not a man of them moved, for they were checked, as was not unnatural, by finding that their captain was seeking to act in defiance of the opinion given by the two other officers..

> Acton said, "Then I'll go by myself,' and moved forward accordingly; but he soon found himself quite alone, at a distance of some thirty or forty yards in front of his men. Presently, however, James Tyrrell, a private of the 77th, ran out of the ranks and placed himself by the side of his captain, saying, 'Sir, I'll stand by you.' Then a soldier sprang out from the company which was on the right of the 77th men .. . The officer and the two soldiers moved forward towards the battery, and they compassed a few yards without being followed; but then suddenly, to Acton's infinite joy, the whole of his 77th men rushed forward after their captain.

Nor could the other two companies now remain behind, and they also followed Acton in an attack which proved completely successful.

Medals awarded to Lieutenant John Brophy, 1854-56

Distinguished Conduct Medal 1854; Crimea War Medal 1854-56, with clasps: Alma; Balaklava; Inkermann; Sebastopol; Turkish Crimean War Medal, British issue; Médaille Militaire, France 1861

Generously donated by Miss P Styles

NAM. 1975-04-78

John Brophy (or Brophey) was born in East London in 1821 and enlisted in 1839 into the 63rd (The West Suffolk) Regiment of Foot at Newcastle-under-Lyme. He served with the Regiment in Burma, and in the Crimea as a colour-sergeant. He earned the Distinguished Conduct Medal for his bravery at the Battle of Inkerman by rescuing the Queen's Colour from enemy hands when Ensign Clutterbuck, who was carrying it, was killed. Brophy was severely wounded in the action, resulting in his medical discharge in 1855. However, on his return home he was almost immediately commissioned Lieutenant and Paymaster in the 3rd Lancashire Militia. Later he was appointed a member of the Queen's Bodyguard of the Yeoman of the Guard, with whom he served until 1890. In 1867 Brophy applied unsuccessfully to the War Office for his gallantry in the Crimea to be rewarded with the Victoria Cross, an award which had not been instituted at the time of his action. Brophy died in London in 1891.

Medals awarded to Major-General Henry Adams, 1842-56

1st China War Medal 1842; Crimea War Medal 1854-56, with clasps: Alma, Inkermann

Generously donated by Major P R Adams

NAM. 1976-08-2

Henry William Adams (1805-54) was first commissioned ensign in the 12th (East Suffolk) Regiment of Foot on 31 July 1823. He was lieutenant-colonel successively of the 18th (Royal Irish) Regiment of Foot (1840-44) and the 49th (The Hertfordshire) Regiment of Foot (1844 until his death). Having previously seen action in the First China War, he was appointed brigadier-general on 21 February 1854 and given command of the 2nd Brigade of the 2nd Division. At the Battle of Inkerman on 5 November 1854, he defended the Sandbag Battery against heavy odds during the early stages of the fighting with 700 men of the 41st and 49th regiments until a wound in the ankle forced him from the action. Promoted major-general on 12 December 1854, he died of his wound at Scutari a week later.

Side drum, 1854

Russian Infantry

37cm. w x 34.5cm. h

Generously donated by the Royal United Service Institution

NAM. 1951-12-35-3

Russian Infantry side drum captured by Drum-Major Robert Beck, of the 88th Regiment of Foot (Connaught Rangers) at the Battle of Inkerman on 5 November 1854.

Officer's Coatee *c*1837-57; Waist Belt *c*1846; Sash *c*1846

1st (or Grenadier) Regiment of Foot Guards

Wool cloth, gilt-metal buttons; buff leather, gilt-metal buckle, gilt-metal stud fittings; fine crimson net, twisted crimson silk tassels, plaited crimson silk tassel bosses

Generously donated by Lady M Russell

NAM. 1965-03-18, -1, -4, -6

Worn by Captain (later Lieutenant-Colonel) Sir Charles Russell VC (1826-83). He was first commissioned as an ensign in the 35th (Royal Sussex) Regiment of Foot on 25 August 1843, becoming a lieutenant on 9 June 1846. He transferred to the Grenadier Guards in 1847 and was promoted lieutenant and captain on 13 September 1853 and major on 2 November 1855. He retired as a lieutenant colonel in 1868.

At the Battle of Inkerman Russell won his Victoria Cross. According to Kinglake, some Guardsmen in the Sandbag Battery were heard to say 'If an officer will lead, we will follow', whereupon Russell, leaping out through the left embrasure, shouted 'Follow me, my lads!' He fired his revolver at a group of Russians and was upon the point of being bayoneted in the back by one of them when the only man to have followed, Guardsman Anthony Palmer, saved his life by shooting the Russian dead. Kinglake continued: 'Russell was a man of slight build, not disclosing great bodily strength, yet in one of his struggles for the mastery - which also were struggles for life - he was able to tear a rifle from the hands of a Russian soldier, and he kept it to the end of the day.'

Officer's Coatee, Full Dress, *c*1848-55

49th (Princess Charlotte of Wales's or Hertfordshire) Regiment

Wool cloth, gold embroidery, metal thread, gilt-metal buttons

Generously donated by Mrs L J Hill

NAM. 1959-07-23-1

The coatee belonged to Lieutenant Arthur Savory Armstrong of the 49th Regiment of Foot who was killed in the early stages of the Battle of Inkerman when the Russian artillery on Shell Hill cannonaded Home Ridge. Much of the Russian gunnery was aimed at the encampment of the 2nd Division behind the ridge and it was here that Armstrong was hit. 'Being the adjutant, and therefore on horseback, he was exposed to a fire which spared men on foot', Kinglake explained.

Mug inscribed 'Sergeant Davies defending the Colours at Inkermann', 1854

Hard paste porcelain of Continental manufacture, probably transfer-printed in England, unmarked, *c*1855, 10.7cm. h x 10.2cm. w x 13.7cm. d

Generously donated by Miss Edna Rowe

NAM. 1999-01-144

This mug reproduces an image from a print in *Cassell's Illustrated Family History* showing a Grenadier Guardsman, Sergeant Davies, defending the Regiment's Colours against Russian infantry. The subject has been identified as Colour-Sergeant Poolfield Davis, 1st (or Grenadier) Regiment of Foot Guards, who served at the Battle of Alma but not, as it emerges, at the Battle of Inkerman. A letter amongst the National Army Museum's Collection of Wetherall Papers from Captain George Higginson, Adjutant of the 3rd Battalion 1st (or Grenadier) Regiment of Foot Guards, dated 5 February 1855, explains the history behind this myth:

> There is another Serjeant of the 3rd Battalion who is the source of much annoyance to us all: I allude to Serjt. Davies and his correspondence with the Newspapers regarding his exploits, &c. Now we all know very well that he saw less of the fighting at Alma than any soldier in the Battalion as he chose to remain at the rear with Burgoyne who was severely wounded early in the action. He was sent on board ship two days before the battle of Inkermann, and yet he actually has the impudence, in one of the letters I have read in a Newspaper, to say that he was present in all the affairs from 20th Sept. to 7th November!! The N.C.O.[s] of the Battalion are furious, of course. I should be inclined myself to laugh, and let the great overgrown brute swagger a la Bobadil were it not that I hear people are making him presents and writing him flattering notices on his prowess, his claim to which he has not the candour to disavow.

Identical mugs were also produced, in which the name in the title is given as Sergeant Thomas. Sergeant-Major William Thomas of the Grenadier Guards was noted in his records for having shown 'Gallant conduct for Battle of Alma where he carried the … colour after the officer carrying it was wounded.' Although Thomas was commended for his bravery in a different action, it seems likely that his name was substituted when it was realised that he was more worthy of public acclaim than Davies.

SERGEANT DAVIES DEFENDING THE COLOURS AT INKERMANN

Two Russian letters recovered from the Battlefield of Inkerman, 1854

Manuscript, 20.5cm. h x 24cm. w; 20.6cm. h x 16.9cm. w

Generously donated by Mr Antony Whitaker

NAM. 1994-01-215 –15, -16

These letters were recovered by Colonel George Bell, 1st (The Royal) Regiment of Foot. The letters - the first of which was endorsed by Bell 'From "Inkerman's" Blood-stained field' - emerge upon their translation as curious items for him to have discovered. The first of them, written to one Nikolai Vekentiev, dates from 1849, five years earlier; the second, a bureaucratic letter written to Lieutenant-Colonel Michin at the fortress of Suchum, is even older, dating from 1821.

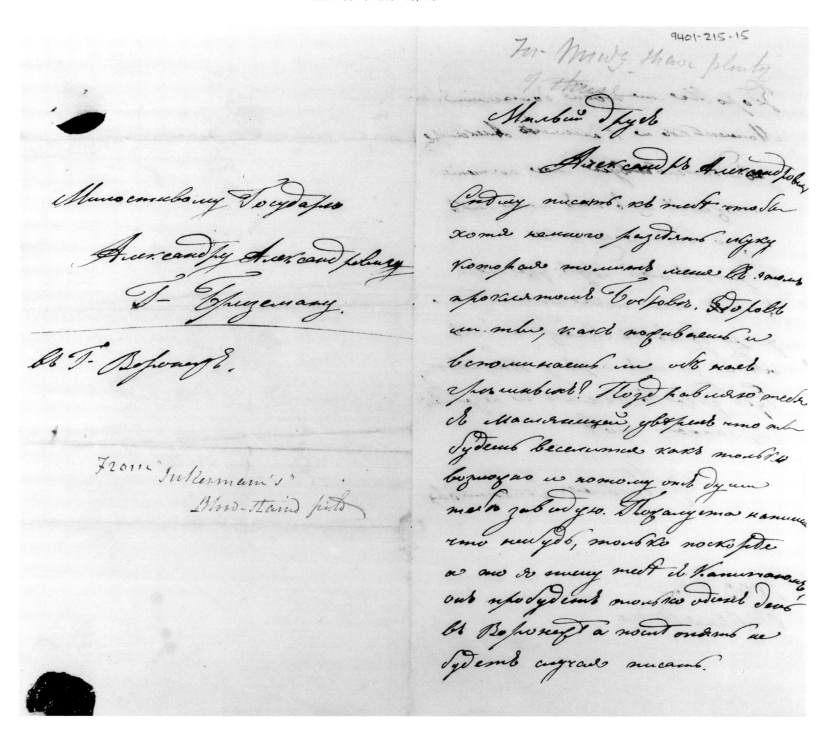

continued from over...

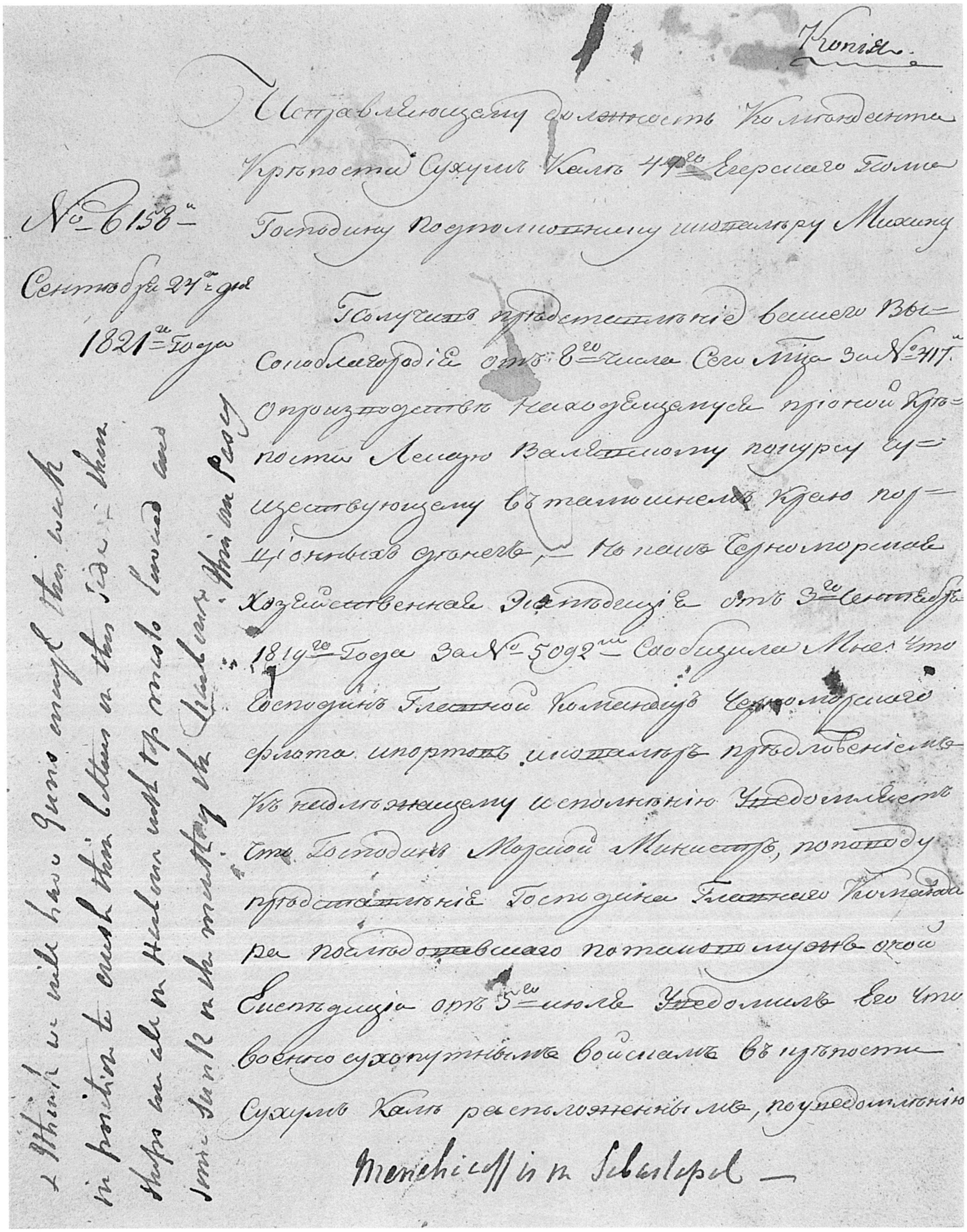

Копія

№ 6158

Сентября 24го дня 1821го Года

Исправляющему должность Коменданта Крѣпости Сухумъ Калѣ 44го Егерскаго Полка Господину Подполковнику [illegible]

Получивъ представленіе вашего Высокоблагородія отъ 8го числа сего Мѣсяца за № 417 о произвождствѣ находящемуся при оной Крѣпости Лекарю [illegible] существующему въ тамошнемъ краю порціонныхъ денегъ, — но понѣ Черноморская Хозяйственная Экспедиція отъ 3го Сентября 1819го Года за № 5092 сообщила Мнѣ что Господинъ Главной Командиръ Черноморскаго флота и портовъ [illegible] предложеніемъ къ надлежащему исполненію увѣдомляетъ что Господинъ Морской Министръ, по поводу представленія Господина Главнаго Командира [illegible] оной Экспедиціи отъ 5го іюля увѣдомилъ его что военно сухопутнымъ войскамъ въ крѣпости Сухумъ Калѣ расположеннымъ, по [illegible]

I think we will have guns enough this week in position to crush their batteries on their side; then ships are all in Harbour and the masts lowered and some sunk in the mouth of the Harbour. This on [illegible]

Menchicoff is in Sebastopol —

Lieutenant-General Sir George Brown's Commendations for Inkerman, 1854

Manuscript, 32.5cm. x 20cm.

Generously donated by the Royal United Service Institution

NAM. 1968-07-287-3

When Lord Raglan asked his divisional commanders to compile reports in the aftermath of a battle, he did so partly in order that the names of officers who had distinguished themselves might be brought to his attention. The most deserving would earn inclusion in his official dispatch, guaranteeing them some form of recognition. This summary of Lieutenant-General Sir George Brown's recommendations for the Light Division after Inkerman is taken from the Raglan Papers, and shows the well-deserved praise accorded the field officers of the 77th (The East Middlesex) Regiment of Foot for their conduct during the battle. Majors Straton and Dixon received brevet promotions as a result.

Medals awarded to Lieutnenant-General George Boldero, 1854-56

Crimea War Medal 1854-56, with clasps: Alma, Inkermann, Sebastopol; Order of the Mejidie, Turkey, 5th Class; Sardinian War Medal; Turkish Crimean War Medal 1855, Sardinian issue (reverse).

Generously donated by Miss V G Hammill

NAM. 2000-03-18

Major (later Lieutenant-General) George Neeld Boldero (1829-98) was first commissioned in the 87th Regiment of Foot (Royal Irish Fusiliers) in 1847, transferring to the 21st (Royal North British Fusiliers) Regiment in 1850. He fought as a captain in the Crimea and was awarded the brevet of major on 12 December 1854.

Letter written by Captain George Boldero, 1854

Manuscript, 17.8cm. h x 11.4cm. w

Generously donated by Miss V G Hammill

NAM. 1989-01-133

Boldero's active service in the Crimea was brought to an end at Inkerman by a severe wound in the right arm. Eight days after the battle he arrived at Scutari Hospital, from whence he wrote his father this brief letter.

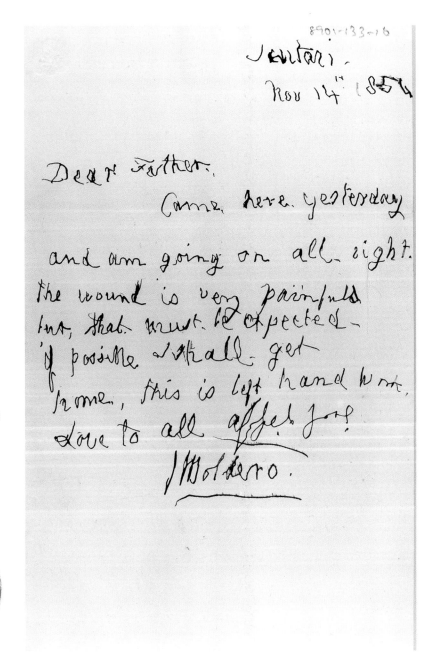

Medals commemorating the Battle of Inkerman, 5 November 1854

Bronze, John Pinches Ltd, 41mm. diam

Generously donated by the Royal United Service Institution

NAM. 1963-05-23-3

White metal, John Pinches Ltd, 41mm. diam

Generously donated by Mr J C Crisp

NAM. 1960-12-100-3

Bronze and white metal versions of the same medal, showing obverse and reverse. The obverse, in bronze, depicts British and Russian soldiers in close combat, with the word INKERMANN above. The reverse carries the names of the participating regiments and corps, arranged by divisions in the form of a rose.

The medal is one of a set of three, struck in silver, bronze and white metal by Pinches, with two other similar medals, commemorating the battles of Alma and Balaklava.

The Russian Army and the Campaign of Sevastopol

Alan J Guy

Her victory in the Napoleonic Wars had bequeathed to Russia, numerically speaking, by far the most formidable army in Europe. Its peacetime strength was fixed at 800,000 men, rising to 850,000 under Tsar Nicholas I (1825-55). Such numbers were necessary, partly because a system of recruitment based on serfdom did not allow for the establishment of a genuine reserve, but mostly to support a defensive posture from the Baltic to Kamchatka imposing enough to make any foreign aggression impossible. But powerful as an army of 850,000 might look on paper, it was insufficient to achieve that ambition. After a disappointing campaign on the Danube frontier in 1828, when it proved

Tsar Nicholas I.
NAM. 1960-12-323-6

almost impossible for the Russians to mobilize an army of 180,000 men, only the Turkish commander's foolishness in giving battle the following year enabled General I I Diebitsch to dictate terms at Adrianople. By this time his striking force had been reduced to 10,000 men. In 1831, when Polish and Russian armies clashed in battles on a Napoleonic scale at Grachow and Ostralenka,[1] the Tsar could hardly bring together a field army of 150,000. Between 1854 and 1856, after an absolutely stupendous effort, Russia succeeded in mobilizing 31,954 officers and 1,742,343 men, augmented to over 2,500,000 by irregulars and militia.[2] This army was believed to be greater in number than any European power had ever raised before, but was still not enough for the task in hand. Out of that great armament, only 320,000 were ever present in the Crimean theatre at one time (March 1855) and numerical superiority on the battlefield was achieved only once, at the mismanaged Battle of Inkerman on 5 November 1854. Where was the rest of the Russian army? What was it doing, and why?

In the more or less total absence of any geo-strategic thinking in early-nineteenth century Russia (intellectual officers had been tainted by their involvement in the Decembrist Rising of 14 December 1825) external security policy was based on a 'two-power standard' of military preparedness, according to which the western army was to equal in number those of Austria and Prussia combined. Throughout the Crimean War the good sense of this western emphasis was borne out by the need to guard against the sullen neutrality of Prussia and the menaces of the Austrians. In practical terms, it meant that 293,000 troops were tied down in Poland and the Western Ukraine, with another 121,000 in neighbouring Bessarabia and along the Black Sea. When Nicholas toyed with the possibility of reinforcing the Crimea at the expense of the central position, Marshal Prince I F Paskevich (who enjoyed in Russia the military reputation of the Duke of Wellington in England, and of whom Nicholas stood somewhat in awe) retorted, 'Should we not leave the Crimea? Why do they ascribe such importance to it? The Crimea is Sevastopol with fourteen ships in it. Compare which is better: to sacrifice those ships, or to be deprived of Bessarabia, Volhynia, Polodia, part of Ekaterinoslav, Kherson, Kiev, when Austria will be against us!'[3] Nicholas hastened to reassure his mentor that he had no intention of abandoning Poland without a fight, but as a result he sank deeper and deeper into creeping strategic paralysis, for the security of Poland and the Crimea was far from being his only problem. In the early 1830s, following the hard-won Turkish and Polish Wars, he had had a blinding intimation of what might happen if the fleets and armies of Britain and France lined up against him alongside the Turks, the armies of the central powers and possibly even the Swedes, who bitterly resented Russian encroachments in the Baltic. As well as pointing out to him how vulnerable he was in central

A panoramic view of the Russian Empire, published in London in 1855. The railway to Odessa, so clearly marked, did not in fact reach the city until 1866: it would greatly have eased Russian logistical difficulties if it had existed.
NAM. 1973-02-4-8

Europe, Prince Paskevich had highlighted the exposed position of the capital, St Petersburg, itself - a shrewd analysis as it turned out, for it was doubtful how long the outwork at Kronstadt could have withstood the great naval armament being prepared by the British for the (unfought) Baltic campaign of 1856. In response to this northern threat another 260,000 men, many of them picked troops, stood on guard in Finland and along the Baltic coast, equipped with the very latest shell guns, electronically-detonated sea mines and other anti-warship 'infernal machines.'[4] Up to 183,000 more fought during the War against the Turks and Islamist guerrillas on the Caucasus Frontier, ultimately

with much success, for the fall of the great Turkish fortress of Kars on 26 November 1855 offered the possibility of a counterpoise to the loss of Sevastopol two months earlier. Another 500,000 men were deployed on internal security duties inside the empire. The Crimean Peninsula itself was among the places least well defended in 1854, Tsar Nicholas, Paskevich and Prince A S Menshikov, the theatre commander, having underestimated what the allied fleets and armies could achieve there and thinking the province was capable of looking after itself.

In such circumstances it would have been theoretically possible for the Tsar to adopt an over-arching plan, the so-called 'Scythian Strategy' (*skifskaia strategiia*) of trading space for time which, despite its pejorative Asiatic overtones, had served the country well in 1812, was sanctified by history and actually taught at the Russian General Staff Academy. It would be employed during the Crimean War, but on a small scale and not in the Crimea itself. Some forts on the coast of the Caucasus were evacuated, and some minor works on the Gulf of Finland abandoned. At Petropavlovsk on the Pacific Coast of Kamchatka, after inflicting a punishing defeat on a British squadron on 30 August 1854, the Russian garrison withdrew into the interior and the warships based there hid deep in northern waters where they could not be located.[5] At Sevastopol however, as A J P Taylor has mischievously pointed out, the Russians extended the courtesy to their enemies of standing to fight at one of the few places they could be got at and made to bleed.[6] By so doing they acquiesced in a situation which put them on the back foot strategically. In contrast, however risky the Allies' strategy may have been, it had the clear and achievable intention of using their fleet to project a military force capable of destroying Russian naval power in the Black Sea.[7]

Having opted to defend Sevastopol, the situation for the Russians was then complicated by the fact that even had it been possible to pour more men into the Crimea, factors of time, distance and logistics made it very difficult to maintain them there. First, there was no railway connection to the Crimea, and in any case it had already been calculated that there was not enough rolling stock in the country to move so much as a corps, let alone an army. Troops made their way to the theatre of war on foot; sometimes over dirt-track roads nearly impassable in the wet and which in winter might reduce the number of effectives completing the trip by as many as nine out of every ten. Once in the Crimea, the Russian soldier was beset by logistic horrors as bad as anything suffered by the Allies and possibly worse. Water was very scarce. The Crimean Peninsula produced little other than cattle and grapes. Food and ammunition for the men and fodder for the countless horses accompanying the army had to be carted vast distances, at soaring expense, from distant parts of Russia. The local Tartar population was indifferent, if not hostile. When Allied naval units broke into the Sea of Azov in May 1855, ravaging the coastline and terrorizing the inhabitants, incalculable quantities of provisions and feed went up in flames; the Russian supply trains and cavalry could no longer operate effectively and the roads inland had to be protected by forts.[8]

Looking back from the twenty-first century on these accumulated difficulties, one wonders whether Menshikov's first instinct to pull out of Sevastopol after his (avoidable) defeat on the Alma may have been a master stroke, the field army, it could be argued, being much the more valuable asset. Alternatively, was the decision to defend Sevastopol taken as a means as much to save the wounded field army as to keep it in being as a credible threat? Assuming this to be the case, it was clearly better to tempt the Allies into wearing themselves out against the town's fortifications than to

The Russian retreat from the Alma.
NAM. 2002-10-139

leave them free to seek out and probably destroy the army in battle. That done, however, could the town thereafter be given up without irretrievably losing face? Research in the newly opened Russian archives may eventually throw more light on this complex decision-making process but, as is sometimes the case in a game of chess which is going badly, Tsar Nicholas in 1854 found himself in a position of 'move compulsion' - he had to make a move, but all the possible moves only made things more difficult.[9] What is certain, however, is that for Nicholas the one thing worse than war was dishonour, a view shared by his principal advisers, who could only accept an exit strategy from the War that enabled them to preserve at least the semblance of the nation's self-respect. The 'Scythian Strategy', moreover, born in 1812 out of a gross miscalculation of Napoleon's military power (Russian intentions had been to advance, not to retreat) had been a strategy for an army with no choice. This time, it could be said, there were far too many choices.

Confident at least in the ability of the Russian soldier to 'out-suffer' his opponent, the ingenuity of the defending engineer, Lieutenant-Colonel E de Todleben,[10] and the inspirational leadership of the three naval officers who commanded inside Sevastopol, Vice-Admiral V A Kornilov, Admiral P S Nakhimov and Rear-Admiral V I Istomin (all three of whom were to die during the siege), Tsar Nicholas chose to fight on there. In 1855 his son, Tsar Alexander II, would do exactly the same in an even worse situation. To the very last hour of the town's agony, neither Menshikov, nor his successor as theatre-commander, Prince M D Gorchakov, had the strength of mind to stand up to this moral pressure, coming as it did direct from the autocrat. Yet by the end of the siege in September 1855 the defenders of Sevastopol were dying at an unsustainable rate of up to 2,500 a day.

Concerning the valour and endurance of the Russian soldier, especially in the defence, there was no disagreement. He was in most cases an agricultural serf, chosen for the draft by the elders of his peasant commune. To return a serf trained in the military arts to the life of a serf was thought to be socially dangerous, so enlistment brought with it the reward of legal freedom. On the other hand, to return a free man to his village after a term of short service was thought to be equally risky, in that it might lead to unregulated serf emancipation. To avoid both difficulties Russia chose to stand aside from the European trend towards short service and the build-up of trained reserves by setting a period of service of twenty-five years under arms. In these circumstances, few draftees would ever return to their homes. In fact, the recruit was looked upon as being as good as dead by his family and friends, who accompanied him to the first milestone with lamentations worthy of a funeral. Forever separated from home and peasant life the

soldier was taught to rely instead on the small-unit fraternity of his company or platoon *artel* which, by replicating some features of the village commune and giving him a degree of control over the management of his pay and rations, provided him with a surrogate family, and a focus for personal loyalty and soldierly cohesion. His acculturation to arms was based upon an unselfish love for Holy Russia, reverence for the Tsar and a devotion to the Orthodox faith, which however superficial it might have been in points of doctrine, had much to offer in terms of regimental *ésprit de corps*. The defence of Sevastopol commenced with a religious procession; icons hung and

Russian manpower: the raw material. A deserter painted by Colonel The Honourable George Cadogan.
NAM. 1998-06-128-41

lamps and tapers burned in the heart of the Malakhov and other defences throughout the siege.

Given the popular conception of the limitless number of Russia's people, it is at first surprising to find that the crippling strategic overstretch described earlier was complemented by an equally alarming shortage of manpower. Steady growth in the population of Russia since the eighteenth century underpinned the regular establishment of 850,000 men - but only just, for the true size of the recruit base was small in relation to it. In the early 1830s, when Tsar Nicholas and his military administrators turned in some desperation to this matter, it was calculated that about 16.5 million male peasants were eligible for the draft - over half of them living far away from any likely theatre of war - which complicated any mobilization a great deal, it might be added. Making allowances for age and fitness, fewer than four million men were actually worth the taking, of whom some 75,000 were needed each year. In other words, at any one time the Russian army accounted for about twenty per cent of all the men in the state liable and fit to serve.[11] Seeing that taxation based on the product of agricultural labour accounted for about thirty per cent of Russia's annual income, landlords and peasant communes naturally did their best to prevent the most useful men in their communities from being drafted: first or only sons were usually exempt; timely bribes could redeem others. As for the remainder, evasions, feigned illnesses and self-mutilations soared to alarming proportions. Small wonder, therefore, that the draft was bulked out by the friendless, by the local 'troublemaker', or by the petty criminal discharged by the courts into the hands of the recruiter. In the 1830s, Tsar Nicholas, alarmed by the insufficiency of trained men, brought in a system of indefinite furloughs for soldiers who had served twenty of their twenty-five years, by which he hoped to build up a reserve 150,000 strong. This body of men, together with a mass of untrained recruits, comprised the huge army of 1854-56, but was little more than a palliative. As for the reservists themselves, they remained trapped between the civilian world and the military - exiled from the paternal hearth but, as they were liable for recall at any time, unable to settle to any livelihood.

Whatever its numerical shortcomings, even in time of peace the cost of Nicholas' army was so great it nearly bankrupted the state. It is one of the tragedies of his reign that the troops which, in his own way, he cared for so much, were nevertheless subjected by him to devastating economies. He was more than pleased when able to cut the cost of a uniform jacket by reducing the number of buttons. More importantly, excessive reliance on the bayonet - which flew in the face of a tradition of aimed fire originating in wars against the Turks - can best be explained by chronic shortages of powder and ball. Some men, it was said, spent their entire military career without ever firing their muskets, or else having to make do with clay bullets. The Russian soldier's smoothbore percussion musket was totally outclassed by the Minié rifles of the British - deadly at ranges of 455m. upwards, as opposed to less than two hundred. In the Russian service expensive rifles could only be spared for a few sharpshooters. The great Suvorov's catchphrase, 'the bullet is a fool; the bayonet is a clever fellow' was by now a counsel of necessity, not a matter for choice.[12] To make things worse, dogged even in peacetime by institutional failures of supply, the Russian army often found it necessary to follow a path of economic self sufficiency which was highly negative in terms of military effectiveness. The notorious 'agrarian militarism' of the military settlements of Tsar Alexander I (1801-25) was by now in eclipse, but large amounts of time and manpower were taken up in agriculture, trade and construction work that would far better have been spent on training - so much so that one modern authority has characterized the whole military apparatus of Nicholas I as a 'quasi-reserve army'.[13] In this struggle for unit solvency and subsistence, training in anything more sophisticated than the famous parade step took second place, and the massive attack columns of the Crimean battlefields owed as much to this as to a sound tradition of defence in depth against the Turks.[14]

Prince A S Menshikov.
NAM. 1968-07-322-10

Shortcomings on such a scale were, sadly, not to be compensated for by inspired or even competent generalship. Russia's generals in the Crimea kept up a long tradition of internecine competitiveness, tale-bearing, toadying and buck-passing, which makes their British and French opposite numbers look angels by comparison. It is amazing that known incompetents (or at best the unwilling) were kept in high command for so long. Prince Menshikov outwardly possessed all the attributes of a soldier, sailor and diplomat that should have qualified him well for independent command, yet when he began his infamous 1853 mission to Constantinople, the prelude to the War itself, he claimed to be suffering from gout, earache, nosebleeds, hoarseness, a throat abscess, headaches, toothache and constipation - notable handicaps for a commander-in-chief designate.[15] His courtier's wit was in practice more like verbal savagery, the Prince having an unforgivable word ready for everyone: the news that female nurses had arrived in the Crimea was greeted by him with the comment that they would do nothing but spread syphilis.[16] He openly admitted to having no grasp of tactics, and preferred to give no orders at all rather than interfere in things he did not understand. On the crucial day at Inkerman he shuffled combat command onto the unfit shoulders of General P A Dannenberg - having already been warned by Prince M D Gorchakov,

Prince M D Gorchakov.
NAM. 1968-08-25

who had sent Dannenberg from Bessarabia as a job-lot with the men of 4 Corps under him, that he could not be trusted to act independently. For the loss of that decisive battle, where tens of thousands of Russian soldiers were never brought into action, Dannenberg blamed his colleague, Lieutenant-General F I Soimonov, who was conveniently dead. Menshikov blamed Dannenberg.[17] Tsar Nicholas closed the circle - first by sacking Dannenberg and then, belatedly, Menshikov - but when the Prince's time came to leave the Crimea in the spring of 1855, to be replaced by Gorchakov, one wag in the army was heard to say that they might yet regret him. And so it proved, for at the last major field engagement of the campaign, the Battle of Chernaya Rechka on 16 August 1855, Gorchakov, who had not wanted to fight in the first place but who was not prepared to say no to his imperial master, demonstrated that he was no more an effective commander than his predecessor.[18]

Tsar Nicholas died on 2 March 1855. Before the end he had ceased to wish to hear tidings from the War. The first reaction of his son, Alexander, was to fight on; 'Sevastopol is not Moscow', he declared on hearing of the town's fall, 'the Crimea is not Russia. Two years after the burning of Moscow, our victorious armies were in Paris. We are still the same Russia, and God is on our side.'[19] By the beginning of 1856 however, diplomatic pressure, civil unrest and economic breakdown combined with military exhaustion to bring Russia to the conference table at Paris. The advocates of peace at Alexander's court had by now reached the conclusion that submitting at this stage of the War to what were relatively lenient terms would not prejudice the country's power-base in the longer term. Another year of campaigning certainly would. Choosing therefore to look upon the Peace of Paris (April 1856) as little more than a truce, Alexander was even able to dress it up as a vindication of Russian war aims against the Sultan. The reactions of the men vanquished on the battlefields of the Crimea were, unsurprisingly, more troubled, the underlying reasons for their defeat being much less clear than they are today. Their mood is perhaps best caught by Count Leo Tolstoy, then an artillery sub-lieutenant, in the sombre closing paragraph of his 'Sevastopol in August 1855';

> As almost every man crossed the waterlogged pontoon to the northern [Severnaia] suburb of the stricken town, he took off his cap and crossed himself, But behind this feeling of self-preservation there was another, a deeper feeling, sad and gnawing, akin to remorse, shame and anger. Almost every soldier looking back at the abandoned town from the North side, sighed with inexpressible bitterness in his heart and made a menacing gesture towards the enemy.[20]

After the Russian withdrawal pre-set fires raged in Sevastopol for two days. The surviving warships had been set alight or scuttled. The powder magazines were blown up. Fearful of being caught in the explosions the Allies did not venture to march in until the fires had burned out. Their standards were only raised over the captured town on 10 September 1855.

Notes

1   It is a mistake to assume, as some have done, that the Alma was the first full-scale battle between European nations since Waterloo: at Grachow (25 March 1831) and Ostralenka (26 May 1831) tens of thousands were engaged, with Napoleonic Wars veterans prominent on both sides: see Tadeusz Stachkowski 'The Polish-Russian War of 1831', *History Today*, Vol. XXIX (1979) pp310-17, 386-93.

2   Statistics from a secret Russian War Ministry study, 'Data for the Estimation of Russia's Military Strength' (1870), quoted by Robert F Baumann 'The Russian Army, 1853-1881', in Frederick W Kagan & Robin Higham (eds), *The Military History of Tsarist Russia*, New York & Basingstoke (2002) p138.

3   John Shelton Curtiss, *Russia's Crimean War*, Durham, NC, (1979) p439.

4   For the new technology of control-detonated mines and contact-detonated 'infernals' in Baltic naval operations, see D K Brown, *Before the Ironclad: Development of Ship Design, Propulsion and Armament in the Royal Navy, 1815-60*, London (1990) pp152-4.

5   For the Petropavlovsk operations, see Barry M Gough, *The Royal Navy on the Northwest Coast of North America, 1810-1914*, Vancouver (1974) pp108-30.

6   A J P Taylor 'Crimea: The War that would not boil' (1951), reprinted in Chris Wrigley (ed); Taylor, *From Napoleon to the Second International: Essays on Nineteenth Century Europe*, Harmondsworth (1993) pp216-28, *passim.*

7   Hew Strachan, 'Soldiers, Strategy and Sebastopol', *The Historical Journal*, Vol XXI, (1978) pp303-25 analyses British strategic thinking behind the Sevastopol expedition. For the British fixation on the threat posed by enemy fleets and arsenals, which decades of warfare against France had prepared them for in doctrinal terms, see Andrew D Lambert, *The Crimean War: British Grand Strategy against Russia*, 1853-56, Manchester & New York (1990), *passim.*

8   See Professor Lambert's bullish assessment of the impact on Russian fighting power of the Sea of Azov operations; *The Crimean War: British Grand Strategy*, pp230-4. Professor Curtiss, who cleaves to the Russian historians of the War, is much more sceptical; Curtiss, *Russia's Crimean War*, pp431-2. Stephen M Harris provides an excellent intelligence-based analysis which qualifies both points of view; see his *British Military Intelligence in the Crimean War, 1854-56*, London (1999) pp105-14.

9   For the concept of *Zugzwang* - 'move compulsion', I am indebted to Professor David Saunders, who applies it to the foreign and domestic policies of Nicholas I; Saunders 'A Pyrrhic Victory: The Russian Empire in 1848', in R J W Evans & Hartmut Pogge von Strandmann, *The Revolutions in Europe, 1848-1849: From Reform to Reaction*, Oxford (2000) p151.

10   As well as his celebrated works of fortification at Sevastopol, Todleben raised a four volume literary monument to his achievements there, plus a volume of maps and plans. After the War he became a kind of

international consultant on fortifications; see Quentin Hughes 'Russian Views of the English Defences in 1864', *Fort: Journal of the Fortress Study Group*, Vol VII, (1979) pp69-76. In contrast to some parts of the Russian military machine, the engineers, along with the artillery, were an élite corps and highly regarded. Todleben, despite his fame, was not immune from criticism; his insistence on fortifying the gorge (rear) of the Kornilov bastion on the Malakhov to allow for all-round defence may have contributed to the failure of Russian counter attacks on the French storming parties during the fall of this vital position on 8 September 1855. The allies launched twelve attacks that day, of which only that on the Malakhov was successful.

11   See the extended discussion in Frederick W Kagan; *The Military Reforms of Nicholas I: The Origins of the Modern Russian Army*, Basingstoke (1999) pp221-3.

12   This maxim was derived from A V Suvorov's *How to Win: A Talk to Soldiers in their own Language* (1795). It has sometimes been wilfully misunderstood so as to make Suvorov look unnecessarily eccentric and reactionary - curious character though he certainly was. In his writings, Suvorov had urged the Russian soldier to fire sparingly but accurately: all he had meant was that a bullet might go astray - a good bayonet thrust wouldn't; see Christopher Duffy, *Eagles over the Alps: Suvorov in Italy and Switzerland, 1799*, Grand Rapids, Michigan (1999) pp16-17.

13   Elise Kimmerling Wirtschafter, *From Serf to Russian Soldier*, Princeton, NJ, (1990) p95.

14   Russian tactical formations are conveniently set out in Robert H G Thomas & Richard Scollins' excellent volume in the Osprey 'Man at Arms' series; *The Russian Army in the Crimean War, 1854-56*, London (1991) pp19-24.

15   David M Goldfrank 'Policy Traditions and the Menshikov Mission of 1853', in Hugh Ragsdale (ed), *Imperial Russian Foreign Policy*, Cambridge (1993) p135.

16   As recorded by one of the Russian Crimean War heroes little known in the west, Dr N I Pirogov of the Academy of Sciences, who served at Sevastopol; see John Shelton Curtiss 'Russian Sisters of Mercy in the Crimean War,1854-1855', *Slavic Review*, Vol XXV (1966) p85.

17   Albert Seaton, *The Crimean War: A Russian Chronicle*, London (1977) is unsparing on the generalship of Menshikov and Dannenberg (see especially pp157-78), but their failure to get large bodies of troops into action is characteristic of the loose command and control methods of the time; see Brian Holden Reid, *The American Civil War and The Wars of the Industrial Revolution* London (1999) p41.

18   Leo Tolstoy, who served under Gorchakov at the siege of Silistria, admired him and thought that he was worshipped by the troops, see R F Christian (ed), *Tolstoy's Letters*, Vol I, London (1978) p25. Others, relieved at the departure of Menshikov from the Crimea, had their doubts but kept an open mind. Tsar Alexander II, who knew his limitations, maintained a relentless pressure on Gorchakov to do something, with predictably unfortunate results. Colonel Seaton's verdict is harsh; *op.cit.* pp194-208, but as he points out, Gorchakov

retained the Tsar's favour and succeeded Paskevich as commander of the western army, *ibid.* p218.

19   Norman Rich, *Why the Crimean War? A Cautionary Tale*, Hanover, New England & London (1985) p157.

20   Leo Tolstoy, *Tales of Army Life*, Oxford (1935) 'Sevastopol in August 1855', p229. In the Russian calendar the evacuation of the southern sector of the town took place during the night of 27-28 August (8-9 September, new-style) 1855, hence the title of Tolstoy's work.

Administrative Breakdown

On 14 November 1854 a great storm swept the Crimea. The tents of the Allied encampment outside Sevastopol were flattened. Worse, much of the British shipping gathered beyond the narrow confines of Balaklava harbour was driven onto the rocks. The mighty steamship the *Prince*, carrying the Army's warm winter clothing, sank. Twenty days' supply of hay for the Commissariat's horses were also lost. Combined with the onset of winter and the turning of the earthen track between Balaklava and Sevastopol into a quagmire, this loss of forage crippled the Army's already inadequate transport. Overworked horses died from starvation in their traces. Without transport, rations for the troops before Sevastopol were interrupted. There was no fuel to cook the food. Thinly clothed, lacking shelter and exhausted by unremitting trench duty, the soldiers succumbed to cholera and dysentery in their thousands. Medical provision was scandalously deficient; there were no ambulances to convey the sick to Balaklava. Those that survived the voyage back to Constantinople found the hospitals at Scutari ill-equipped and the medical staff overwhelmed. Men lay untreated for weeks; the mortality was appalling. By January 1855, such was the rate of attrition in the British Army in the Crimea that, without reinforcement, it was within thirty days of ceasing to exist.

'The gale off the port of Balaklava, 14th Nov. 1854'

Coloured tinted lithograph by R Carrick after William Simpson (1823-99), number four in the first series of Simpson's 'Seat of War in the East', published by Paul and Dominic Colnaghi & Co, London, 15 January 1855, 37cm. h x 55.5cm. w

Crookshank Collection, transferred from the British Museum

NAM. 1971-02-33-490-4

The hurricane that struck the Crimea on 14 November 1854 sank no fewer than twenty-one British and fourteen French ships. Among them was the mighty steamship the *Prince*, carrying the Army's winter clothing, and the *Resolute* with its cargo of ten million Minié rounds. The loss of twenty days' issue of hay for the horses also proved of crucial importance: lacking nourishment, the Army's horses – vital for the conveyance of supplies from Balaklava to the encampment before Sevastopol – died in ever-increasing numbers.

'Commissariat difficulties. The Road from Balaklava to Sevastopol, at Kadikoi, during the wet weather', 1854

Tinted lithograph by Edmund Walker (*fl.*1836-62) after William Simpson (1823-99), number 13 in the first series of Simpson's 'Seat of War in the East', published by Paul and Dominic Colnaghi & Co, London, 9 February 1855, 38.2cm. h x 56.8cm. w

NAM. 1969-08-30

The road from Balaklava to Kadikoi was notoriously treacherous in wet conditions, causing many horses and oxen transporting supplies from the harbour to perish stuck fast in the mud. According to the historian of the Crimean War, Alexander William Kinglake (1809-91):

The road growing worse and worse daily under the action of rain, was before long in such a condition as to be impassable for wagons, unless they were forced through the clay by powerful teams; and a time was even at hand when the Commissary-General would find himself compelled to abandon altogether the use of wheeled carriages, trusting only thenceforth to the expedient of sending up his supplies on the backs of horses and mules... Already, cold, wet, and hard work (to be followed at times and too often by a more or less prolonged want of food) were not only killing those beasts, but fast weakening our artillery teams...

Captain Arthur Layard, 1855

Photograph by Roger Fenton

NAM. Negative 4616

Captain Arthur Layard (1819-55) of the 38th (The 1st Staffordshire) Regiment of Foot was the younger brother of the radical Member of Parliament, Austen Henry Layard. His letters to his brother are generally critical of the higher military authorities, that of 12 December 1854 being among the most scathing:

> The continuous rain we suffered from, up to three days ago, did us a great deal of mischief. In the first place it has completely destroyed our transport service. The road to Balaklava was in a dreadful state. The mules &c. were overworked and underfed, the consequence was they died, the Commissariat could not get our rations or our forage, the troops were and are all on short rations and the mounted officers, the Artillery and Cavalry up here are obliged to send in for their forage and I hear we shall have shortly to send in for our rations ourselves. Our wretched Ambulance establishment of course went to the back. And only yesterday, don't hide the fact from any one in England, the French volunteered and took down to Balaklava eleven hundred 1100 of our sick, 200 going down from this Division, an officer of the staff attached to it going down with them. The sick were conveyed in the litters etc on the mules and reached the ships safely. The mules appeared in excellent condition, just as fresh as when they first landed at Gallipoli. Our animals are all dead or the few that remain are but a bag of dying bones. There is not an officer in the Army that does not blush at our being obliged to go for help to our friends the French.

Arthur Layard died of disease on 7 August 1855.

'15 sick of ours went down to Balaclava to embark for Scutari today, and their places will be filled ere evening – the French have to carry most of our sick on their mules; as we have no means – I enclose slight sketch of some sick being take down by our Cavalry, and a more sickening sight it is difficult to imagine. 3rd January – 1855'

Pencil sketch by Captain (later Colonel) Henry John Wilkinson (1829-1911), 1st Battalion, 9th (The East Norfolk) Regiment of Foot, 1855, 15.6cm. h x 21cm. w

Generously donated by the Royal United Service Institution

NAM. 1972-07-6-63-2

Major William Forrest of the 4th (Royal Irish) Regiment of Dragoon Guards commented thus on the use of cavalry horses to carry the sick to Balaklava:

The sickness in the Army generally, continues, I fear as bad as ever, and the neglect of the sick is as disgraceful as ever, or very nearly so. The only means of transporting the poor fellows, from the Front, down to Balaklava, is upon Troop-Horses. One of our Officers went in charge of one of these Parties a few days since; the day was bitterly cold: when he arrived at the Division, to which he was ordered to go, he found that the Medical Officer had received no intimation of the intended removal of the sick, consequently there was great delay before the different cases could be selected for removal, and when they at last started, these poor Fellows had no extra clothing, beyond a blanket to wrap round them, and many of them had no shoes; they were altogether in a most pitiable state; many of these poor fellows actually crying; Men, who probably had fought at Inkerman, or at all events, were of the same stamp, as those who did.

Crimea War Medal 1854-56, with clasp: Sebastopol

Awarded to Sergeant Frederick Newman, 97th (Earl of Ulster's) Regiment of Foot

Generously donated by Mrs C A Fitzgerald

NAM. 1968-11-25

Frederick Newman (1828-54) enlisted in the 97th (Earl of Ulster's) Regiment of Foot on 20 February 1844 and, until he returned to England in May 1853, had spent almost all his military career abroad in the Mediterranean, Jamaica and North America. He served as a Hospital Sergeant from 1849 onwards and in this capacity went with his Regiment to the Crimea in November 1854, dying of fever the following month.

Hospital Sergeant Frederick Newman, 97th (Earl of Ulster's) Regiment of Foot

Carte de visite photograph by A Simmons, 258 Westminster Bridge Road, London, 14.3cm. h x 10.3cm. w

Bequeathed by Mrs C A Fitzgerald

NAM. 2002-03-167-1

Newman is photographed wearing around his waist a sergeant's floss silk crimson sash. He was an unhappy soldier and since 1848 had been hoping that his uncle would buy him out of the Army. The money that he had been saving for the purpose he had paid to buy out his younger brother, who enjoyed the Army even less than he did.

Letter written by Hospital Sergeant Frederick Newman, 1854

Manuscript, 18cm. h x 22.2cm. w

Bequeathed by Mrs C A Fitzgerald

NAM. 2002-03-167-36

The 97th (Earl of Ulster's) Regiment of Foot arrived in the Crimea in November 1854 from Piraeus in Greece where it had already been ravaged by cholera, losing 120 men within three months. On 29 November Newman wrote to his parents:

> We are now about 3 miles from Sebastopol and under canvas tents, the rain pouring in torrents and all around miserable. Cholera has broke out amongst the poor fellows who are exposed in the Trenches day and night with nothing but their big coats to shelter them from the rain or cold..

> ..We get biscuits Salt Pork or Beef and one gill of Rum with some Sugar Rice and unroasted Coffee. Just like our government, the idea of sending coffee here not roasted. We manage it somehow, by grinding it in a broken bomb shell with a round shot to crush it. Water is very scarce and extremely muddy. I have not washed my face nor yet shaved since I landed here on the 20th inst being satisfied with enough to drink without washing my face and as for a clean shirt I think when I can find it convenient to wash one then I will put one on. So I am washerwoman and cook and everything else at the same time. ..This terrible Cholera .. has made fearful ravages here. I have just commenced to write again and there are now six poor fellows lying dead. I am rather loose in my bowels, but take as much care of myself as possible.

Newman resumed the same letter on 2 December:

> It is a cold, windy morning and my feet feel like ice. We have lost 25 men by Cholera and we have now 18 in Hospital with this disease and 25 with Diarrhea. I must say we are fearfully situated and any man who lives to go to England from this ought to be a good man all his life after.

Twelve days later Newman too was dead from fever.

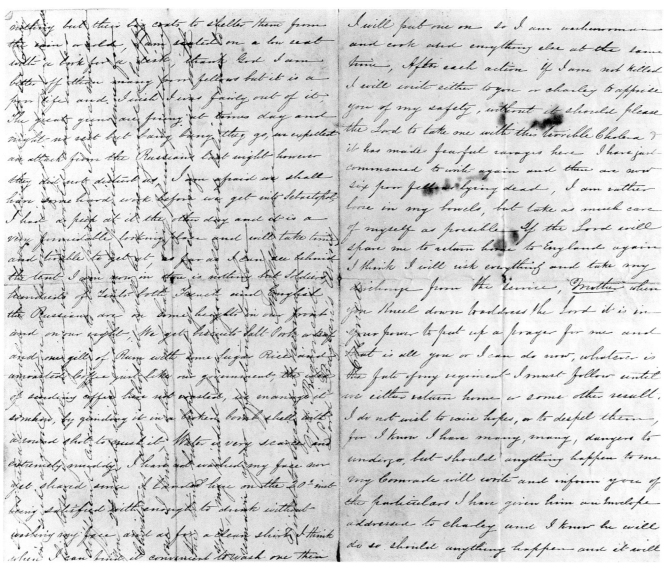

Writing case, *c*1854

20cm. l x 14cm. w x 7.5cm. d

Generously donated by Mrs C A Fitzgerald

NAM. 1968-12-23

The remains of a label reveal that the writing case was used by Hospital Sergeant Frederick Newman of the 97th (Earl of Ulster's) Regiment of Foot, en route to the Crimea and after he arrived there. His administrative duties meant that the writing case was an essential tool of his trade.

'Crimean War 1854', winter 1854-55

Watercolour, inscribed lower left 'Colr Sergt R. Adkinson Crimean Vet 1908', by Colour-Sergeant Richard Adkinson (b.1835), 19th (1st Yorkshire North Riding) Regiment of Foot, 1908, 24.7cm. h x 37.4cm. w

Generously donated by Mr J R Barker

NAM. 2003-07-2

Richard Adkinson, born on 28 April 1835 in Kibworth, Leicestershire, enlisted in the 19th Regiment of Foot on 30 December 1852 and was promoted corporal in March 1854. In the Crimea, Adkinson was wounded at the Alma but returned to duty during the siege of Sevastopol. He went on to serve in India from June 1857 until January 1872.

Although this watercolour of a party of the 19th (1st Yorkshire North Riding) Regiment of Foot trudging through thick snow from Balaklava to Sevastopol in the winter of 1854-55 was not made on the spot, it depicts an identifiable location with the plateau of Sevastopol ahead and the route to the British encampment round the col to the left. In the worst of the winter, with wheeled transport unable to negotiate the unmade roads and most of the horses dead, soldiers were forced to complete the twelve mile round journey to Balaklava themselves in order to collect their supplies. Adkinson's composition, showing a colour sergeant and a corporal helping exhausted soldiers, records the camaraderie that was so essential for the survival of the Army in such conditions.

Paintings by other ranks depicting the Crimean War are rare as, unlike officers, they did not receive instruction in drawing and lacked ready access to materials.

Letter of E Griffiths, 1855

Manuscript, dated Camp before Sebastopol 31 January 1855, 18.3cm. h x 22.5cm. w

Generously donated by Mrs M Robert

NAM. 1975-01-50

When Lord Raglan was attacked for incompetence and indifference to the sufferings of the troops, his champions would allege that it was only malcontent officers who wrote letters of complaint home. The private soldier, they maintained, remained cheerful. This letter, signed 'E Griffiths', shows such not to be the case. Although it is impossible to positively identify E Griffiths, his unusual enthusiasm for the generalship of the Duke of Cambridge suggests that he was a Guardsman, in which case he was perhaps Evan Griffiths of the Scots Fusilier Guards, killed before Sevastopol on 10 August 1855. His written dialect is certainly one suggestive of a Welshman:

[Well we have an horspitl hear but a man must bee all but gon before he goes ther] so that i must walk about as long as i can and then when i can walk about no longer drop into my grave such is tha usag of your british armey in the crimea such is what tha think good a nof for them that are gaining laurels and victouries it is enough to brak a mans hart and i think that is what tha are try to do. .. what use lord Ragland is out hear that is tha man that can sit down and wright is dispatch home and talk about tha position of the armey when on the 5th of november at inkerman he was not never among it to see them onley [knowing] what he was toald such cowardic i never saw in a generl officer for i had tha chance of seeing him from wher i was so i tell you the truth the man is old and foolish not fit for this servies but he answers lord aberdeen very well. if the Duak of Camberage had camanded us at inkirman Sebastopel would have been ours and tha whoule of tha eneney put to tha rout insted of anoying us in the way thay are.

165

Letter of Lieutenant Henry Alderson, Royal Artillery, 1854

Manuscript, dated 'Camp before Sebastopol December 29' 1854, 20.8cm. h x 27cm. w

Generously donated by Mr P Holt

NAM. 1980-11-54-1

For much of the Crimean War hostilities were played out against a backdrop of peace talks conducted in Vienna. Some officers wished for peace to spare them their ordeal before Sevastopol. Most, however, were unwilling to countenance peace before the fortress had fallen. Lieutenant Henry James Alderson (d. 1909) of the Royal Artillery, writing to his mother, hoped for both. He was also pleased to hear that there was to be a Crimea War Medal and that the desperate nature of the fighting at Inkerman was fully recognised at home.

If the last Shave be true we shall walk into Sebastopol without further bore, as peace is to be proclaimed and Sebastopol given over as a material guarantee. I hear the medal &c is already struck or is going to be. I shall be lucky as I shall get the "Alma" clasp which is "bono" being in the siege train as the others of course won't. It seems from the notice taken of it the Authorities are really about to acknowledge that "Inkerman" was the hardest fought action there ever was. I can assure you that out here where we have better opportunities for knowing the ins & outs of it it considered that there never was an action like it.

Gunners of the Royal Regiment of Artillery resting in the trenches of Sebastopol, c1855

Watercolour and pencil, signed lower right 'HJA', by Lieutenant (later Major-General Sir) Henry James Alderson (d. 1909), 10th Battalion Royal Artillery, c1855, 26cm. h x 38cm. w

Generously donated by Mr R E Alderson

NAM. 1955-01-4-9

Alderson appears to have drawn purely for his own pleasure and that of his friends and family. His letters to his mother held in the Museum Collection include a number of sketches and in them he also enquires as to whether other drawings had arrived safely in the post. Alderson served in the Crimea from 1854 to 1855, and saw action at the Battles of Alma and Inkerman, and the siege of Sevastopol, in particular in the trenches with the siege train, and the bombardments of October 1854, and April and June 1855. In recognition of his service, Alderson received the Crimean Medal with three clasps, the Turkish Medal and was made a Knight of the Legion of Honour. He went on to be appointed Assistant Superintendent of Experiments at the School of Gunnery in the 1870s, Assistant to the Director of Artillery and Stores in the 1880s and was President of the Ordnance Committee in 1891.

'Inkerman Lodge. The Winter Quarters of Brigadier General Bell', 1855

Drawing, signed 'W K Elles 38th Regt' (Ensign William Kidston Elles, 38th (The 1st Staffordshire) Regiment of Foot), 'Near Sebastopol 1855 1st January', 13.2cm. h x 19.8cm. w

Generously donated by Mr A Whitaker

NAM. 1994-01-215-5

Brigadier-General (later General Sir) George Bell (1794-1877) of the 1st (The Royal) Regiment of Foot was in the process of drafting a letter to the editor of *The Times* highlighting the wretched condition of the Army in the Crimea ('Sir John Campbell who commands the 4th Division lives in a little cave, by candle light! Col. Bell has a wall 4 feet high built round his Tent, to break off the wind, other officers have mud walls around') when on 30 November 1854 he had a visitor:

I was sitting at my ration dinner at 4pm when Lord Raglan came to pay me a friendly visit. Kind & unexpected, an honor not contemplated. He is a man of remarkable memory and asked of things I thought had been forgotten. Told me that my old friend General Egerton was breaking down & confined to his room, was amused at my Fortification around my tent, with my shot & shell arranged on my front battlement! One of these round shot I told him entered one of my tents without harm, & a shell with its Fuze burned out, paid us a camp visit.

Bell commanded the 1st Brigade of the 3rd Division until his return to England in 1855. He was convinced that his letter to *The Times* had blighted his career.

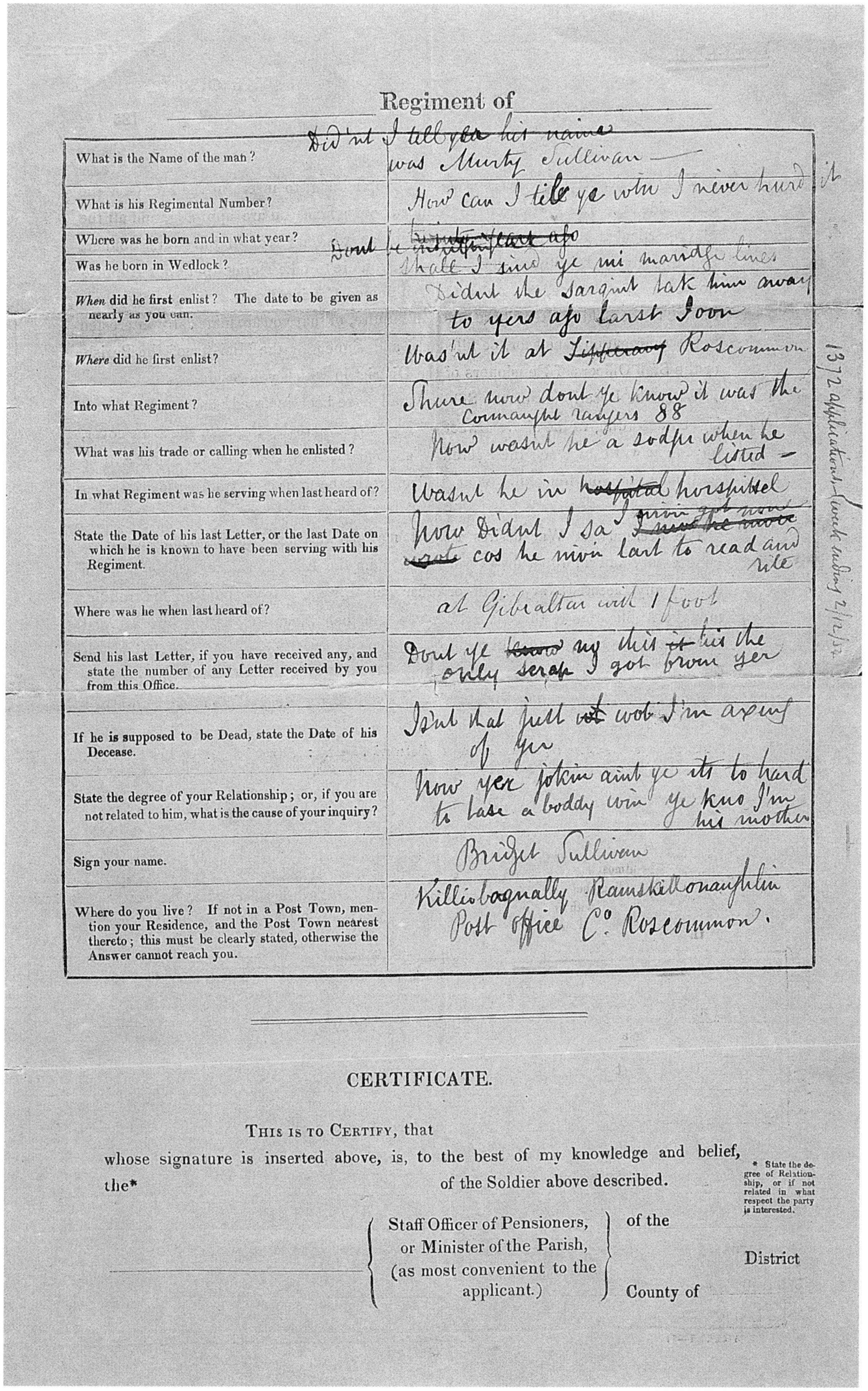

Regiment of

What is the Name of the man?	Did'nt I ~~tell yea his name~~ was Murty Sullivan —
What is his Regimental Number?	How can I tell ye win I never hurd it
Where was he born and in what year?	Dont he ~~twenty year ago~~ ago
Was he born in Wedlock?	Shall I send ye mi marridge lines
When did he first enlist? The date to be given as nearly as you can.	Didnt the sargint tak him away to yers ago larst Soon
Where did he first enlist?	Was'nt it at ~~Tipperary~~ Roscommon
Into what Regiment?	Shure now dont ye know it was the Connaught rangers 88
What was his trade or calling when he enlisted?	Now wasnt he a sodger when he listed —
In what Regiment was he serving when last heard of?	Wasnt he in ~~hospital~~ horspittel
State the Date of his last Letter, or the last Date on which he is known to have been serving with his Regiment.	Now Didnt I sa ~~I never got none~~ ~~I never he wrote~~ ~~wrote~~ cos he nivir larnt to read and rite
Where was he when last heard of?	at Gibraltar with 1 foot
Send his last Letter, if you have received any, and state the number of any Letter received by you from this Office.	Dont ye ~~know~~ ny this ~~it~~ his the only scrap I got from yer
If he is supposed to be Dead, state the Date of his Decease.	Isn't that just ~~wot~~ wot I'm axing of yer
State the degree of your Relationship; or, if you are not related to him, what is the cause of your inquiry?	Now yer jokin aint ye its to hard to lase a boddy win ye kno I'm his mother
Sign your name.	Bridget Sullivan
Where do you live? If not in a Post Town, mention your Residence, and the Post Town nearest thereto; this must be clearly stated, otherwise the Answer cannot reach you.	Killiobagnally Ramskillonaughlin Post office C^o Roscommon.

1372 applications (week ending 2/12/54)

CERTIFICATE.

THIS IS TO CERTIFY, that
whose signature is inserted above, is, to the best of my knowledge and belief, the* of the Soldier above described.

* State the degree of Relationship, or if not related in what respect the party is interested.

Staff Officer of Pensioners, or Minister of the Parish, (as most convenient to the applicant.) of the District County of

W.O. Form 118, 1854

Printed and manuscript, 34cm. h x 20.5cm. h

Generously donated by Vice-Admiral Sir John Lea

NAM. 1986-06-90

War Office 118 was the form filled in by relatives wishing to enquire about the well-being of a soldier with whom they had lost touch. This example has been filled in by a War Department clerk posing as an Irish woman of poor intelligence named Bridget Sullivan of County Roscommon. In the margin he noted '1372 applications – week ending 2/12/54' – presumably about loved ones in the Crimea.

The system of enquiry was far from infallible. In response to an application concerning John Pine of the 1st Battalion, The Rifle Brigade, his family was told that 'he was put on board ship at Balaklava for Scutari on the 21st Jany [18]55, but did not arrive at his destination and is therefore supposed to have died on passage'. In fact, as they discovered from one of his comrades, John Pine had died at the base hospital at Kulali, near Constantinople.

Wooden signpost, *c*1854-56

82cm. l x 17.5cm. w x 3cm. d

Generously donated by Lieutenant-Colonel
V Hughes

NAM. 1960-08-50

This wooden signpost, painted on
both sides 'To Headquarters and
Balaklava', was brought back from
the Crimea by Cornet John Gibsone
of the 17th Regiment of Light Dragoons (Lancers). Gibsone was
commissioned into the regiment on 8 December 1854 and joined it in the
Crimea on 14 July 1855. He retired as a captain in 1863.

Chair used at Balaklava, *c*1854-55

92cm. h x 57cm. w x 55cm. d

Generously donated by Mrs F M B Musgrave

NAM. 1965-05-51

Balaklava, the harbour chosen by the British in which to land supplies for
their Army in the Crimea, was small and cramped. As the stores
accumulated aboard ship and at the harbour side, administration
descended into chaos. Compared to the soldiers encamped before
Sevastopol, the commissariat officials at Balaklava – roundly condemned
by the troops for their slavish adherence to red tape - lived in relative
comfort: at least they had chairs in which to sit.

Poster issued by the Postmaster General, 1854

Printed, 44.4cm. h x 28cm. w

NAM. 1998-05-4-1

At a time when the Army's logistical support had almost completely broken down, the mail service stood out as a beacon of relative efficiency. Appointed by the Postmaster General, the Army Postmaster was independent of the military and employed, in the main, civilian staff. In spite of a shortage of steamers with which to carry the mail to Constantinople, and the occasional difficulty in getting the Army to move the mail bags from the Balaklava Post Office to the quayside, during 1855 over 750,000 letters were sent through France to the Army and Navy in the Black Sea theatre, with 1,200,000 letters sent back in return.

Instructions No. 161, 1854.

By Command of the Postmaster General.

NOTICE TO THE PUBLIC.

GENERAL POST OFFICE,
October, 1854.

IN order to prevent the delay of Letters and Newspapers for Invalid Officers and Soldiers belonging to the British Forces in the East, who may be in the Military Hospital in Turkey, by such Letters, &c. being forwarded to the Head Quarters of the Army, a separate bag will, in future, be made up in London for the correspondence referred to, and Letters and Newspapers will be forwarded in this bag if they are plainly addressed to

"The Hospital, Scutari,
"Constantinople,"

and if the postage upon them is duly paid in advance.

The dates fixed for dispatching from London the Mails for Constantinople, viâ France, are the evenings of the 3rd, 9th, 13th, 19th, 23rd, and 29th of every Month, but when the Month has 31 days, the Mail is made up on the 30th instead of on the 29th.

'W H Russell The Times Correspondent in the Crimea', c1855

Proof lithograph by and after Thomas Herbert Maguire (1821-95), with a facsimile of William Howard Russell's autograph, published by Henry Graves & Co, London, 26 October 1855, 61.5cm. h x 43.6cm. w

NAM. 1972-09-56

William Howard Russell (1820-1907), the celebrated correspondent of *The Times*, is shown wearing the jacket which he adopted as part of his dress in the East. In his memoirs, Russell noted that, having lost his bags on the way to the Crimea:

> I must have been, to say the least, odd-looking. Boxes of clothes, &c., from Poole and Silver were somewhere on the sea; but I was, on the whole, but poorly equipped for the invasion of the Crimea. I wore a Commissariat officer's cap with a broad gold band; a Rifleman's patrol jacket, for which I had given egregious largesse to the owner; cord breeches; a pair of butcher-boots and huge brass spurs.

During the 39 years that elapsed between Britain's last war in Europe, the Napoleonic Wars, and the outbreak of the Crimean War in 1854, journalism had been transformed. Technological advances such as the development of the telegraph had encouraged the public to demand accurate, informative and up-to-date news from around the world. In order to satisfy these requirements, newspapers sent representatives to the Crimea to deliver unprecedented records of a war as it unfolded. As speed and accuracy of war reportage became paramount, newspapers placed greater emphasis on their reporters being present at the events they described. The journalists, who had to rise to the challenges of living and working in the battlefield's dangerous environment in order to provide a commentary on the progress of the conflict, were the world's first genuine war correspondents. These reporters provided the public with eye-witness accounts from the front line, personal perspectives on the world of the ordinary soldiers and subaltern officers, which could be read alongside the bland official reports released by the government. In February 1854, in his quest to provide the public with accurate information on the progress of the war, John Delane (1817-79), the editor of *The Times*, asked the Irish-born journalist, William Howard Russell, to accompany the Brigade of Guards when it left Britain for Malta as part of the expeditionary force bound for the East. His series of dispatches published between 9 and 13 October 1854 describing the twin horrors of minimal medical treatment and appalling hygiene endured by the patients at Scutari were instrumental in persuading Florence Nightingale to gather together her party of nurses.

What distinguished Russell from other correspondents' accounts of the battles of the Crimean War were the brilliant powers of description with which he illuminated his reports. Notwithstanding his avowal that, 'The rattle of musketry, the thundering of the batteries, the crackling of the flames, the whiz and ping of bullets near at hand, were very disconcerting, and unsuited to philosophic observation of events', Russell's vivid descriptions of such battles as the Alma, Balaklava and Inkerman, and the assaults on the Malakhov and the Redan, came to form the basis of the public's perception of these events. Moreover, Russell and *The Times* brought not only the exploding shells, the smoke, the confusion, the heroism and the death of the battlefield into the homes of Britain, but also the spectre of the soldier abandoned to starvation, cold and disease through official neglect. *The Times* appealed to its politically active readership and shared its concern about the administrative failures and consequent neglect of the soldier. Russell's letters stirred the conscience of the nation; there followed in January 1855 a parliamentary vote on an opposition motion calling for an enquiry into the Government's mismanagement of the war. It was carried overwhelmingly, whereupon the Prime Minister, Lord Aberdeen, resigned.

Journal of Acting Assistant Surgeon Henry Bellew, 1854-55

Manuscript, 19.5cm. h x 27cm. w

Generously donated by Miss A I Bellew

NAM. 1951-12-21-1

Henry Walter Bellew (1833-92), who qualified as a surgeon on 6 October 1854, was destined to join the Bengal Establishment of the East India Company. However, he would only be the requisite twenty-two years old on 30 August 1855 and so, hearing that the Army of the East desperately needed surgeons, he applied to the Army Medical Department and was appointed acting assistant surgeon. He embarked 2 December on the steamship *Alma* and arrived at Constantinople on 2 January 1855. Told that his services were required immediately, he was sent to Hyder Pasha Hospital at Scutari. On 4 January, 120 new patients arrived:

They were with few exceptions in a truly pitiable state of filth and utterly helpless from wounds & debility. On being brought inside the hospital several were found to be dead, many were at their last gasp, and others it was evident had but a short time to live & suffer. Almost all the living were in a lamentably exhausted condition and filthy to a degree not to be described. All were swarming with vermin, huge lice crawling all about their persons & clothes. Many were grimed with mud, dirt, blood &c & gunpowder stains. Several were more or less severely wounded and others were completely prostrated by fever & dysentery. The sight was a pitiable one & such as I had never before witnessed. The poor fellows endured their sufferings with heroic fortitude amounting in appearance to indifference as to their fate. Both Barnett & I exerted our best energies to render what aid lay in our power and were busy to a late hour easing the aches of those placed under our care. There has been somehow unaccountable neglect in the arrangements for this Hospital. Until some hours after the arrival of the men there were neither stores, attendants nor the necessary refreshments on the spot. During this afternoon I attended single handed to the wounds & wants of 74 helpless men. From many, on my knees as they lay on the floor, I cut away the clothes as the easiest & safest way of ridding them of their filth & vermin.

'Graves at the head of the harbour of Balaklava', 1854

Coloured tinted lithograph by C Haghe after William Simpson (1823-99),
number 21 in the first series of Simpson's 'Seat of War in the East',
published by Paul and Dominic Colnaghi & Co, London, 13 March 1855,
36.8cm. h x 55.4cm. w

Crookshank Collection, transferred from the British Museum

NAM. 1971-02-33-490-21

In the description accompanying this print, the artist recorded that the
scene represented the burial of a sailor from one of the ships in the harbour
of Balaklava:

> War has its victims other than those who perish by the sword and
> bullet; fever and cholera are ever in its train, and not infrequently
> carry off those whose vocation is not in the battle-field, for whom
> alive there are no laurels, and dead no glory. At Balaklava there
> are many graves whose tenants were of this class, men who
> perished at their post and in the faithful discharge of their duty, and
> who sacrificed their lives to their country as surely and not less
> heroically than the soldier who falls at the summit of the breach he
> has mounted, and with the shout of victory ringing in his ears.

'Our Cavalry, Dead Horses', 1854

Pen and ink and watercolour by Lieutenant (later Colonel) Henry John Wilkinson (1829-1911), 1st Battalion, 9th (The East Norfolk) Regiment of Foot, 1854, 13.4cm. h x 20.5cm. w

Generously donated by the Royal United Service Institution

NAM. 1972-07-6-12

'On the heights at many a spot there lay the putrefying bodies of horses which had died under the toil of bringing up supplies for our army, and still lay where they fell for want of "hands" to bury them'; so wrote Alexander Kinglake, the historian of the Crimean War. While it is true that overwork killed a vast number of horses, the real problem was the lack of forage, as

Lord Raglan explained in a letter to the Secretary of State for War on 23 January 1855:

> I did not after the storm attempt to get fresh horses, for the Com[missary] General did not encourage me to hope that he could feed them, and there was no use in buying horses, and letting them die of starvation, and want of due care.

> I got some from Eupatoria for the Commissariat; and they, like the snow, have melted away, and I now have sent for some to Constantinople, but they may share the same fate, if the forage which should have been sent from England does not arrive.

Our Cavalry Dec.r 1854

'Before Sebastopol; Novr 1854.

The Sentry

'Before Sebastopol: Novr 1854. The Sentry'

Pen and ink and watercolour by Lieutenant (later Colonel) Henry John Wilkinson (1829-1911), 1st Battalion, 9th (The East Norfolk) Regiment of Foot, 1854, 23.9cm. h x 18.4cm. w

Generously donated by the Royal United Service Institution

NAM. 1972-07-6-54-2

According to a manuscript note below the drawing, a copy of it was made for 'Genl Sir Richard England at his own request', presumably as a souvenir of the campaign. The shivering sentry certainly became a by-word for misery, Lieutenant Thomas Lynden Bell of the 28th (The North Gloucestershire) Regiment of Foot writing home on 8 January 1855:

> We never see our Commander in Chief. .. I heard an anecdote of him lately viz he made an excursion to see the Camps (having perhaps had a hint) and rode up to the sentry of some regt (the sentry did not know him). His Lordship said, "Well my man I suppose you have got the warm clothing all right." The poor fellow said nothing but merely pulled open his great coat. He had no trousers, only drawers, with garters round the calves of his legs made by himself. Such is the story, I believe it though I will not vouch for its truth.

'The Trenches No 4 Battery. Left Attack', 1855

Watercolour by Captain (later Colonel) Henry John Wilkinson (1829-1911), 1st Battalion, 9th (The East Norfolk) Regiment of Foot, 1855, 12.3cm. h x 18.9cm. w

Generously donated by the Royal United Service Institution

NAM. 1972-07-6-43

A fellow officer of Wilkinson's in the 9th (The East Norfolk) Regiment of Foot, Captain Hopton Bassett Scott, wrote home on Christmas Day 1854 describing a scene not unlike that depicted by the artist:

We must still man the trenches day after day, and wretched work it is. I spent one day with 100 men and a subaltern in a small trench cut across the Simpheropol road about 400 yds from the town. The enemy's sharp-shooters quite commanded our position, so much so that if we stood up for a moment half a dozen rifle balls whizzed about us. To enliven our position it rained in torrents, and as there was no outlet for the water which poured down the roads, the trench gradually filled, so that we had to bolt for it one by one to a cover about 50 yards in rear. They made very good practice, but did not quite hit off the elevation, so there were several narrow escapes but no casualty save a hole in our grog but which was fortunately above the water line, or rather spirit level. We spent from 6 A.M. till 9 P.M. in that trench unable to move a muscle and in a deluge of rain, some of the poor fellows wretchedly ill.

'Night Scene - winter - in the Trenches before Sebastopol taken on the spot by Capt H. J. Wilkinson 9th Regt February. 1855'

Watercolour, signed lower right 'H.J.W.', by Captain (later Colonel) Henry John Wilkinson (1829-1911), 1st Battalion, 9th (The East Norfolk) Regiment of Foot, 1855, 10.3cm. h x 15.9cm. w

Generously donated by the Royal United Service Institution

NAM. 1972-07-6-15

Following the public outcry at the condition of the troops in the Crimea during the winter of 1854, the Government had sent out fresh supplies of warm clothing. On 23 January 1855, Lord Raglan reported to Henry Pelham Pelham-Clinton, 5th Duke of Newcastle (1811-64) and Secretary of State for War the 'Great progress … in disembarking and issuing to the troops vast quantities of warm clothing of all descriptions; and I believe I may assert that every man in this army has received a second blanket, a jersey frock, flannel drawers and socks, and some kind of winter coat in addition to the ordinary greatcoat'. However, as this watercolour shows, although their living conditions were improving by February 1855, the soldiers huddled against the elements in the trenches before Sevastopol remained far from comfortable.

'Camp. R. B. November 30', 1854

Pen and ink by Joseph Archer Crowe (1825-96), 'special' artist for *The Illustrated London News*, 1854, 17.8cm. h x 22.8cm. w

Generously donated by the Royal United Service Institution

NAM. 1968-06-319

Below this sketch of the camp of the Rifle Brigade, there is a manuscript inscription describing the scene, 'The tent is a fascimile – the men cannot

be too ragged and "worn" looking. Hills at altitude of Chernaya background -'. These instructions were intended to assist *The Illustrated London News* in producing an engraving after the drawing; however, the subject was not selected by the editors for publication.

The subject of the study lower right entitled 'Colville. Capt. Rifle Brig.' is Captain (later Colonel) the Honourable William James Colville (1827-1903) of The Rifle Brigade, the artist of two humorous uniform studies included elsewhere in this exhibition (NAM. 1974-02-131-1 & -2).

The following twelve watercolours by William Simpson have been grouped together out of chronological sequence to enable them to benefit from the lower levels of lighting employed in one section of the exhibition gallery, and also to allow the visitor to see Simpson's paintings displayed side by side.

'Lord Raglan's Quarters before Sebastopol Novr 1854'

Watercolour and pencil, signed lower right 'Wm Simpson' and inscribed as title, by William Simpson (1823-99), 1854, reproduced as plate nine in Simpson's 'Seat of War in the East', first series, published by Paul and Dominic Colnaghi, London, 1855, 26.1cm. h x 42cm. w

Bequeathed by Henry Edward Hugh, 9th Duke of Newcastle

NAM. 1992-01-114

The key to the print published after this watercolour indicates Captain Brandling and the tents of his troop of Royal Horse Artillery in the left foreground, with the camp of the heavy cavalry behind them. In the centre of the picture, an ambulance is shown travelling in the direction of General Scarlett's tents to the right, with the camps of the Third and Fourth Divisions in the distance behind them. The clouds of smoke on the horizon indicate the French Batteries to the far left, and then those of the Russians. The large area of smoke at centre-left marks the English attack and the next puffs of smoke, the Russian White Tower or Malakhov Batteries. According to the description published to accompany the print after this watercolour, 'The emaciated body of a dead horse in the foreground tells its own tale, and informs us that the difficulties and disasters of winter have already commenced'.

'The Valley of the Shadow of Death, Caves in the Woronzoff Road behind the 21 Gun Battery', December 1854

Watercolour and pencil, signed and dated lower right 'Wm Simpson/ Decr 1854', by William Simpson (1823-99), 1854, reproduced as plate 36 in Simpson's 'Seat of War in the East', first series, published by Paul and Dominic Colnaghi, London, 1855, 25.6cm. h x 44.6cm. w

Bequeathed by Henry Edward Hugh, 9th Duke of Newcastle

NAM. 1992-01-116

The so-called 'Valley of the Shadow of Death' was the Vorontsov Ravine to the rear of the British right attack, the position of which is indicated in this picture by the puffs of smoke on the horizon. The valley was given this name because of the enormous number of Russian shot and shells fired from the Malakhov which overshot their target and rolled into it. This drawing, made before the second bombardment, shows only a fraction of the shells that came to fill the ravine by the end of the war. By April 1855, according to the published description of the plate after this watercolour: 'The whole extent of the road from side to side, for a very considerable distance, was literally paved with round-shot of all calibres, and with large and small fragments of shell, so that a horse had the greatest difficulty in picking his way through the labyrinth of obstacles thus presented.'

'Interior of Lord Raglan's Head Quarters. A Council of War', 1855

Watercolour, signed and dated lower left 'Wm Simpson/ 1855', by William Simpson (1823-99), 1855, reproduced as plate eight in Simpson's 'Seat of War in the East', second series, published by Paul and Dominic Colnaghi, London, 1856, 28.5cm. h x 46.4cm. w

Bequeathed by Henry Edward Hugh, 9th Duke of Newcastle

NAM. 1992-01-118

Seated in the centre of the scene is Lord Raglan, with the Turkish commander-in-chief, Omar Pasha, and his French counterpart, General Canrobert, to the left. The respective French and British naval commanders, Admirals Bruat and Sir Edmund Lyons, are pictured to the right. The setting, which the published description of the print after this watercolour describes as a 'modest farm-house', served as the British Headquarters for the duration of the conflict.

'Disembarkation - Kertch', 24 May 1855

Watercolour and pencil, signed and dated lower right 'Wm Simpson/ 24th May/ 1855', by William Simpson (1823-99), 1855, 29.3cm. h x 50cm. w

NAM. 1963-01-115

The port of Kerch guarded access to the Sea of Azov, an important supply route for Sevastopol. Much to the disgust of the British, a previous Anglo-French expedition to capture Kerch had been abandoned in sight of its objective when the French force was suddenly recalled. However, on 22 May 1855 a second expedition was launched.

Permitted by Lord Raglan to accompany both expeditions, Simpson recorded in his autobiography his impressions of the disembarkation at Kamish Burun, on the west side of the Straits of Kerch: 'I went ashore after some of the troops had landed. The spot was a small bay, with a flat beach and a fishing village. The people of that village had all run away, and evidently they had done so in a very great hurry. In one house I saw a pot on the fire with food in it; the fire was still red, and the liquid in the pot still simmering.'

'From Chapman's Attack' or 'Town Batteries or Interior Fortifications of Sebastopol from the advanced parallel of Chapman's Attack, 23 June 1855'

Watercolour and pencil, signed and dated lower left 'Wm Simpson/ 23rd June/ 1855', by William Simpson (1823-99), 1855, reproduced as plate six in Simpson's 'Seat of War in the East', second series, published by Paul and Dominic Colnaghi, London, 1856, 33.7cm. h x 50.3cm. w

Bequeathed by Henry Edward Hugh, 9th Duke of Newcastle

NAM. 1992-01-121

The soldiers in the foreground are shown manning a Rifle Pit in the British Left attack, also know as Chapman's Attack. Below them to the right, the Vorontsov road runs down to Sevastopol's Man of War Harbour; the water's edge is protected by the Russian Strand Battery. Atop the high ground to the right, the Barrack Battery is well-placed to sweep any attack made from this direction.

'Camp of the 3rd Division', 15 July 1855

Watercolour and pencil, signed and dated lower right 'Wm Simpson/ 15th July 1855', by William Simpson (1823-99), 1855, reproduced as plate 12 in Simpson's 'Seat of War in the East', second series, published by Paul and Dominic Colnaghi, London, 1856, 29cm. h x 43.8cm. w

Bequeathed by Henry Edward Hugh, 9th Duke of Newcastle

NAM. 1992-01-122

The figures in the foreground are shown using cannon balls as bowls. The print after this watercolour was accompanied by a detailed key showing the distribution of the regiments within the camp which, according to the description, was published: 'For the satisfaction of those to whom these camps are associated either in the past or in the present with the absent living or the unforgotten dead'.

The dark, stormy sky shown moving in from the right of the picture forced the artist to seek refuge in one of the tents of the 63rd (The West Suffolk) Regiment of Foot in order to finish his painting.

'Camp of the 4th Division, July 15th 1855'

Watercolour and pencil, signed and dated lower right 'Wm Simpson/ 15th July 1855', by William Simpson (1823-99), 1855, reproduced as plate nine in Simpson's 'Seat of War in the East', second series, published by Paul and Dominic Colnaghi, London, 1856, 23.3cm. h x 44.2cm. w

Bequeathed by Henry Edward Hugh, 9th Duke of Newcastle

NAM. 1992-01-123

The key which accompanied the print after this watercolour detailed the distribution of the regiments within the 4th Division's camp. To the left are the tents of the 57th (The West Middlesex), 20th (The East Devonshire) and 17th (The Leicestershire) Regiments, with those of the 55th (The Westmoreland) Regiment of Foot to their right. Behind them are the tents of the Royal Regiment of Artillery attached to the 2nd Division, with the French camp beyond. The two huts behind the mounted officers mark the position of the Royal Regiment of Artillery of the 4th Division, with the camp of the Guards and Highlanders in lines beyond. In the centre of the picture are the tents of the 39th (The Dorsetshire) Regiment of Foot, those of the 49th (The Princess Charlotte of Wales's) Regiment of Foot and the Rifle Brigade far right.

'The Battle of Tchernaya, 16th August 1855'

Watercolour and pencil, signed and dated lower right 'Wm Simpson/ August 1855', by William Simpson (1823-99), 1855, reproduced as plate 14 in Simpson's 'Seat of War in the East', second series, published by Paul and Dominic Colnaghi, London, 1856, 29cm. h x 49.3cm. w

Bequeathed by Henry Edward Hugh, 9th Duke of Newcastle

NAM. 1992-01-124

The Battle of the Chernaya was the final attempt made by the Russians to break the siege of Sevastopol. By August 1855 the defenders of the town were suffering such heavy casualties from the Allied bombardment that the effort could no longer be delayed. The Russian attack, however, was bloodily repulsed by the French, assisted by the Sardinian Army.

On the left of the picture the Russians are shown being thrown back from the slopes of the Fediukine Heights. In the middle distance they have already begun retiring over the Tractir Bridge. To the right French Zouaves (a type of soldier, originally of North African origin) defend the Aqueduct Bridge.

'Redan and Advanced trenches of British Right Attack, Sebastopol burning in the distance'

Watercolour, signed and dated lower right 'Wm Simpson/ 1856', by William Simpson (1823-99), 1856, reproduced as plate 38 in Simpson's 'Seat of War in the East', second series, published by Paul and Dominic Colnaghi, London, 1856, 27.9cm. h x 50cm. w

Bequeathed by Henry Edward Hugh, 9th Duke of Newcastle

NAM. 1992-01-129

On the night of 8-9 September 1855, following the French capture of the Malakhov, the Russians evacuated the south side of Sevastopol and set fire to the town. A column of British infantry can be seen in the foreground carrying away firewood salvaged from the ruins; they also have some Russian prisoners. In the distance, towards the left, a flag flies from the Redan; the Malakhov is the prominent feature occupying the middle right of the picture.

'Interior of the Redan. Taken from its left face, looking towards the salient angle, looking South', September 1855

Watercolour and pencil, signed and dated lower right 'W Simpson/ Sept 1855', by William Simpson (1823-99), 1855, reproduced as plate 20 in Simpson's 'Seat of War in the East', second series, published by Paul and Dominic Colnaghi, London, 1856, 29.1cm. h x 43.8cm. w

Bequeathed by Henry Edward Hugh, 9th Duke of Newcastle

NAM. 1992-01-126

Although the British twice failed to take the Redan, the French capture of the Malakhov left Sevastopol untenable and in the course of the following night the Russians evacuated the town on the south side of the harbour. The fighting inside the Redan on 8 September had been desperate and although by the time Simpson executed his painting a degree of tidying-up had taken place, the acuity of the observation made by Lieutenant-Colonel Anthony Sterling can still be grasped: 'The inside of the Redan, when I saw it last, was filled with broken gun-carriages, and strewed with dead men and firelocks and clothes. Standing on the parapet, you looked down on a deck, as you would standing on a frigate's hammock nettings. Assaulting the Redan was very much like boarding a frigate from boats.'

'Docks at Sebastopol with ruins of Fort St Paul', 1855

Watercolour and pencil, signed and dated lower right 'Wm Simpson/ 1855', by William Simpson (1823-99), 1855, reproduced as plate 26 in Simpson's 'Seat of War in the East', second series, published by Paul and Dominic Colnaghi, London, 1856, 29.1cm. h x 43.9cm. w

Bequeathed by Henry Edward Hugh, 9th Duke of Newcastle

NAM. 1992-01-125

The six dry docks were the centrepiece of the Russian naval base of Sevastopol. Their destruction would be the single most important act in preventing the resurgence of any threat from Russia's Black Sea fleet. At the end of December 1855 and throughout the following January, a series of mines were exploded which obliterated them completely.

'The Duke of Newcastle addressing the Circassians on the Banks of the Kuban, 3rd Octr 1855'

Watercolour and pencil, signed and dated lower right 'Wm Simpson/ 1857', by William Simpson (1823-99), 1857, 27cm. h x 44.4cm. w

Bequeathed by Henry Edward Hugh, 9th Duke of Newcastle

NAM. 1992-01-132

After resigning as Secretary of State for War upon the downfall of Lord Aberdeen's government in January 1855, Henry Pelham Pelham-Clinton, 5th Duke of Newcastle (1811-64), travelled to the Black Sea and the Crimea to see for himself the condition of the Army and the nature of the terrain. In the autumn of 1855 he journeyed to Circassia in the north-east Caucasus where he is depicted, standing before tents, surrounded on either side by Circassian Chiefs. The artist, William Simpson, recorded in his autobiography:

The first night we enjoyed Circassian hospitality was a new experience. We had had a long and tedious day's journey among the hills, and reached a chief's residence. This consisted of a number of small huts, built of wattle and daub, with thatched roofs, one of which was the konag, or guest house. A separate house for strangers is a necessary consequence of Mohammedan ideas respecting wives and women folk in general. These konags were small places with mud floors and raised mud ledges, on which the rugs or sleeping carpets were placed. They were sofas by day and beds at night. Our repast was provided in this wise. Some one had to go and catch a sheep or goat, and it had to be killed and cooked before supper was possible. This took three or four hours, and the customs of Circassia were not spoken of in favourable terms as we waited.

"Position of the British Army before Sevastopol, shewing the line of railway"

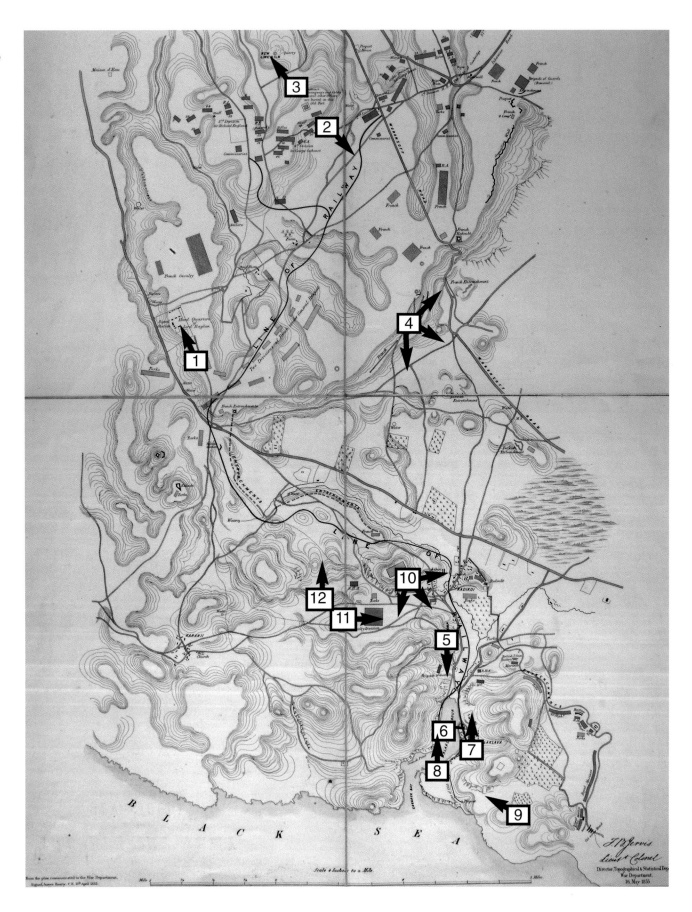

1. South view of Lord Raglan's Headquarters (Robertson)
2. Camp of the 2nd, 4th and Light Divisions from Cathcart's Hill (Robertson)
3. Sevastopol from Cathcart's Hill (Fenton)
4. Panorama of the Plains of Inkerman and Balaklava showing, in the distance (left to right), the Russian-held Inkerman Heights beyond the River Chernaya; the Fedukine Heights; the North Valley and Voronsov Road; and the Causeway Heights. It was from approximately here that Lord Raglan watched the Battle of Balaklava and the Charge of the Light Brigade (Fenton).
5. View south looking towards Balaklava (Robertson)
6. Railway sheds and workshops at Balaklava (Fenton)
7. Balaklava, looking north (Robertson)
8. Balaklava Harbour, looking north (Robertson)
9. The Castle Hospital and Balaklava Harbour (Robertson)
10. Panorama looking south-east from Frenchman's Hill (Robertson)
11. View east towards Kadikoi from the cavalry encampment (Fenton)
12. View north towards the Plateau of Sevastopol from the cavalry encampment (Fenton)

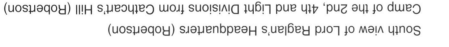

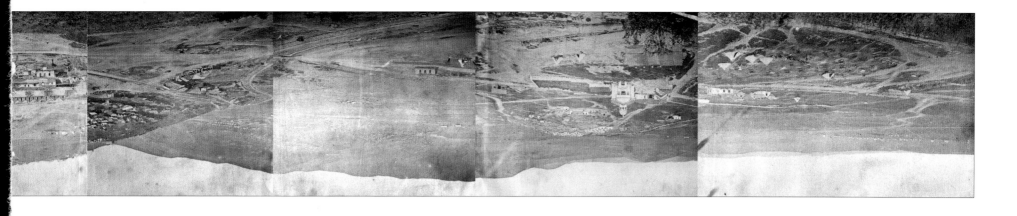

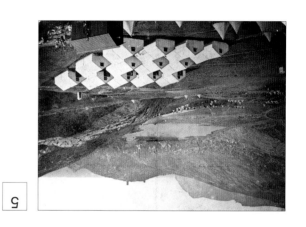

The British line of supply from Balaklava to the Camp before Sevastopol

Art and War Reportage in the Crimean War I: The Illustrated London News

Emma Armstrong

The Illustrated London News, a Pictorial Family Newspaper, containing Essays on Public Affairs; Literature; Fine Arts; Music; Drama; Sporting Intelligence; Science; and a complete record of all the events of the week, at home, abroad, or in the colonies; the whole illustrated in a high style of art by wood-engravers of the first eminence...[1]

Founded in May 1842 by Herbert Ingram (1811-60),[2] *The Illustrated London News* was the world's first illustrated newspaper. Although previously a number of newspapers had included illustrations of news events from time to time, *The Illustrated London News* was the first to include high quality wood engravings as a regular feature of its publication. The images were included not merely to complement the written word; instead they formed the substance of the journal, and it was through the interplay between text and images that the periodical sought to create meaning. The first half of the nineteenth century had seen a transformation of the newspaper readership, which now incorporated an increasing number of the middle-classes. In 1851, for the first time, Britain's towns were home to more of the population than the countryside.[3] The illustrated press, a novel form of weekly newspaper, was developed to cater to the demands of this new audience. Costing sixpence, *The Illustrated London News* provided the new urban readership not only with news and information, but engravings of the latest fashions, spectacles and art. In so doing the paper offered its readers a window onto the world of knowledge, culture and taste to which they might aspire.

Even before the outbreak of the Crimean War, it was clear that there was enormous public interest in military matters. When in June 1853 the Army assembled on Chobham Common for over two months of exercise and manoeuvres, the huge military gathering became a public spectacle entailing splendid royal reviews which, on one day alone, was witnessed by 30,000 spectators. In an attempt to profit from the popularity of Chobham Camp, a number of artists and print dealers exploited the demand for a visual record of the event. For example, James Wyld published a 'Plan of the Encampment of Chobham Common with the surrounding country',[4] to assist visitors travelling to the camp and in identifying the location of each regiment's encampment. *The Illustrated London News* published a daily diary of activities.

Chobham also offered the Army an opportunity to test its uniform, weaponry and equipment in the field. However, by conducting these investigations in such an arena, it invited public scrutiny of military matters. *The Illustrated London News* commented in January 1854, 'The Encampment at Chobham has awakened that degree of public

interest in the condition of our army without which it is impossible to effect any great reform in this country'.[5] As the country moved towards war, public interest in the state of the armed forces increased, fed by extensive press reportage. In January 1854, *The Illustrated London News* published maps and views of the Black Sea, commenting that,

In the present interesting crisis, ... we feel called upon to give a full and faithful portraiture of this important spot, which may, before very long, become the scene of events materially affecting the destinies of Europe.[6]

While it had been common practice for *The Illustrated London News* to employ London draughtsmen to construct images out of news reports from the daily press, at the outbreak of war in 1854 there were insufficient visual or written records of the Crimea for artists in Britain to use as reference on the area. The first illustrations of the Russian naval port of Sevastopol appeared in *The Illustrated London News* in June 1854,[7] and were after drawings by a naval officer, Lieutenant (later Rear-Admiral) Montagu Frederick O'Reilly (1822-88), whose work was a regular feature of the journal until the end of the War.[8] During the course of the War, *The Illustrated London News* published a number of drawings by members of the armed forces, while another newspaper carried advertisements offering the substantial inducement of £100 for the best collection of drawings by an officer of the British Army or Royal Navy serving in the Crimea showing battles, sieges and genre scenes connected with the War.[9]

Paintings with imaginary reconstructions of battles no longer satisfied public demand, so for the first time newspapers commissioned artists to accompany the British Army to war. Initially *The Illustrated London News* sent three correspondents, Edward Angelo (or Arthur) Goodall (1819-1908), Joseph (later Sir Joseph) Archer Crowe (1825-96) and Constantin Guys (1802-92), to report as direct observers of the war in the Crimea. In November 1854, the journal advertised,

On Saturday next, November 11th, 1854, will be Published an extra sheet of *The Illustrated London News*, containing descriptions and sketches, from Constantine Guys, Esq., and Joseph Crowe, Esq., the Special Correspondents of *The Illustrated London News*, at the Seat of War, witnessing the Great Operations at the Siege of Sebastopol.[10]

Of these artists, Constantin Guys was the most experienced in reporting conflict. Indeed, he is sometimes acknowledged as the first war artist for his work in *The Illustrated London News* from the 1848 Paris Revolution, which had helped to double the paper's circulation in

'Sebastopol and it's fortifications on the Black Sea'.
Wood engraving after Lieutenant (later Rear-Admiral) Montagu Frederick O'Reilly (1822-88),
Royal Navy, published in *The Illustrated London News*, 3 June 1854 p523.
NAM. Negative 98463

three months. However, it was his Crimean drawings that established his reputation.

As part of the avant garde group in Paris which included Emile Zola, Edouard Manet and Charles Baudelaire, Guys was the subject of the latter's analytical essay, 'Le Peintre de la Vie Moderne', first published in 1863. Although at the artist's request, his identity was not divulged, Baudelaire wrote that,

> Monsieur G. does not like to be called an artist. Is he not perhaps a little right? His interest is the whole world; he wants to know, understand and appreciate everything that happens on the surface of our globe. The artist lives very little, if at all, in the world of morals and politics.[11]

Guys was the first of *The Illustrated London News*' 'Special Correspondents' to cover the preparations for war in the Crimea. His drawings of Shumla in Bulgaria, dated 17 January 1854 were published in *The Illustrated London News* on 4 March,[12] whilst his drawings of Scutari were published on 9 and 24 June.[13] He used a particularly free and expressive style, working initially in pencil, over which he applied thin ink and watercolour washes before reinforcing the line with more ink. Baudelaire wrote of his sketches,

I have studied his archives of the Eastern War - battlefields littered with the débris of death, baggage-trains, shipments of cattle and horses; they are tableaux vivants of an astonishing vitality, traced from life itself, uniquely picturesque fragments which many a renowned painter would in the same circumstances have stupidly overlooked.[14]

The artist Edward Goodall was attached to the Naval Brigade headquarters in the Crimea, remaining there for a year. Unlike Crowe who also sent the periodical descriptions of the scenes he drew, Goodall appears to have confined himself to providing mainly visual records of the war. Consequently he was usually referred to as 'Our Special Artist' whereas Crowe was cited as 'Our Special Correspondent and Artist.' Where Goodall's pictures were accompanied by descriptions, they were often taken from the despatches of *The Times* correspondent William Howard Russell (1820-1907), 'in one of his vivid letters...'.[15] Since Goodall's scenes were very much simplified, his drawings were easily translated to wood engravings. However, his technique meant that some of the illustrations appeared stilted or staged. The photographer Roger Fenton (1819-69) was contemptuous of Goodall's work, and wrote of him in a letter to William Agnew (1825-1910) on 9 April 1855;

His sketches seem to astonish everyone from their total want of likeness to the reality, and it is not surprising that it should be so, since you will see from the prints sent herewith that the scenes we have here are not bits of artistic effect which can be effectually rendered by a rough sketch, but wide stretches of open country covered with an infinity of detail.[16]

A talented watercolourist, Joseph Crowe had been a reporter for the *Daily News* from 1846-52. Travelling via Shumla, Silistria and Varna, he arrived in the Crimea in September 1854, where he was made welcome by an old friend of his father's, General Sir George de Lacy Evans, commanding the 2nd Division. Unlike newspaper correspondents such as William Howard Russell, artists like Crowe, although employed by

the press, were not regarded with the same suspicion and were allowed to occupy tents close to those of the Army. However, living and working so near to the action also had its disadvantages. Crowe's autobiography is filled with accounts of his encounters with mortars and bullets, such as on the early morning of 5 November 1854 at the Battle of Inkerman, where he recorded that,

now there was complete light, I could see every shot and shell that came booming along from those sixty guns of "The Mount." I had to get through the fire, and I watched the shot as they came, and stopped or jumped to dodge them, and this so successfully that I found myself at last on the rising ground near our camp.[17]

'Our artist on the battlefield of Inkerman'.
Wood engraving after Joseph (later Sir Joseph) Arthur Crowe (1825-96),
published in *The Illustrated London News* , 3 February 1855 p116.
NAM. Negative 98122

Crowe suffered frostbitten toes after the Battle of Inkerman and travelled to Britain for surgery, returning in June 1855 and remaining in the Crimea until February 1856. His watercolours from 'the seat of the war in the east' are characterised by a vivid fluidity which, unfortunately, was lost when they were transferred to print. Whilst the dense nature of box-wood used for wood engraving ensured that long print runs could be achieved, it also meant that it was hard to work, making it difficult to reproduce such subtleties of drawing as variations in the thickness of line. In addition, sketches were often revised and redrawn by the engravers in London in order to heighten their sense of drama.

As the Crimean War progressed, public demand for eyewitness news of the war increased still further, prompting the paper to despatch three more correspondents to report on the conflict; Oswald (later Sir Oswald) Walters Brierly (1817-94), William Luson Thomas (1830-1900) and Robert Thomas Landells (1833-77).

Oswald Walters Brierly studied naval architecture at Plymouth before going on to become an accomplished marine artist. In 1839, he exhibited two marine paintings at the Royal Academy, then embarked on a voyage round the world, which included accompanying a surveying expedition of the Great Barrier Reef, the Louisiade Archipelago and of other parts of the coast of Papua New Guinea. In 1854 Brierly was employed by *The Illustrated London News* to accompany the Allied Fleet during the Crimean War, initially in the Baltic, but later in the Black Sea. The following year he published a series of lithographs entitled, 'The English and French fleets in the Baltic.' After the war he enjoyed a successful career as a painter of historical naval scenes. In 1874, he was appointed Marine Painter to Queen Victoria and was knighted in 1885.

The son of the engraver and illustrator Ebenezer Landells, Robert Landells worked for *The Illustrated London Magazine* from 1853 until 1855, when he was hired by *The Illustrated London News* and sent to the Crimea. He continued to work for that newspaper until 1871, reporting on the Schleswig-Holstein War of 1864, the Austro-Prussian War of 1866 and the Franco-Prussian War of 1870-71.

The artist William Thomas was a social reformer who went on to found another illustrated periodical, *The Graphic* in 1869, which proved a successful rival to his former employer. In February 1855 Thomas was working for *The Illustrated London News* in Britain drawing military hospitals and those returning officers who received the thanks of the House of Commons.[18] However, by March he had arrived in the Crimea, probably as a replacement for Crowe who had temporarily returned to Britain suffering from frostbite. In a caption to one of his

illustrations, Thomas acknowledged that he too suffered from the harsh conditions, noting, 'I send two Sketches taken from Life in the Trenches. You may depend on their exact truthfulness: the want of finish to be found in them may be laid to my scarcely being able to hold a pencil in my hand from excessive cold'.[19] However, by May he had returned to Britain, when a number of his drawings such as the 'Distribution of the Crimean Medals by Her Majesty, at the Horse Guards' were published in *The Illustrated London News*.[20]

In addition to these correspondents in the Crimea, in May 1855 *The Illustrated London News* sent John Wilson Carmichael (1800-68) to the Baltic to report on the naval war. The future father-in-law of his fellow correspondent William Thomas, John Carmichael was the son of a shipwright. He went to sea as a boy and was apprenticed in his father's profession before becoming an artist.[21] Carmichael, who was also commissioned by the Lords of the Admiralty to record the naval operations in the Baltic, remained with the Royal Navy until the end of the Crimean War in 1856. He went on to have a distinguished career as a marine painter in oils, exhibiting 21 paintings at the Royal Academy between 1835 and 1859.

In order to supplement the work of the correspondents in the Crimea, *The Illustrated London News* also employed the French graphic artist Gustave Doré (1832-83), working freelance in London from reports and photographs. Doré's romantic illustrations contrasted with those more realistic images submitted by the special correspondents, drawn from life. In his double-page battle scenes such as 'The Battle of the Tchernaya',[22] Doré's work was more akin to traditional depictions of battles, characterised by dramatic, crowded images of closely-packed ranks of identical soldiers charging the enemy.

Doré was also employed by a rival newspaper, *The Illustrated Times*, which had been founded in June 1855 by Henry Vizetelly (1820-94), after he had helped Ingram set up *The Illustrated London News* in 1842. The publication of this new cheap newspaper costing twopence was made possible by the abolition of the newspaper tax, or 'tax on knowledge' as it was called. In the preface to the first issue, *The Illustrated Times* boasted, 'Those who possess our volume, possess a reflection of the history of the time, a living picture of all that has happened during it – at once literary and artistic'. *The Illustrated Times* attempted to achieve the same goals as *The Illustrated London News*, but on a smaller scale. Instead of the team of correspondents that the larger, established newspaper sent to the Crimea, *The Illustrated Times* sent just one, Julian Portch (d. 1865), who returned from the war with rheumatic fever, from which he was later paralysed. Like *The Illustrated London News*, *The Illustrated Times* included the work of serving

'The Battle of the Tchernaya'.
Wood engraving after Gustav Doré (1832-83),
published in *The Illustrated London News,* **29 September 1855 pp392-3.**
NAM. Negative 98462

soldiers. One such artist was Captain (later Lieutenant-General) Henry Hope Crealock (1831-91), 90th Regiment of Foot (Perthshire Volunteers) who served at the siege and fall of Sebastopol, commanded a party of the Regiment at the storming of the Quarries and was mentioned in despatches for his conduct during the attacks on the Redan in 1855. However, *The Illustrated Times* was never really able to rival the success of *The Illustrated London News*, and it was subsequently taken over by Ingram in 1859 before being discontinued in 1872.

At the beginning of the war, in common with their fellow correspondents and those of such newspapers as *The Times*, it was rare for the artists employed by *The Illustrated London News* to be named. Indeed, there was anonymity at all levels of the gathering and dissemination of the news by editors, correspondents, artists and engravers. However, by selecting the images for publication and altering the compositions before engraving, the editor of *The Illustrated London News* gave uniformity to the journal's production, which denied the identity of the artists. The drawings are only credited to a 'Special Correspondent' or 'Special Artist' in order to establish their veracity as eyewitness records. However, by the end of 1855, most of the illustrations of the Crimean War were either signed or their artists named in the text.

As illustrative journalists, the 'special artists' had to know what to draw as well as to display the ability to make rapid sketches under difficult circumstances. In general these artists made studies in the field which they worked up into more finished drawings in pen and ink and watercolour later on in camp. Many of the artists employed by *The Illustrated London News* had been trained as engravers, which meant that they were familiar with the constraints of the medium and may have drawn accordingly. In addition, they often added inscriptions to their sketches or included an explanatory letter before sending the drawings back to London with the mail. These notes not only provided the newspaper's editor with information about the scene, but also included topographical annotations to assist in the engraving. On their arrival in London, the newspaper's staff transferred the images to wood-engravers' blocks, sometimes editing them or combining elements from more than one study. The topography was usually faithfully reproduced, but figures and props were often moved for dramatic effect. Such alterations at the behest of the editor were intended so that the illustrations could better reflect the accompanying text when the report was published within about three weeks of the event.

In order to capitalise on the topical value of its illustrations, *The Illustrated London News* made every effort to reduce the delays in printing its drawings, even dividing its images into a number of separate blocks of wood so that a team of engravers could work on one picture simultaneously. The newspaper also announced the imminent publication of images and explained the difficulties it had to surmount in order to deliver illustrations from the Crimea, thereby promoting itself as working tirelessly to provide a public service.

Initially the journal had been filled with illustrations of the Army in their splendid uniforms embarking on a glorious adventure in the East. The newspaper included dozens of images of regiments leaving their barracks and onboard ships bound for Malta. However, as the war progressed, such optimistic scenes were replaced by sobering images of the boredom of camp life, military routine and, in the winter of 1854-55, a force depleted by disease and deprivation in the deadly siege before the Russian naval base of Sevastopol. Although an appetite for battle scenes still existed, the nature of the Crimean War in which there were long periods of comparative inactivity between engagements, meant that the journals needed to fill their pages with alternative images of the conflict.

The Illustrated London News was slow in condemning the failing administration of the war. Indeed, it had attacked *The Times* for its criticism of the Allied commanders, and forcefully contested the veracity of Russell's reports of the conditions in the camps. However, by the winter of 1854-55, it no longer denied the mismanagement of the war;[23] and, in February 1855, in describing Lord Aberdeen's late Government as, 'the strongest Administration the country has enjoyed for many years,' admitted that the Ministry had allowed,

> by some defect of management - some blundering in details – some incapacity existing somewhere, or some obstruction, that must be discovered and removed – the noblest army that ever left our shores … to perish of disease and famine ... Compared with such facts as these, of what value was any Administration, however well-intentioned and honest as a whole, and however illustrious as regards the personal and public character and position of its component members? Clearly of none.[24]

Although generally *The Illustrated London News* presented a realistic view of the war, there were instances when it depicted the Army as the Government might have wished it to be seen, rather than as it was. For instance, Captain (later Lieutenant-Colonel) George Frederick Dallas, 46th (The South Devonshire) Regiment of Foot, wrote in the spring of 1855,

> I got, by the way, a paper, I think the 23 December, which tells pretty well the truth about the Army here … and an *Illustrated* with pictures of us here only dressed as we ought to be not as we are. I can assure you that to this date, the 12th. Janry. we have neither the huts, fur caps, boots, or anything in the "picture".[25]

During 1855, *The Illustrated London News*' images of the war became increasingly positive, showing improved hospital facilities, camp kitchens in the Crimea and receptions and investitures for heroes returning home. However, interest in the war waned during the summer and there was a marked decline in the number of Crimean images

WINTER CLOTHING FOR THE BRITISH TROOPS IN THE CRIMEA.

'Winter clothiing for the British Troops in the Crimea'.
Wood engraving, published in *The Illustrated London News*, **23 December 1854 p649.**
NAM. Negative 36024

appearing in *The Illustrated London News* until the fall of Sevastopol prompted an enormous resurgence. On 29 September the journal advertised,

> We have received, direct from Sebastopol, from our several Correspondents and artists, Splendid pictures of the Storming and Burning of Sebastopol. We are also informed by those gentlemen that by successive posts they will forward to us Drawings and Sketches of the Interior and Ruins of Sebastopol. These, as we receive them, will appear from week to week in *The Illustrated London News*, Price 5d, with a Supplement Gratis every week.

Indeed, such was the fascination with Sevastopol, the capture of which had taken so many months and cost so many lives, that the newspaper continued to publish views of the ruins until mid-December.

While the development of photography would later rival and then largely usurp the role of the war artist, in 1854 photography was insufficiently developed to capture anything more than posed images, due to the considerable exposure time needed by the wet-plate collodion process. Photographs could only be reproduced in newspapers if they were redrawn and engraved in the same way as artists' drawings. With its relatively fast production rate and new pictorial content meanwhile, *The Illustrated London News*' coverage of the Crimean War raised its circulation from just over 100,000 copies per week in 1854, to 130,700 by June 1855. Following the lifting of the stamp duty later that year, it rose again to an unprecedented 200,000.[26] The public's insatiable appetite for news from the front and visual records of the progress of the war was encouraged and fed by *The Illustrated London News*, so that even by November 1854, it had become the most popular newspaper in Britain, outstripping sales of *The Times*.[27] During the Crimean War *The Illustrated London News* published nearly 1,000 illustrations in all, which remains the most complete visual record of the conflict.

Notes

1   *The Illustrated London News,* 2 July 1842 p127.

2   Ingram, a staunch Liberal who favoured social reform, also founded *The Daily Telegraph* in 1848.

3   C Hibbert, *The Illustrated London News Social History of Victorian Britain*, London (1975) p45.

4   NAM. 1979-06-36.

5   *The Illustrated London News*, 7 January 1854 p17.

6   *The Illustrated London News*, 14 January 1854 p31.

7   *The Illustrated London News*, 3 June 1854 p523.

8   *The Illustrated London News*, 21 Oct 54 p392 reproduced a sketch by O'Reilly of the occasion on which he obtained a private audience with the Sultan of Turkey to discuss his sketches of Sevastopol. The Sultan later awarded the artist with the order of the Mejidie.

9   *The Naval and Military Gazette*, 28 October 1854.

10   *The Illustrated London News*, 29 September 1855 p374.

11   C Baudelaire, *The Painter of Modern Life*, London (1964) p7.

12   K W Smith, *Constantin Guys. Crimean War Drawings 1854-1856,* Cleveland, Ohio (1978) Cat. No.1 and p67 and *The Illustrated London News*, 4 March 1854 p196.

13   *The Illustrated London News*, 10 June 1854 p558 and 24 June 1854 pp598-599.

14   C Baudelaire, *The Painter of Modern Life,* London (1964) p18.

15   *The Illustrated London News*, 22 September 1855 p346.

16   T Agnew and Sons, *Agnew's 1817-1967*, London (1967) p75.

17   Sir Joseph Crowe, *Reminiscences of Thirty-Five Years of My Life,* London (1895) p164.

18   *The Illustrated London News*, 4 November 1854 p43.

19   *The Illustrated London News*, 10 March 1855 p233.

20   *The Illustrated London News*, 26 May 1855 p497 and pp505-506. Although the work of William Luson Thomas is usually signed, he is often confused with his brother, George Housman Thomas (1824-69), who also produced drawings for *The Illustrated London News*. Both George and William Thomas appear to have attended the presentation of Crimean medals by Queen Victoria, since George was commissioned by the Queen to paint the scene.

21   John Wilson Carmichael is inaccurately called James in a number of reference sources.

22   *The Illustrated London News*, 29 September 1855 pp392-393.

23   *The Illustrated London News*, 17 February 1855 p144.

24   *The Illustrated London News*, 3 February 1855 p97.

25   Quoted courtesy of Michael Hargreave Mawson, editor of *Eyewitness in the Crimea, The Crimean War Letters of Lieutenant Colonel George Frederick Dallas*, London (2001).

26   *The Illustrated London News*, 8 April 1854, p309 and 30 June 1855, p286.

27   *The Illustrated London News*, 4 November 1854 p429 records, 'Our number, at present time, has considerably increased over and above average – the sale now being upwards of One Hundred and Twenty Thousand weekly; being double the circulation of the Times, and far beyond that of all other Newspapers, weekly or daily, published at the price of 5d. or above'.

Political Reaction and Public Response

When the first battle casualties and cholera victims were sent back to the hospital at Scutari from the Crimea, it had been *The Times* journalist William Howard Russell who, in a series of dispatches published between 9 and 13 October 1854, had alerted the public to the appalling conditions existing there. The response was immediate. *The Times* Fund was the first of many public subscriptions set up to provide comforts for the troops. Florence Nightingale led a party of nurses to assist at Scutari. Her efforts there on behalf of the sick and in battling the torpor of the medical authorities were inspiring. *The Times* meanwhile shifted the focus of its attack to Raglan and his headquarters staff. They were accused of both incompetence and indifference to the sufferings of the troops. The Government of Lord Aberdeen became worried that it would be attacked in turn; it tried to persuade Raglan to dismiss Generals Airey and Estcourt from his staff, as well as the Commissary-General, William Filder. It was too late. In January 1855 a parliamentary motion was passed criticising the Government's conduct of the war and it resigned. Lord Palmerston's new Government appointed commissions of inquiry. It reorganised army administration. It implemented existing plans for a Land Transport Corps and the building of a railway at Balaklava. With these measures and the coming of spring, the supply situation in the Crimea quickly improved.

Henry Hope Crealock served in the Crimea from 5 December 1854 to 10 February 1855, and again from 28 March 1855. He commanded a party at the storming of the Quarries and was mentioned in despatches for his conduct during the attacks on the Redan in 1855.

The scene of stags and dogs is reminiscent of the work of Sir Edwin Henry Landseer (1802-73), although the heads of the animals have been transformed into caricatures of British Army officers. The conceit of the drawing is that the central figure of Major-General Richard Airey (Quartermaster-General), the noble stag, is being hunted by a group of hounds (Crealock's clearly executed his work in early 1855 when Airey was subject to intense criticism at home). The hounds include Lieutenant-General James Simpson, sent out by Lord Panmure, Secretary of State for War, to report on the efficiency of Lord Raglan's staff; the Reverend Henry Wright, principal chaplain to the forces in the Crimea, and Major-General Richard Dacres, commanding the Royal Artillery. The stags sheltering on the far bank are members of Airey's department, including the original owner of the drawing, Major George Willis.

'The noble animal at bay', *c*1855

Watercolour, signed lower left 'H H Crealock del', by Captain (later Lieutenant-General) Henry Hope Crealock (1831-91), 90th Regiment of Foot (Perthshire Volunteers) (Light Infantry), *c*1855, from an album of watercolour and pen and ink drawings compiled by Major (later Colonel) George Harry Smith Willis, 77th (The East Middlesex) Regiment of Foot, *c*1854-56, 34 cm. h x 32.6 cm. w

Generously donated by the Trustees of the Middlesex Regimental Museum

NAM. 1994-01-1-417-49

'Group of the 47th in Winter Dress'

Photograph by Roger Fenton, 14.6cm. h x 15.9cm. w

Generously donated by Lieutenant-Colonel N Lovett

NAM. 1964-12-151-6-21

The 47th (The Lancashire) Regiment of Foot was part of the 2nd Division. By the time the photographer Roger Fenton arrived in the Crimea it was already spring and he had to ask the troops to don their winter clothing specially.

Replacements for the warm clothing lost on the *Prince* had begun to reach the Army in January. The gratitude of the soldiers was tempered by regret, as Captain William Radcliffe of the 20th Regiment noted: 'I spoke to a man yesterday that was carrying some sheepskin Coats on his back, & said what capital ones they were. He said, "Yes Sir, it's a pity they didn't come before so many poor fellows were in their Graves". I could not but agree with him.'

'Panoramic view of the entrenchment of Allied Armies of England and France before Sebastopol'

Tinted lithograph by and after Thomas Packer, a plate from the series 'Packer's Panoramic Views of the Crimea', published by Stannard and Dixon, 18 April, 1855, 44.7cm. h x 69.4cm. w

Crookshank Collection, transferred from the British Museum

NAM. 1971-02-33-361

By April 1855, when this print was published, the railway between Balaklava and the British encampment before Sevastopol was in operation. The crisis of supply had passed. Still, although drastically foreshortened, it is possible to appreciate from the panorama how vital was the line of communication between Balaklava and the British camp, fully comparable in importance to the *voie sacree* at Verdun in 1916.

Florence Nightingale, *c*1862

Marble, signed and dated at back 'J.STEELL D.S.A. Sculpt. Edinburgh 1862', by Sir John Robert Steell (1804-91), 1862, 5 cm. h x 46cm. w x 30cm. d

Generously donated by the Royal United Service Institution

NAM. 1963-10-193

As the 'Lady with the Lamp', Florence Nightingale (1820-1910) was a legend in her own lifetime. Born into a wealthy family, she overcame the narrow opportunities available to girls of her class and, despite the censure of her parents, she completed a course of nursing training in Germany in 1851. Following reports in *The Times* of the soldiers' suffering in the Crimea, Florence answered the appeal for nurses and was appointed 'Superintendent of the Female Nurses in the Hospitals in the East'.

In November 1854 Florence arrived with 38 nurses at Scutari on the Asia Minor side of the Bosphorus, in Turkey. There they were faced with a dirty and vermin-ridden hospital, converted from a barracks, which lacked even basic equipment and provisions. Overflowing more with sick than wounded troops, in February 1855 the death rate rose to 42 per cent, largely from disease. By June 'The Lady-in-Chief', as Florence was known, had improved conditions to such an extent that it dropped to two per cent.

This bust was paid for and presented to Miss Nightingale by the non-commissioned officers and men of the British Army. Publicity-shy and appalled at the adulation she received, when asked to lend this bust to the Victorian Era Exhibition, held to commemorate Queen Victoria's 1897 Diamond Jubilee, Florence initially refused but eventually relented. Confirming her worst fears, the bust was sacriligiously venerated by visitors as if it were a holy relic. Nevertheless, she was touched by the report that an anonymous visitor, possibly a veteran of the Crimea, came every day to dress it with fresh flowers.

Florence Nightingale helping a wounded soldier, *c*1856

Parian ware statuette, designed by T Phyffers, manufactured by Copeland, *c*1856, 24cm. h x 23cm. w x 17cm. d

Generously donated by Mr W W Warner

NAM. 1966-04-1

Until the development of the medium of biscuit porcelain and then Parian ware in the nineteenth century, sculpted portraits, usually carved from marble, had been the exclusive preserve of the rich. Parian ware was superior to biscuit porcelain, being finer and visually more pleasing as well as cheaper than its crude forerunner.

Letter of Florence Nightingale to Lord Raglan, 1855

Manuscript, dated Scutari 8 January 1855, 27.4cm. h x 21.2cm. w

Generously donated by the Royal United Service Institution

NAM. 1968-07-293-9

Florence Nightingale had first written to Lord Raglan from Scutari in December 1854 pointing out deficiencies in medical arrangements. The following month she wrote again:

> I have no excuse to plead for the impertinence of which I am about to be guilty other than that extraordinary circumstances, such as those in which we find ourselves these Hospitals being unparalleled as far as I know in the history of calamity, urge for

extraordinary proceedings, of which one of the most extraordinary is certainly a woman venturing to address a Commander-in-Chief upon a matter within his own province.

I have, however, been, while freed from professional trammels, in a position [to observe as many of the details, possibly more than any one else, throughout these Hospitals now containing 3600 sick. And these three thousand six hundred include those only in the General Barrack Hospitals.

The comforts of the sick do not depend so much upon the skilful surgeon even, as upon the careful orderly & the constant change of these continually neutralizes the orders of the former.

My Lord, I know well that what I am going to suggest may be simply impossible. But I also know that hundreds of lives may depend upon it..

Two things occur to me as desirable, if possible.

(1st) An exceptional Order for the moment from the Commander in Chief that the Convalescents, if good Orderlies, be not sent away to the Crimea.

(2nd) That the Commander in Chief call upon the Commanding Officers to select ten men from each Regiment as Hospital Orderlies to form a depôt here (not young soldiers, but men of good character); also 3 Sergeants from each Regiment, for upon the non-commissioned officer, who now is recalled as soon as he begins to learn his duty when placed in charge of a ward, depends most of the good order of that ward. ...

Florence Nightingale

P.S. .. I throw it, my Lord, upon your kindness & forbearance to me not to betray that I have interfered with you in this matter, whatever decision your enquiries may leads you to].

Raglan was sympathetic but non-committal, quoting, as he was wont to do, precedents set by the Duke of Wellington during the Peninsular War.

Letter of Lieutenant-General Sir John Burgoyne on Florence Nightingale, 1855

Manuscript, dated British Embassy Constantinople, 27 March 1855, 18cm. h x 226cm. w

Generously donated by the Royal United Service Institution

NAM. 1968-07-293-9

When Florence Nightingale and her nurses first arrived at Scutari in early November 1854 their presence was resented by the doctors of the Army Medical Department. Only when the influx of casualties following the Battle of Inkerman proved overwhelming were the services of the nurses reluctantly accepted. By March 1855, however, when Lieutenant-General Sir John Burgoyne visited Scutari on his way home to England, the situation in the hospitals had improved to the extent that old resentments could resurface. Burgoyne's comments in his letter to Lord Raglan reflect the antipathy felt towards Florence Nightingale by the medical establishment:

[Since writing to your Lordship I have visited the great Hospitals in company with Lord William Paulet & Lady Strangford, & they certainly appear to me to be in excellent order, & without wants of any kind unprovided for; the Patients have generally that kind of countenance that indicates amendment, rather than] *despondence.* There is however manifestly an under current of troubles & turmoils in the establishments. Miss Nightingale is decidedly not in favor with the authorities, & from the accounts I hear of her I can hardly wonder at it. Whatever Philanthropy she may have on a great scale, she does not appear to be amiable in ordinary intercourse with her equals or superiors. She likes to *govern*, & bestows all her tenderness upon those who *depend* upon her: for instance, she will not give an atom or a thought upon any *Officer* who may be in the most wretched state. She seems also to *court* popular applause, even unduly. If anything is wanted for the sick, she will *hurry* to provide it from her own funds & stock *for fear* it might be obtained in the regular course. She is considered also very hard, seems to delight in witnessing surgical operations, with arms folded, & where she can be of no use whatever, & is considered [to be of that strong minded class of woman, that is indifferent on religion].

Orders and Medals awarded to Florence Nightingale, 1867-1907

Order of Merit 1907; Order of the Hospital of St John of Jerusalem, Badge of a Lady of Grace 1904; Royal Red Cross, 1st Class, 1883; Geneva Cross, France, 1870-71; Gold medal issued by the Société Française aux blessés des armées de terre et de mer 1867; Norwegian Red Cross Society Badge of Honour 1910 (*shown anti-clockwise from bottom left*)

Generously donated by the Royal United Service Institution

NAM. 1963-10-54

At the time of the Crimean War nurses were not considered eligible for campaign medals; the Zulu War 1879 was the first campaign in which their services would be so recognised. However, Florence Nightingale was among the first 31 recipients of the Royal Red Cross, instituted in 1883 as an award specifically to females for special devotion in nursing sick and wounded servicemen.

Since its institution in 1902, the Order of Merit has to date only admitted eight women, of which Florence Nightingale was the first. This highly prestigious Order, of which British membership is limited to the Sovereign and a maximum of 24 others at any one time, comprises six admirals, six generals and twelve civilians eminent in the fields of art, music and literature.

The Most Venerable Order of the Hospital of St John of Jerusalem was incorporated by Royal Charter of Queen Victoria in 1888. It is generally given in recognition of voluntary work in hospitals, ambulance and relief work. It has undergone many changes and is now divided into six classes under the Sovereign and Grand Prior of the Order.

Gold enamelled brooch, presented to Florence Nightingale by Queen Victoria, 1855

Gold, with diamonds and enamel, said to have been designed by Prince Albert the Prince Consort (1819-61), manufactured by R & S Garrard & Co, 1855, 5.8cm. h x 4.4cm. w

Generously donated by the Royal United Service Institution

NAM. 1963-10-280

Sometimes referred to as the 'Nightingale Jewel', this brooch is engraved verso with a dedication from Queen Victoria, 'To Miss Florence Nightingale, as a mark of esteem and gratitude for her devotion towards the Queen's brave soldiers, from Victoria R. 1855'. The brooch was not intended to serve merely as a piece of jewellery, but rather, in the absence of a medal or established decoration suitable for presentation to such a female civilian, it stood as a badge of royal appreciation. the letter from the Queen which accompanied the brooch acknowledged the invaluable work that Miss Nightingale had done for the Army in the Crimea:

> …I need hardly repeat to you how warm my admiration is for your services, which are fully equal to those of my dear and brave soldiers, whose sufferings you have had the privilege of alleviating in so merciful a manner. I am however, anxious of marking my feelings in a manner which I trust will be agreeable to you, and therefore send you with this letter a brooch, the form and emblems of which commemorate your great and blessed work, and which, I hope, you will wear as a mark of the high approbation of your Sovereign!

The design of the brooch, which was supervised by Prince Albert, was illustrated and described in full in *The Illustrated London News* on 2 February 1856:

> The form of the Jewel is oval. The ground or field is of pure white enamel, bearing a crimson cross, on which, in diamonds, are the letters "V.R." and the Royal crown; from the centre issue gold rays, implying Heavenly sympathy; this is inclosed by an oval band of black enamel – black being an emblem of good council – on which, in gold, are the words, "Blessed are the merciful". On each side spring branches of palm in gold and green enamel – denoting the peaceful occupation and triumphant result of her gentle though firm labours; the colour green may also be considered to imply eternal friendship. The label bearing the word "Crimea" is in azure blue, similar to that of the riband of the Crimean medal. The whole is surmounted by three brilliant diamond stars, the celestial signification of which is obvious.

Bracelet presented to Florence Nightingale by the Turkish Sultan in 1856

Silver, gold, cornelian and diamonds, manufacturer unknown, *c*1856, 4.7cm. h x 18.4cm. w x 0.5cm. d

Generously donated by the Royal United Service Institution

NAM. 1963-10-281-2

The magnificent bracelet is centrally set with an oval cornelian stone engraved with Arabic text, surrounded by numerous small rose-cut and 28 cushion-shaped diamonds, supported on each side by three rows of nine cushion-shaped diamonds; with a rectangular clasp set with three rows of cushion-shaped stones. The total weight of diamonds is approximately 8.6 carats.

This bracelet was presented to Florence Nightingale by the Sultan before her return to Britain on 28 July 1856. The gift was accompanied by a financial donation for the nurses and hospitals. In a letter from Queen Victoria to the Secretary of State for War, Fox Maule, 2nd Baron Panmure (and later 11th Earl of Dalhousie), dated 27 July 1856, the Queen referred to Miss Nightingale's application for permission to accept these presents:

> The Queen returns this letter of Miss Nightingale's. She had already heard of the gifts of the Sultan's, through Lord Stratford, who communicated with Lord Clarendon on the subject, and asked the Queen's permission for Miss Nightingale to accept the bracelet, as well as the sum of money for the Nurses and Hospitals. The Queen entirely approves of the intended distribution of the money.

On her death, this bracelet was one of a number of items, along with the 'Nightingale Jewel' and the marble bust of Florence Nightingale displayed in this exhibition, that were donated to the Royal United Service Institution by the executors of her estate, in accordance with her desire that they should be 'where the soldiers could see them'.

Medal commemorating Florence Nightingale, *c*1859

White metal, John Pinches Ltd., 41mm. diam

The obverse depicts a half-length figure of Miss Nightingale reading a book, within a beaded oval frame. On either side are sprays of roses, thistles and shamrocks. The reverse carries an oval badge flanked by palm sprays and bearing the words: BLESSED ARE THE MERCIFUL. Above it are three mullets and at the centre is a cross in splendour surmounted by a crown and the letters VR. Below is a scroll inscribed: CRIMEA, and around the edge of the medal the inscription: AS A MARK OF ESTEEM AND GRATITUDE FOR HER DEVOTION TO THE QUEEN'S BRAVE SOLDIERS.

NAM. 1979-07-133

'Florence Nightingale May 15 1856'

Pencil, from an album of paintings, sketches and ephemera by Colonel (later General Sir) The Honourable George Cadogan (1814-80), 1st (or Grenadier) Regiment of Foot Guards, 1854-56, 47cm. h x 36cm. w

NAM. 1998-06-128-70

Inscribed 'Miss Nightingale's hair had been cut short after an illness', this pencil sketch of Florence Nightingale is the one referred to in an inscription on the next drawing in the album as the more faithful of the artist's portraits of the sitter.

On 2 May 1855, Miss Nightingale left the barrack hospital in Scutari in order to witness for herself the conditions of the Army at Balaklava. Within a few days of her arrival in the harbour, she was struck down with 'Crimean Fever'. Although it was feared that she was near to death, by 24 May Lord Raglan was able to telegraph London that Miss Nightingale was out of danger. However, her recovery was slow, hampered in part by her demanding schedule. In a letter to Sidney Herbert, Secretary at War, dated just over a month before this drawing, Miss Nightingale recalled that, 'During the greater part of the day I have been without food necessarily, except a little brandy and water (you see I am taking to drinking like my comrades in the Army)'. Furthermore, her companion, Mrs Samuel Smith, wrote on 31 December 1855:

> I go to bed at 11; she habitually writes till 1 or 2, sometimes till 3 or 4; has in the lst pressure given up 3 whole nights to it. We seldom get through even our little dinner (after it has been put off one, two, or three hours on account of her visitors), without her being called away from it. I never saw a greater picture of exhaustion than Flo last night...

'Florence Nightingale May 14 '56 her own signature. Miss Nightingale done from nature but not advance[d] enough to be very like – (the profile in the small book is more like)', 1856

Pencil, pen and ink and watercolour, from an album of paintings and sketches and ephemera by Colonel (later General Sir) The Honourable George Cadogan (1814-80), 1st (or Grenadier) Regiment of Foot Guards, 1854-56, 47cm. h x 36cm. w

NAM. 1998-06-128-71

'Florence Nightingale in the Military Hospital at Scutari', *c*1855

Coloured lithograph by and after Joseph Austin Benwell (*fl.* 1856-86), published by Peter Jackson, The Caxton Press, London and Liverpool, *c*1856, 30cm. h x 43.7cm. w

NAM. 1978-10-57

In this night scene, Florence Nightingale is shown on her inspection rounds of the cramped wards of the hospital at Scutari. In what was to become an iconic image of her, Miss Nightingale is seen holding a lamp in her hand.

Florence Nightingale's lantern, *c*1855

11.5cm. w x 34.5cm. h

Generously donated by the Rev J Compton Bracebridge

NAM. 1962-12-29-1

It is believed that Florence Nightingale used this folding candle lantern while she was working at the base hospital at Scutari. It is a disposable item made locally out of cheap materials and was probably one of the lanterns available at the military hospital at Scutari for the night rounds in the wards.

Henry Wadsworth Longfellow immortalised Florence Nightingale as the 'Lady with a Lamp' in his poem 'Santa Filomena', which was published after her return from the Crimea:

> …A lady with a
> Lamp shall stand,
> In the great history
> of the land, A noble
> type of good,
> Heroic womanhood.

Florence Nightingale's field glasses, 1854-56

Santi, Rue St Ferreol 6, Marseille, France, 16cm. l x 12.5cm. w

Generously donated by the Royal United Service Institution

NAM. 1963-10-216

On 21 October 1854, five days after Sidney Herbert, the Secretary at War, wrote asking for her assistance, Florence Nightingale and her party of nurses left London for the East, crossing the Channel to Boulogne and travelling through France to Marseilles. From there she sailed on the fast mail boat *Vectis* to Constantinople, where she arrived on 3 November. The manufacturer's details suggest that she acquired her field glasses – which are made of blackened brass – when in Marseilles. They are inscribed 'Miss Nightingale "Vectis" Oct 1854'.

Model of Florence Nightingale's carriage

51cm. l x 16cm. w x 23cm. h

Generously donated by Miss M Alexander

NAM. 1967-06-76

On her second visit to the Crimea in March 1856, the exertion of travelling to the scattered field hospitals took its toll on Florence Nightingale's delicate health and, to spare her riding, she was given a mule cart. This however overturned one night on the rough tracks and so Colonel William McMurdo of the Land Transport Corps presented her instead with this, her Crimean carriage, which also served as an ambulance. *The Illustrated London News* commented on 30 August 1856:

> It is very light, being composed of wood battens framed on the outside, and filled with basket-work. … The interior is lined with a sort of waterproof canvas. It has a fixed head on the hind part, and canopy extending the full length, with curtains at the side to inclose the interior. The front driving-seat removes, and thus the whole forms a sort of small tilted waggon, with a webbed frame, suspended on the back part, on which to recline, and well padded round the sides. It is fitted with patent breaks to both the hind wheels, so as to let it go gently down steep hills.

The original carriage is in the Collections of the Florence Nightingale Museum Trust.

'The Crimean Army Fund Station at Kadi-Koi erected by Mr St Leger Glyn, and Mr Jervois Smith', 1855

Tinted lithograph by Robert M Bryson (*fl.* 1863-76) after artist unknown, published by Paul and Dominic Colnaghi & Co, London, 7 May 1855, 37.8cm. h x 48.5cm. w

Generously donated by Lieutenant-Colonel A C Lovett

NAM. 1969-10-554

'The Crimean Army Fund' was set up and administered by *The Times* newspaper in response to its reports of the privations of soldiers in the Crimea in the winter of 1854-55. The public response to the Fund was immediate and the first of a number of ships, carrying gifts to a value of £60,000, sailed for the Crimea in December 1854. Although by the time the Fund's goods arrived the government had supplied warm clothing to the troops at Balaklava, it was able to clothe the entire 39th (The Dorsetshire) Regiment of Foot, recently arrived in Constantinople from Gibraltar dressed only in light summer uniform.

In addition to the £22,100 raised by the Fund to purchase goods, a number of manufacturers and suppliers contributed their wares to the relief effort. For example, the distillers of Campbeltown in Scotland sent 700 gallons of whisky for the use of the Highland regiments. The Fund purchased and distributed such goods as clothing, food, beer and spirits, books, cutlery, tobacco, stationery, coffee-mills, soap and candles, which were much appreciated by the troops as they provided not only physical comfort, but also the sense of being remembered by their country. The Fund also received gifts from private benefactors of knitted clothing and Christmas hampers - often accompanied by written messages from the women who had prepared them - which brought memories of home to the men in the field. According to William Howard Russell, 'The moral effect of these offerings upon the mind of the soldier was beyond measure good'.

Not wishing to burden the Army with the administration of the aid, the Fund's representatives conveyed the supplies directly to the hospitals and built a Crimean Fund Station at Kadikoi to distribute the goods straight to the troops in the field. While the Fund's agents used their discretionary powers to hand out some of the supplies as gifts, most were sold to the soldiers at very low prices.

Letter of Austen Henry Layard MP, 1854

Manuscript, dated HMS *Agamemnon* at Balaklava, 8 October 1854, 18.3cm. h x 22.2cm. w

Generously donated by Miss P Layard

NAM. 1956-02-51-3

Austen Henry (later Sir Henry) Layard (1817-94) had made his reputation in the archaeological excavations at Nineveh before turning his attention to politics and becoming a Liberal Member of Parliament in 1852. When war broke out between Russia and Turkey his interest in the East was rekindled and in 1854, in company with John Delane, editor of *The Times*, and Alexander Kinglake, future historian of the war, he followed the Army to the Crimea. He watched the Battle of the Alma from the maintop of HMS *Agamemnon* and in this letter to his parliamentary colleague, H A Bruce (a future Liberal home secretary), was highly critical of the failure to have followed up victory with the immediate capture of Sevastopol. Lord Raglan and his personal staff came in for particular condemnation:

[I have been greatly struck at the great superiority of the navy in all that relates to details &] management & in energy – enthusiasm – to the army. This may be a good deal owing to the want of a military leader who can inspire troops with confidence and inject into them a part of his own spirit. Both the commissariat & medical arrangements are exceedingly bad. The men are exposed to great unnecessary suffering and the ravages of the cholera have been doubled by the want of common precautions. Up to this day the men have

not had their tents and the officers only received them two or three days ago. You would be surprised at the state of things. The fact is there is no master mind to grasp the whole subject, to give orders and to see that they are carried out. I could not put my finger upon one man (with the exception perhaps to a certain degree of Sir Colin Campbell) and say 'there is a man to command an expedition'. There are a number of red waistcoated gentlemen, with their hands in their pockets, cousins & nephews of Lord Raglan, or officers in the Guards, idling about. Men of undoubted gallantry, but without a spark of enthusiasm or energy, all rating the thing a great bore and longing for Pall Mall. At Varna what with this spirit & the terrible ravages of the cholera the army was well nigh demoralised.

217

The Prospects and Conduct of the War. Speech delivered in the House of Commons, on December 12, 1854. By Austen Henry Layard Esq., M.P. for Aylesbury

Printed, 33pp, 22cm. h x 14.3cm. w

Generously donated by Miss P Layard

NAM. 1956-02-51

Layard left the Crimea on 12 November 1854, having witnessed the battles of Balaklava and Inkerman. He reached to England in time to take part in the special session of Parliament on 12 December. His speech, which was printed in pamphlet form for wider distribution, was wide ranging in its criticism of the Government's conduct of the War. Having failed to provide the army in the Crimea with an efficient ambulance corps, the Government was to blame for the two days that were lost collecting the wounded after the Alma. Moreover, it had placed in command generals too old for the task: 'service in the Peninsula must no longer be the qualification for high and responsible posts in the Crimea', Layard concluded.

THE PROSPECTS AND CONDUCT OF THE WAR.

SPEECH

DELIVERED IN THE HOUSE OF COMMONS,

ON

DECEMBER 12, 1854.

BY

AUSTEN HENRY LAYARD, Esq.,
M.P. FOR AYLESBURY.

LONDON
JOHN MURRAY, ALBEMARLE STREET.
1854.

Letter of the Duke of Newcastle to Lord Raglan, 1854

Manuscript, 29 December 1854, 23.1cm. h x 18.6cm. w

Generously donated by the Royal United Service Institution

NAM. 1968-07-283

After the appearance in *The Times* on 23 December 1854 of an editorial accusing the Army's high command of incompetency, lethargy, aristocratic hauteur and official indifference, the Secretary for War, the Duke of Newcastle became seriously alarmed. Letters had been arriving in England for some time now complaining about the abandoned state of the army in the Crimea. Unless something were done the Government would be attacked next. Newcastle therefore wrote to Raglan complaining of the want of method exhibited by the Army's staff: 'The truth is, General Airey and General Estcourt are much complained of as not being up to their work'. However, when Newcastle suggested that they should be replaced, Raglan leapt passionately to their defence.

Letter of Major-General James Estcourt, 1855

Manuscript, 8 January 1855, 22.2cm. h x 36.6cm. w

NAM. 1962-10-95

Major-General James Bucknall Bucknall Estcourt (1802-55) had first been commissioned into the Army in 1820. He served in Canada and went onto half pay as a lieutenant-colonel in 1843, sitting as Member of Parliament for Devizes between 1848 and 1852. In 1854 he was appointed Adjutant-General of the Army of the East. On 8 January 1855, during the worst of the winter, he wrote a long letter to the Adjutant-General in England, Major-General George Wetherall (1788-1868) blaming Lord Lucan and the Commissary-General William Filder for the Army's difficulties. He had good things to say about Florence Nightingale and her nurses ('of great comfort to the sick men') but was critical of officers who had returned home on flimsy pretexts ('Neither Bentinck nor Paget can return and fill exactly the places they had in the estimation of the Army'). He added in his postscript: 'I have written too fully to admit of your showing my letter to any one. I have been uncharitable in it, and I might appear to be a croaker, and to be desponding. I am not these however I hope.'

Pattern 1822 Infantry Officer's Sword

Charles Herbert, 8 Pall Mall East, London, 94cm. l

NAM 2000-05-130

In 1834, the then Captain James Estcourt accepted an invitation from his friend, Colonel F R Chesney of the Royal Artillery, to act as his second in command in the Government-sponsored Euphrates Valley expedition. The intention was to try to find a shorter overland route to India. Estcourt's unusual silver mounted, eastern-style scabbard – which sheathes his standard Pattern 1822 Officer's sword - is thought to have been acquired by him during the course of his two years in Mesopotamia.

'Major General Estcourt & Staff'

Photograph by Roger Fenton, 17.6cm. h x 16.9cm.

Generously donated by Lieutenant-Colonel N Lovett

NAM. 1964-12-151-7

Estcourt, who is standing in the middle of the picture, is photographed wearing his sword with its distinctive scabbard; even the broken sword knot is visible. When appointed to act as Adjutant-General to the Army of the East, Estcourt had been a surprise choice, having seen no previous active service; indeed, he had expected to go with the Army as Judge-Advocate. Lieutenant-Colonel Anthony Sterling doubted his suitability for the appointment: 'The Adjutant-General is a very amiable man, a perfect gentleman and a good Christian, but as innocent of the meaning of discipline as a sucking baby.' He died of cholera on 24 June 1855.

Major-General James Simpson

Photograph by Roger Fenton

NAM. Negative 46765

Major-General (later General Sir) James Simpson (1792-1868) was first commissioned into the Army in 1811, served in the Peninsula and, in 1815, at Quatre Bras, where he was severely wounded. He was second in command to Major-General Sir Charles Napier in Scinde in 1845. In February 1855, he was chosen by the new Government to go out to the Crimea as chief of staff, an appointment hitherto unknown in the British Army but one copied from the French. Simpson was instructed by the Secretary for War, Lord Panmure, to report on the fitness of Raglan's existing staff; Panmure fully expected that Simpson would recommend their recall. In fact, Simpson lavished praise on Airey and Estcourt and both remained in post. Following the death of Lord Raglan on 28 June 1855, Simpson succeeded him as commander-in-chief, but he did so reluctantly and resigned his command within five months.

Second Report from the Select Committee on the Army before Sebastopol; with the Minutes of Evidence and Appendix

Printed 23 April 1855, 729pp, 33cm. h x 43cm. w x 5cm. d

Books 28825

Parliament had reassembled on 23 January 1855 and the Radical MP John Roebuck laid down a motion that a committee be charged 'To enquire into the condition of the of our army before Sebastopol, and into the conduct of those Departments of the Government whose duty it has been to minister to the wants of that army'. The Government made the motion a vote of confidence and resigned after it was heavily defeated on 29 January. Lord Palmerston, who headed the new Government, hoped that the change would be sufficient to placate the parliamentary opposition but in a vote on 23 February the creation of a committee was insisted upon. The so-called Roebuck or Sebastopol Committee had eleven members, including Roebuck himself and Henry Layard, but its deliberations were hampered by a lack of suitable witnesses (most of whom were still in the Crimea) and it was reduced to interviewing either those generals since returned home like the Duke of Cambridge, De Lacy Evans, Lucan and Cardigan, or battlefield tourists like George Dundas, MP for Linlithgow, who, as he admitted, had only spent a fortnight in the Crimea.

MINUTES OF EVIDENCE.

Lunæ, 5° die Martii, 1855.

MEMBERS PRESENT.

Mr. Roebuck.	Lord Seymour.
Mr. Drummond.	General Peel.
Sir John Pakington.	Mr. Bramston.
Colonel Lindsay.	Mr. John Ball.
Mr. Layard.	Sir John Hanmer.
Mr. Ellice.	

JOHN ARTHUR ROEBUCK, Esq., IN THE CHAIR.

George Dundas, Esq., a Member of the House; Examined.

1. *Chairman.*] YOU are a Member of the House of Commons?—Yes.
2. During the past autumn you went to the Crimea?—Yes.
3. Did you go there in any official capacity?—No.
4. At what time did you arrive at the Crimea?—On the 15th of December.
5. And at Balaklava?—On the 17th.
6. And at what time did you leave?—On the 29th.
7. What opportunities did you possess of seeing the condition of the army, and the condition of the men?—While at Balaklava I had many opportunities of seeing the state of matters there, from being constantly on shore, and I rode up to the front every day when the weather would permit me.
8. Dividing the parts of the army, did you see the condition of the cavalry?—Yes, the cavalry camp was about a mile from Balaklava. I went to the cavalry camp on the day of my arrival. There had been a few days previously very bad weather, and the state of the land was very muddy. I found, on my arrival in the cavalry camp, the horses of the cavalry standing at their pickets; they had no rugs on; they were totally unprotected from the weather, and, apparently, they had had very little indeed to eat; many of them had died quite recently, as the ground in the vicinity of the camp was covered with their dead bodies, and many must have died even during the preceding night, as they were at their pickets on the ground; that is to say, their bodies were lying on the ground; indeed, almost every other horse was on the ground; some of these were dead, others I saw dying; and I was led to suppose, not only from the attenuated state of the horses, that they had been in want of forage, but from observing that the tails and manes of many of them had been eaten off. I may add, that the horses of the Scots Greys seemed to be in a worse condition even than the darker-coloured horses; from what reason I can hardly tell; however I do not think that the horses of either regiment could have been in a condition to have carried their riders in a charge.
9. How far were those horses from the harbour?—Hardly a mile.
10. Was there much forage in the harbour at that time?—So I understood; and indeed I saw a considerable quantity of bran in bags, which was lying

G. Dundas, Esq. *M. P.*

5 March 1855.

0.21.   A   upon

Letter of Major Nigel Kingscote, 1855

Manuscript, dated 24 March 1855, 22.6 cm. x 37.2 cm.

Generously donated by Miss Katharine and Miss Dorothy Potter

NAM. 1973-11-170

Major (later Colonel Sir) Robert Nigel FitzHardinge Kingscote (1830-1908), Scots Fusilier Guards, was, in common with most of Lord Raglan's aides de camp, one of his nephews. A fierce defender of Raglan's reputation, in this letter to his father, after describing the great Russian sortie of 22 March and commenting on the precariousness of French morale, Kingscote rounds on the critics of Lord Raglan and the Army: 'I look upon Mr Roebuck's committee as a farce. They examine men who were not here when our difficulties really commenced and as to Mr Layard he *lies* horribly and Mr Dundas must be nothing more or less than an idiot.'

'The Staff at Headquarters'

Photograph by Roger Fenton, 17.7cm. h x 16.2cm. w

Generously donated by Lieutenant-Colonel N Lovett

NAM. 1964-12-151-2

In this photograph Major Nigel Kingscote is the bearded figure standing on the extreme left. Among the other relatives of Lord Raglan pictured are Colonel Poulett Somerset (seated on steps, right), Lord Burghersh and Major The Honourable Leicester Curzon (second and third from the right, respectively). Raglan's nepotism, although not unusual for the time, was nevertheless the subject of comment. Kingscote was dismissive: '*The Times* makes out my Lord's staff are all nearly related and therefore the fate of Europe hangs on a family party. I had no idea we were of so much importance.'

Lord Raglan's dispatch pouch, *c*1854-55

Buckskin

45cm. l x 22cm. w

Generously donated by Mr Percival

NAM. 1970-05-20

White buckskin pouch, marked 'Field-Marshal The Lord Raglan, G.C.B.' There are slight traces of red sealing wax suggestive of its use as a dispatch pouch. Certainly, official bags were issued for the purpose. On 10 April 1854 Sidney Herbert, the Secretary at War, wrote to Raglan

That 24 leather bags, with "the Secretary at War" written on each, have been forwarded from the Stationery Office, and shipped on board the "Emperor" at Woolwich for the purpose of being used in the transmission of letters for the Secretary at War, from the Army under your Lordship's command, and to state that printed leather labels to be attached to the bags have also been prepared and forwarded in order that no inconvenience might arise, from having to write separate addresses to each.

Orders and Medals awarded to Major-General Sir Edward Wetherall, 1854-57

Order of the Bath, Badge of a Companion (CB) 1857; Crimea War Medal 1854-56, with clasps: Alma, Balaklava, Inkermann, Sebastopol; Indian Mutiny Medal 1857, with clasp: Central India; Legion of Honour, France, 5th Class c1856; Order of the Mejidie, Turkey, 3rd Class c1856; Turkish Crimean War Medal 1855, Sardinian issue (*anti-clockwise from top*)

Bequeathed by Lieutenant-General Sir H E de R Wetherall

NAM. 1979-12-88

Edward Robert Wetherall (1815-69) was commissioned into the 1st (The Royal) Regiment of Foot in 1834 and served with it during the Canadian Rebellion of 1837. Promoted captain in 1845, he transferred to the Scots Fusilier Guards in 1854. He was appointed Assistant Quarter-Master General in the Army of the East in 1854, and in 1855 became a colonel and aide de camp to the Queen. In 1857, during the mutiny of the Bengal Army, he was made Chief of Staff of the Central India Field Force. He was created a Knight Commander of the Order of the Star of India in 1867 and promoted major-general in 1869, the year in which he died. In spite of the fact that he temporarily commanded the Land Transport Corps in the winter of 1855-56, he is probably best remembered among historians of the Crimean War as the officer who led Lord Lucan and the Army's advanced guard down the wrong fork of the road at the beginning of the flank march around Sevastopol, 25 September 1854.

'North View Head Quarters English Army'

Photograph by James Robertson, 23.4cm. h x 30cm. w

Generously donated by the Royal United Service Institution

NAM. 1964-08-327-13

Lord Raglan moved his headquarters from Balaklava to this farmhouse at Khutor on the Chersonese uplands on 5 October 1854. Here he lived for the next nine months until his death. About two and a half kilometres from Sevastopol and seven from Balaklava, Raglan expressed satisfaction at finding 'a good house in the centre of the position, which is undoubtedly an immense advantage'.

'Dr Sutherland and Robert Rawlinson Esq The Sanitary Commission'

Photograph by Roger Fenton, 24.5cm. h x 24.5cm. w

NAM. 1984-05-142-2

John Sutherland (1808-91), who graduated MD from the University of Edinburgh in 1831, had worked as an inspector at the Board of Health since 1848. Having made his mark with his inquiry into the cholera epidemic of 1848-49, in 1855 he was asked by the new government of Lord Palmerston to head a commission to inquire into the sanitary condition of the Army of the East. Sutherland and the other two members of the commission, Dr H Gavin (accidentally shot and killed, April 1855) and Robert (later Sir Robert) Rawlinson (1810-98), a sanitary engineer, reached Constantinople in March 1855 and reduced the death rate in the hospital at Scutari by half within a matter of weeks. Continuing on to the Crimea, the commission's measures to overhaul sanitary conditions in the field hospitals and camps proved equally efficacious. Most of Sutherland's recommendations in the reports of the Royal Commission on the Health of the Army in 1858 and the State of the Army in India in 1863 were put into practice.

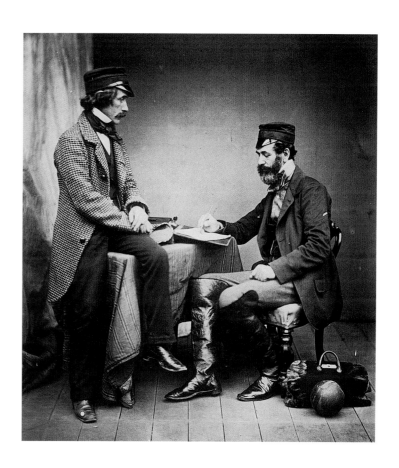

Writing case belonging to Dr John Sutherland of the Sanitary Commission, *c*1855

45.5cm. l x 15cm. w x 30cm. d

Generously donated by Mrs N McDonald Hobley

NAM. 1980-06-5

Writing case used during the Crimean War by Dr John Sutherland, Sanitary Commission (Army of the East) and inscribed with his name and unit.

Although a non-combatant, Sutherland's colleague Robert Rawlinson had a narrow escape from death, as Lord Raglan related in a letter to Lord Panmure on 12 June 1855:

> Poor Mr Rawlinson of the Sanitary Commission in conducting a friend down the ravine leading to the left attack on Sunday was grazed by a 68 P[ounde]r shot just below the hip, & knocked off his horse. The wound is very slight, & he is doing so well that he will be moved down to Balaklava in my carriage this afternoon. … Mr Rawlinson is of a nervous disposition, & it was desirable that he should remove from the hospital to which he was first taken, for the heavy firing disturbed him.

Officer's Full Dress Coatee, *c*1848-55

97th (Earl of Ulster's) Regiment of Foot

Wool cloth, metal thread and bullion, kerseymere turnbacks, gilt metal buttons, satin lining

NAM. 1991-06-15

The front of this double-breasted full dress officer's coatee bears two rows of half domed, gilt metal, regimental buttons, manufactured by Jennings of London. Tail ornaments of embroidered gold, silver, scarlet and sky blue bearing the silver Roman numeral XCVII adorn each of the coatee's tails.

The 97th Regiment arrived in the Crimea from Greece in November 1854. Attached to the Light Division, the Regiment first saw action in earnest when, under Captain Hedley Vicars, it helped repulse the great Russian sortie from Sevastopol on the night of 22 March 1855. A favourite of the well-known Crimean sutler Mrs Mary 'Mother' Seacole, who knew the Regiment of old from when it was stationed on Jamaica, the 97th suffered severely in the second assault on the Redan, 8 September 1855.

Land Transport Corps Percussion Carbine, .650in., 1855

C Rose, Tower of London, 108cm. l

NAM. 1987-10-3

Although the patent inadequacies of the Commissariat in Bulgaria had prompted Lord Raglan to request the formation of a Land Transport Corps as early as June 1854, nothing was done until the last days of the Aberdeen administration in January 1855, when the extreme difficulty of transporting supplies from Balaklava to Sevastopol became a scandal. The Corps, part of the regular army, eventually numbered nearly 9000 men. To enable the supply columns to protect themselves against Cossack marauders, the smoothbore Pattern 1840 Constabulary Carbine fitted with the Lovell Pattern 1842 percussion lock was supplied as an emergency issue firearm. Designated the Land Transport Corps Carbine, it fired a spherical ball contained with powder in a paper cartridge. It was issued with the standard Constabulary Pattern triangular bayonet, which was secured with the Lovell bayonet catch in the same way as the Pattern 1842 Musket bayonet.

As with this example, most of the carbines are dated 1855, the year in which the Land Transport Corps was established. This one was manufactured by C Rose at the Tower of London arsenal and is stamped with the Board of Ordnance mark on the wooden butt and 'LTC/ L/ 140' on the brass butt plate, indicating the unit, the company letter and rack number.

Land Transport Corps Sword, Other Rank's, *c*1856

C R Kirschbaum, Solingen, Germany, 72cm. l

NAM 2002-05-55

Created in early 1855, the Land Transport Corps was hastily equipped. Officers carried the Pattern 1821 Light Cavalry Sword but it is believed that the other ranks were equipped with this copy of the French Infantry Sword, Model 1831. Known vulgarly as 'the cabbage cutter' it was based on the ancient Roman *gladius*. As a weapon it was of little practical value but could serve as a cutting tool. It is unclear whether any were actually carried on campaign or even issued.

Orders and Medals awarded to General Sir William McMurdo, 1843-92

Scinde Campaign Medal 1843, for Meeanee and Hyderabad 1843; Crimea War Medal 1854-56, with clasp: Sebastopol; India General Service Medal 1854-95, with clasp: North West Frontier; Volunteer Officers Decoration 1892; Legion of Honour, France, 4th class, *c*1856; Order of the Mejidie, Turkey, 4th class, *c*1856; Turkish Crimean War Medal 1855, Sardinian issue *(left to right, top to bottom)*

Generously donated by Miss F G Doughty

NAM. 1972-06-19

William Montagu Scott McMurdo (1819-94) was commissioned in 1837 into the 8th (or The King's) Regiment of Foot. Later he served in the 22nd (The Cheshire) Regiment of Foot and the 28th (North Gloucestershire) Regiment of Foot before transferring as a captain to the 78th (Highland) Regiment of Foot (or Ross-shire Buffs) in 1843. Having seen active service under Sir Charles Napier (whose daughter he married) in Scinde and later on the North-West Frontier of India, on 2 February 1855 McMurdo, with the rank of lieutenant-colonel, was appointed Director General, Land Transport Corps in the Crimea. His record in command was mixed, largely because of the indifferent personnel with which he had to work, and the state of the Corps was criticised by his *locum tenens*, Colonel Edward Wetherall.

Nevertheless, on his return home he was promoted colonel and appointed aide de camp to Queen Victoria. He later served in India and Ireland, and retired as a general in 1881.

Medals awarded to Lieutenant-Colonel William Napier, 1854-56

Crimea War Medal 1854-56, with clasp: Sebastopol; Order of the Mejidie, Turkey, 5th Class 1856; Turkish Crimean War Medal 1855, British issue

Generously donated by Mr E W Campion

NAM. 1992-11-110

Lieutenant-Colonel (later General) William Craig Emilius Napier (1818-1903) was first commissioned into the 25th (The King's Own Borderers) Regiment of Foot in 1835. He saw active service in Natal and was aide de camp to his uncle, Sir Charles Napier (whose daughter he married), during operations on the Indus in 1845. In the Crimean War he was Assistant Director, Land Transport Corps to his brother-in-law William McMurdo. He ended his active career as a general (1877) and Governor of the Royal Military College, Sandhurst (1875-82).

Field telegraph wire used in the Crimea, *c*1855

Copper wire, gutta-percha insulation, 17.5cm. l x 14cm. w

Generously donated by Lieutenant-Colonel H B C Watkins

NAM. 1965-10-202-4

The electric field telegraph was used for the first time in wartime conditions in the Crimea. In December 1854 a detachment of Royal Engineers arrived to lay an underground cable the seven kilometres between Balaklava and Lord Raglan's headquarters at Khutor. The ground however was so frozen that it was impossible to commence work until the end of February 1855.

The electric telegraph revolutionised communications and the laying of a 547km. submarine cable between Balaklava and Varna in April 1855 enabled officials in London and Paris to communicate with their commanders in the Crimea within 24 hours. For the generals, increasingly plagued by political interference, this proved a mixed blessing, General Sir James Simpson complaining that 'The confounded telegraph has ruined everything'.

Jug, entitled 'Royal Patriotic Fund', 1855

Earthenware, with transfer-printed decoration, designed by G Eyre, manufactured by S Alcock & Co, Hill Pottery, Burslem, 1 January 1855, 20cm. h x 15.2cm. w x 17.8cm. d

NAM. 1961-03-24

One side of this jug is decorated with a scene depicting a group of wounded soldiers on a battlefield, while on the other, a grieving widow is shown surrounded by her children. Above these vignettes floats an angel who indicates a source of charitable aid in a banner inscribed 'Royal Patriotic Fund'. As its first circular of 1854 stated, the Royal Patriotic Fund was established for 'the succouring, educating and relieving those who, by the loss of their husbands and parents in battle, or by death on active service in the present war, are unable to maintain or to support themselves'.

Meetings took place all over the country in order to raise funds to support the widows and dependents of those soldiers, sailors and marines who lost their lives in the conflict. At one such gathering, held on 2 November 1854 in London, Lord John Russell MP commented:

> … we must look to supply the necessities of those widows and orphans, and to give that last consolation which a man dying on the field of battle, or expiring on the bed of sickness, can have; that, though his arm may be wanting, that his family may look to the gratitude of his country for the comfort of their future life.

By January 1855, the fund had already raised £550,000, of which the Queen had given £1,000 and Prince Albert £500.

The Women of the Crimean War

Sam Doty

On 29 May 1854, Captain Arthur Layard, 38th (The 1st Staffordshire) Regiment of Foot, wrote to his brother Austen Henry Layard MP from Gallipoli, a staging post en route to the East.

> On the troops being ordered for service in Turkey, a circular was sent to every regiment directing com[man]d[ing] officers to allow four women per company for each regiment. Many women availed themselves of the priviledge [*sic*] (if one) and came out tho' not near the number authorized. On their arrival here they were told that no covering or tent would be allowed them, so there were these unfortunate beings without a place to rest their heads though the rain & snow, which fell on the arrival of the first batch of troops. The women are living in holes dug in the banks, they cannot go into the tents with the men, our bell tents are crowded now with sixteen men in them without any addition to their numbers. The weather now is luckily fine. I pity the women if it comes on to rain. The poor creatures were conveyed out by the authorities and then left to shift for themselves in a country w[h]ere everything is different to the rest, I may say, of Europe. And this is the age when so much humanity mongering is going on and when our convicts are fed and lodged far better than half the poor peasants and Secretarys at war spout about the ameliorated condition of the soldier and the boons conferred to their wives.[1]

Thus began the war experience of hundreds of women. A proportion of soldiers' wives by custom and later by regulation had always been allowed to follow their husbands on campaign. The only women eligible to go were those 'on the strength', those whose marriages had been authorised by the officer commanding the regiment. Women on the strength were entitled to accommodation in the barrack room for themselves and their children and a ration of food in return for their labour: washing, sewing, cooking and nursing.

On the eve of departure a ballot was held to determine which wives would go with the regiment and which would be left behind; women with children were excluded. All the eligible women drew papers that read 'to go' or 'not to go'. The lateness of the ballot was intended to limit the opportunity of the soldiers to either desert or smuggle the women aboard. However, when the Rifle Brigade embarked at Portsmouth in the ranks, in uniform with closely cropped hair, was the wife of a private. Her husband, an officer's servant, had drilled and dressed her so well that she passed unnoticed until she was on board ship. The incident was recorded in the *Morning Post* as a romantic attempt by the young couple to stay together. It also made the columns of *The Times* where it was seen by Eliza Amelia, Lady Erroll (d.1916), wife of a

Lady Erroll, painted by Colonel The Honourable George Cadogan, Grenadier Guards, at Devna Camp, Bulgaria in 1854.
NAM. 1998-06-128-108

company commander of the regiment, at whose intercession the young wife was allowed to sail with the ship.

Other women who had missed the ballot got aboard by other means. The wife of Sergeant-Major Williams of the 8th (The King's Royal Irish) Regiment of Light Dragoons (Hussars) was engaged as a lady's maid. Mrs Longley, wife of a sergeant of the 17th Regiment of Light Dragoons (Lancers), managed to beg a passage with the wives after appealing to her former employer, Lord John Russell. Some simply crept aboard when a back was turned. But not all stories ended happily. Colour-Sergeant John Wager of the Rifle Brigade, a man with 15 years' service, cut his throat a few hours before sailing because he had to leave his wife and child behind. Wives who remained often had no means of support and although soldiers could remit part of their pay to thier families at home, few of them did so. Many women were forced to return to their own parishes or appeal to the Poor Law Union as their only hope. Many sank into prostitution. Wives from abroad, like the Canadians left by the Rifles at Portsmouth, had no parish to which to return.

The fate of the army wives left at the stations and docksides around the country was widely reported and moved the nation to pity. A fund was established for their relief, the Central Association in aid of Soldiers' Wives and Families.

In keeping with the distinction between 'officers' ladies' and 'soldiers' women' berths were found for as many of those ladies as desired to go. Lady Erroll took ship with a French maid and a chef. Although many left hoping for adventure, including some young officers' mothers, few endured the rigours of camp life for long, preferring to stay in Constantinople or return home. One who did stay, Mrs Fanny Duberly, kept a journal, later published, of her time in the East.[2]

Life on ship was grim for the soldiers and their women. Many of the wives spent the whole journey battened down in the orlop with no privacy and water in short supply. Steam ships removed many of the hazards of sail, but the passage to the East resulted nonetheless in the first female casualty of the campaign. Mrs Parsons with the 6th (Inniskilling) Regiment of Dragoons died in the fire that burnt the *Europa* down to the waterline on the evening of 31 May 1854.[3]

There survive only partial returns of the number of women accompanying the Army of the East. The 38th Foot sailed with 30 wives, the Coldstream Guards with 32 and the 1st Royal Dragoons with eight. The 4th (The King's Own) Regiment of Foot sailed from Leith with 917 rank and file, 37 officers, two ladies and 30 women including a Mrs Evans. When the regiment reached Malta, 17 women went on, five were left in hospital and eight returned home. From the 93rd (Highland) Regiment of Foot only eight of 27 women chose to go on with the regiment after its first landing. Perhaps Captain Layard's letter above illustrates why. The majority of army women went unnamed in the accounts, their lives, deaths and graves unmarked. But once the army was established in the East a steady flow of women either returning to or travelling out from Britain commenced.

Captain Henry Duberly, paymaster of the 8th Hussars, and his vivacious wife, Fanny. Of her conduct Lieutenant-Colonel William Forrest, 4th Dragoon Guards, wrote: 'They say that she is not actually a "bad one" but that she behaves in the most extraordinary way, riding and walking about with anybody, giving men every encouragement to flirt with her, but when the gentleman becomes rather too ardent in his admiration, she suddenly says "Why you must forget that I am a married woman. I shall tell my husband of this, & we shall have such a laugh." They say that she has played this trick to several.'
NAM. 1964-12-151-6-38

Life with the army was extremely hard for lady and woman alike. Those like Mrs Duberly had the advantage of being wealthy, pretty and popular. Tents were erected for her; a bower was built to shade her from the sun. In contrast the likes of Mrs Longley, Mrs Evans and Mrs Butler of the 95th (The Derbyshire) Regiment of Foot had to get by as best they could. Women of this ilk distinguished themselves by establishing laundries where they could, cooking, sewing and nursing. Women of 'lighter' character filled their time less honourably, plying a far older trade. The summer in Turkey was made miserable by the heat and the insects. As the regiments gathered to move to the western shore of the Black Sea even more wives remained behind, some taking up residence in Scutari.

Cholera and dysentery appeared in the camps and struck indiscriminately. Rations and water were in short supply; in fact disease followed the army up the coast more efficiently than the provisions. It was a much reduced force that landed at Kalamita Bay in the Crimea on 14 September 1854. There were no tents, packs or medical support. In the confusion Mrs Evans was left on board ship and it was only the intercession of Lord Raglan himself that allowed her to rejoin the 4th Foot. Mrs Duberly was left without a mount and therefore had to remain on board the *Shooting Star*.

The Allies began their advance on Sevastopol on the morning of 19 September 1854. Notable amongst the Rifle Brigade were the figures of Lady Erroll and her maid, mounted on mules. As the march progressed the intense heat caused the soldiers to shed excess kit, and the two women collected rifles and slung them about their mules. The following day saw the Battle of the Alma. Mrs Evans was one of the first over the battlefield when the fighting finished. Private Evans had survived but the husbands of her friends had not. This was the first of the often repeated scenes of women reclaiming their dead.

Having reached Sevastopol, the army set up camp at Balaklava and the women set about making it as homely as possible. Mrs Evans repaired the colours of the 4th Foot which had been badly damaged at the Alma. Mrs Butler discovered that her husband was ill on a ship in the harbour, and when she found him he had not eaten in five days. Upon his recovery and her return to camp she determined to work as a nurse, shocked by what she had witnessed.

Mrs Longley gathered with other cavalry wives on the morning of 25 October 1854 to watch 'her' regiment as it formed up. She lost sight of her husband as he rode up the valley in the now infamous Charge of the Light Brigade. When he did not reappear she ran down into the valley to search among the dead and wounded until she found his body. A bullet struck her on the wrist but she would not be diverted from her task. With the help of another lancer, within range of the Russian guns, she built a makeshift coffin and buried her husband.

It was William Howard Russell's dispatches in *The Times* that first drew to public attention the fate of soldiers of the Army of the East. His dispatch of 9 October 1854 reported the harrowing conditions and appalling manner in which the wounded of the Alma were being treated. There was an immediate response to its publication on the 13 and 14 October from the philanthropic ladies of Britain. Schemes to send small private groups of nurses out to the East were initiated, one of which involved Miss Florence Nightingale (1820-1910). Aged 34, slender and attractive, Miss Nightingale was working as the superintendent of a ladies hospital in Harley Street. Nursing was an unusual choice of occupation for a woman born into the upper class. The popular image of the nurse was the drunken, slovenly, Mrs Gamp type, made famous by Dickens. Unbeknownst to the ladies frantically organising relief missions, the War Department had already considered the possibility of using females to nurse in Army hospitals, but had shelved the scheme. The Secretary at War, Sidney Herbert, a personal friend of Miss Nightingale, now realised that she possessed all of the qualities needed to lead a group of nurses. On 15 October, Miss Nightingale was officially approached to lead a party of nurses sponsored by the government. Within two weeks 38 women had been assembled and sent to Turkey to the hospitals at Scutari. That first party comprised 20 employed nurses, five Roman Catholic Sisters of Mercy from Bermondsey, five from an orphanage at Norwood and eight Anglican Sisters of Mercy from Devonport. Miss Nightingale had refused to admit 'ladies' to her group, wanting only women she felt would be capable of undertaking the arduous work that lay ahead. She was promised that no other women would be sent to supplement the party unless requested by her.

From the beginning, Miss Nightingale's work in the hospitals of the East consisted of a series of battles. The first was for acceptance. Many serving medical officers were against the introduction of female nurses at all. The party of women had arrived at Scutari on 5 November 1854, but it was several days before they were allowed to work. It was then only the arrival of huge numbers of wounded from Inkerman that enabled the women to leave off sewing slings, stump pillows and palliasses and to get to work properly. Miss Nightingale and her party could only work under the direction of the medical officers and at their discretion. Many of the doctors refused to let them into the wards. One of Miss Nightingale's principal antagonists, the chief medical officer of the East, Dr John Hall, was still disputing her authority and presence as late as March 1856.

It was then that the second battle began, against the hospital buildings themselves. By the end of the war there were 14 British hospitals established in the East, including the general hospital at Balaklava. The most infamous however was the Barracks Hospital at Scutari. Built as a barrack for the Turkish Army, the buildings were in bad repair from the start. Already full of the sick from the summer and destined to house some 2,300 men at their busiest, the wards were insufficiently furnished, verminous, poorly ventilated and badly plumbed. Cracked and blocked waste pipes allowed sewage to run into the rooms and it was later discovered that the drinking water was filtered through a corpse.

Here the third battle was joined, against the weather and the army purveyors. With the onset of winter the true inadequacy of the provisioning of the army became manifest. Men in the trenches outside Sevastopol were still in the remains of their summer uniforms. The hurricane of 14 November 1854 had sunk the *Prince* with her cargo of winter clothes. Food was still issued raw, when it was available, but all of the local firewood had long since been exhausted. The men were arriving at the hospitals emaciated, crawling with vermin and suffering from dysentery and frostbite. Their poor condition was compounded by the distance they had travelled, packed on transport ships with few attendants. Miss Nightingale was moved on 29 December 1854 to write a

The hospital and cemetery at Scutari, lithograph after a watercolour by William Simpson.
NAM. 1971-02-33-491-33

letter of complaint to Lord Raglan.

I regret to say that the three last arrivals of men, in number about seven hundred and fifty, have come down in a wretched state of sickness. They complain (upon the passage) only of want of orderlies & of utensils, by which a great amount of avoidable stench resulted.

Having been informed that there is a quantity of warm clothing in Balaklava harbour, I nevertheless grieve to find that these men (all landed since the 19th) are more ragged & even destitute of clothing than any of the preceding. The number of frost bitten cases might, it appears to me, have been diminished by an examination of the state of the men on their return from the trenches.

The majority of cases are those derived from Dysentery & exhaustion, sometimes both.

These have suffered by the length of the time on board, ten days.

The usual arrangements for landing the sick have certainly not been so prompt as they might have been. The authorities do not seem to perceive the importance of this for the saving of life.[4]

As Miss Nightingale pointedly observes, warm clothing was apparently available, yet remained unissued. The same story was to be repeated across the whole campaign: food, clothing, equipment and even medicine available from store was not issued. This was in part due to army parsimony, but also to the bureaucracy of the Purveyor's Department. Miss Nightingale would fight against such bureaucracy for the whole of her two years in the East. Fortunately, she had not only private money, but money from *The Times* Fund that allowed her to undertake the provisioning of the sick herself.

Soldiers were meant to take their personal equipment to hospital with them: plates, utensils and spare clothes. Nothing was provided for them upon arrival. Most of the men coming from the front arrived empty-handed in their rags having been ordered to leave their packs behind upon disembarkation at Kalamita Bay. Miss Nightingale undertook to make good the deficiencies but found that as the men left hospital they took her stores with them. An insufficient supply of medical comforts had been provided so Miss Nightingale set up kitchens in the hospitals to make the soft, nourishing food that the desperately ill men needed. Her nurses established and managed a laundry and linen stores; soldiers' wives performed the actual washing. They supervised the dispersal of goods from the free gift store, sewed splint pads and stump cushions and wrote letters for the men. This was in addition to meeting the nursing requirements of 40 - 100 patients each. The nurses worked around the carelessness and roughness of the orderlies and made sure that the weak were not neglected. Lives were saved by the simple expedient of feeding men who could not feed themselves. In the end, however, it was the compassion of the women that left the greatest impression. Sarah Anne Terrot[5] of the Devonport sisters recounted that hopeless, vermin-ridden cases were left to die by the orderlies because they were deemed not worth the effort. Washed and tended by the nurses the men may have died all the same, but the nurses' actions were uplifting for the other patients; in a hopeless place, no one was beyond hope.

Another of Florence Nightingale's ongoing struggles was with her own staff. Several of the employed nurses in the first and subsequent parties were dismissed for drunkenness and bad behaviour within weeks of arrival. Some of the nuns were unsuited to the work and sent home. Miss Nightingale was determined that the party should be kept small to make it manageable. Furious letters survive, marking the arrival in December 1854 of an uncalled for second party of 44, comprising 15 Roman Catholic nuns, 22 nurses and nine lady volunteers under Miss Mary Stanley, an acquaintance of Miss Nightingale's. The medical staff at the hospitals refused to employ more women and Miss Nightingale was left with the task of having to accommodate and employ them. She wrote angrily to Sidney Herbert tendering her resignation and drew attention to the fact that of the 84 women then with her, Roman Catholics now numbered no fewer than 25. Nuns had been sent East on the understanding that they came only as nurses and, to avoid religious tensions, should amount to no more than one third of the total nurses in any given hospital. However, the Reverend Mother Bridgeman of Kinsale had come out with different instructions. She understood her group of 15 nuns were under the authority of Miss Nightingale with regard 'merely' to nursing matters, but that she was to remain in charge of the group, who were to stay together in a convent system. Florence refused to accept more than five, to keep a religious balance, and thereby set the stage for a bitter struggle that was to last until the end of the war. The Kinsale nuns went on to work at Therapia and later the Kulali hospitals, where their quiet discipline and nursing skill were praised. There were complaints, however, of proselytising and deathbed conversions amongst the Protestant soldiery. Miss Nightingale did not resign but stayed until the last casualty left the East.

A languishing Florence Nightingale. Her Crimean War exertions were repaid with a lifetime of invalidity.
NAM. 1963-12-227

Florence Nightingale made three journeys to the Crimea itself, the first in May 1855. In the hospitals at the front she found army wives and widows like Mrs Longley working as nurses and incorporated them into her official band. At one point she fell ill and was near to death. She recovered, but throughout the campaign several of her nurses, nuns and ladies died of cholera and fevers; others were invalided home with their health broken.

A steady flow of nurses and ladies passed back and forth from Britain during the campaign. They nursed in Army, Navy and civilian hospitals throughout the East. One of the arrivals was Lady Alicia Blackwood who presented herself with her husband, Dr James Blackwood a Church of England cleric, at Scutari asking what she could do. Miss Nightingale gave her the unenviable task of attending to the army wives. When Miss Nightingale took over the Barracks Hospital there were 200 women and children living in its cellars, left behind when the army moved to the front. The women subsisted in the most appalling conditions of filth and degradation, living and dying anonymously amidst the drunken crowd. Lady Alicia set about cleaning and partitioning the cellars to restore some pride among these abandoned women. She found employment for them in the hospital laundry, established a kitchen and hospital and provided a nursery for the infants. Gifts of clothing were also made available. Unfortunately those who had once been starving were soon complaining about the quality of their food. Those who had once been in rags fell into hysterics when they could not get the best of the new bonnets sent.

Florence Nightingale employed men as well as women. Convalescent officers and men worked as teachers in the schools that she established and as orderlies in her reading and recreation rooms. At the start of the campaign she cried out for shirts, soap, knives and forks, even operating tables. Towards the end she provided means for the men to improve themselves. For all this she was called 'the soldier's friend'. Of the soldiers she wrote:

> Give them an opportunity promptly & securely to send money home - & they will use it.
> Give them a School & a Lecture & they will come to it.
> Give them a book & a game & a Magic Lanthorn & they will leave off drinking.
> Give them suffering & they will bear it.
> Give them work & they will do it.[6]

The soldiers had much suffering to bear, and their wives bore it with them, along with the predictable results of co-habitation. Major-General William Codrington wrote to his wife from the Camp before Sevastopol on 15 January 1855:

In the midst of the snow storm last night, covered by a little patrol tent which is above a deep and square hole in the ground, was produced - a baby! Sure enough; in the night Corporal Burke of the 33d. went to the Asst. Surgeon saying his wife was taken ill, there it was, Nature had its way the child a girl was born, he sent round the whole division for any other woman to assist, there is not one in camp, and the washing the little affair and doing all the needful fell to the lot of Corporal Burke and the Asst. Surgeon.[7]

Few wives endured so long as to stay with the army at the front over the winter of 1854-55. Those that did were generally understood to be among the better sort. There were of course some exceptions, as Major William Charles Forrest of the 4th (Royal Irish) Regiment of Dragoon Guards wrote to his mother on 23 March 1855:

> In my capacity of Comm[andin]g officer … I have been obliged to apply for a passage to England for Mrs Field; she was constantly smuggling spirits into the camp, and was incorrigible. I fancy she thought that there was no method of punishing her. I applied to have her sent away, and my application was successful. …I suspect that she will give us the slip yet, for I see her stalking over the hills with a carpet-bag in her hand, in

The camp of the 4th Dragoon Guards, photographed by Roger Fenton. The woman has been identified as Mrs Rogers, the wife of a non-commissioned officer, whose skills as a cook and laundress were highly valued by Colonel Edward Hodge, commander of the regiment.
NAM. 1964-12-151-6-31

the opposite direction to Balaklava; however I shall take care that she does not return to our camp.[8]

With the coming of spring a new breed of women appeared. Accompanying the soldiers' wives there appeared the battlefield tourists. 'Travelling gentlemen' were a well-known phenomenon, but here and there ladies like the Carews of Devon leavened their number. Such visitors were a welcome diversion among the officer class and balls and concerts were given in their honour. The most popular visits were to the 'Valley of Death' where picnics were held in range of the

Russian guns. However, doubts were expressed about the propriety of ladies - even officers' wives - witnessing actual fighting, as General Codrington wrote home on 7 August 1855:

I saw two ladies up at the look-out - one Mrs Forrest, and Mrs Handcock came afterwards. It is all very well to come once or so, and look at the scene - but I do not like ladies coming there to see the firing as if to a show, when they must feel that every shot may be mangling some poor fellow![9]

Mrs Ellen-Georgina Handcock, with her husband of a year Lieutenant-Colonel The Honourable Henry Robert Handcock, 97th (The Earl of Ulster's) Regiment of Foot, on the evening of 7 September 1855. He is pointing out where he is to assault Sevastopol the following morning (watercolour by Cadogan). NAM. 1998-06-128-48

Amongst the travellers was a woman familiar to many who had served in Jamaica. Mrs Mary Seacole (1805-81) was a stout, motherly woman in her 50s. Born to a Scottish father and a Jamaican mother she grew up around soldiers. Her mother was a 'doctress', skilled in making herbal medicine and cures for the many tropical diseases that struck the susceptible British soldiers. Now a widow, an experienced nurse, traveller and businesswoman, 'Mother' Seacole determined to offer what help she could to her 'sons' in need. She travelled to London late in 1854 and applied to the Secretary of War, the Quartermaster-General, to Miss Nightingale's recruiters and finally to *The Times* Fund to be allowed to serve as a nurse. None would help. She therefore determined to fall back upon her previous occupation, that of sutler and establish a general store and quarters for convalescent officers near the front at Balaklava. Going into partnership with a Mr Day she took passage in January 1855.

Colonel Handcock was killed during the attack on the Redan of 8 September 1855. Cadogan heard that Mrs Handcock encountered the body of her husband at the same spot near the Picket House where he had seen them the night before.
NAM. 1998-06-128-49

Upon arrival at Balaklava she spent some time at the wharf nursing and tending the sick and wounded gathered for the hospital ships:

> I wonder if I can ever forget the scenes I witnessed there? Oh! they were heartrending. I declare that I saw rough bearded men stand by and cry like the softest-hearted women at the sights of suffering they saw.[10]

Her precious stores of food and merchandise were raided from the start. Even after she managed to build her establishment, the British Hotel, at Spring Hill from scrap wood and whatever lay to hand, her livestock and goods were subject to fierce depredations from the Turks and the French. Despite the setbacks the British Hotel was soon well know across the Crimea, particularly because of her cooking and nursing skills. This 'yellow'-hued woman, as she described herself,

Mrs Mary Seacole, modelled for the National Army Museum's Special Exhibition by H&H Sculptures and based on busts of her in Jamaica and the Getty Museum, California.

would go where she was called, and would take payment for the delicacies and medicine she took with her. But 'Mother' Seacole did not work only amongst the officers. She assisted sick soldiers 'by all the means in her power'.[11] Where payment could not be made, none was sought. Mary Seacole also ventured to the front carrying bandages, medicine, cake and lemonade. She was witnessed by Russell of *The Times* who wrote:

> I have seen her go down, under fire, with her little store of creature comforts for our wounded men; and a more skilful hand about a wound or broken limb could not be found among our best surgeons. I saw her at the assault on the Redan, at the Tchernaya, at the fall of Sebastopol, laden, not with plunder, good old soul! but with wine, bandages, and food for the wounded or the prisoners.[12]

Mrs Seacole proved a colourful, almost flamboyant, figure in her bright dresses and ribbons, lent upon occasion to young Guards officers for their theatrical endeavours. She stayed until the last but her carefully garnered store was still full when the last redcoat went home and she returned to England bankrupt.

Florence Nightingale finally left the East a few days after the last of the invalids in July 1856. Her first visit was to the Bermondsey convent and thence home to her family, unannounced. She shut herself away from the clamour and publicity her work had aroused and for a time was virtually prostrate with fatigue. She then busied herself compiling statistics and reports of her time in the East for the Commission of Inquiry into the running of the war. Illness dogged her for the rest of her life, and it is now thought she might have contracted brucellosis in the Crimea. For the next 40 years, driven by the memory of the needless deaths of so many soldiers, she dedicated herself to the improvement of the medical services - from hospital building and sanitation to notes on home nursing and midwifery. Although she continued to eschew publicity the nation mourned when she eventually died in 1910.

Of the unknown number of soldiers' wives who travelled with the Army of the East very little information survives. Mrs Longley volunteered for nursing service in India during the suppression of the mutiny in the Bengal Army and went on to work at King's College Hospital. Mrs Evans continued travelling with her husband and was at the Siege of Lucknow. Mrs Butler's husband never fully recovered after the war and she was eventually left on a meagre widow's pension. She and Mrs Evans were at the end given military funerals and were remembered as heroines of the Crimea by their regiments.

The Crimean War opened one chapter and closed another in the history of the British Army and its women. It was the first war in which women were officially employed by the War Office to serve, under the guidance of Miss Nightingale. It was also the last in which women on the strength followed their husbands to battle. Hundreds of years of tradition ended as the British public called for reform and an improvement in the lot of the Army's soldiers and their women.

Notes

1   NAM. 1959-03-128.

2   F Duberly, *Journal Kept During The Russian War*, London (1856).

3   E S Jackson, *Records of the Inniskilling Dragoons*, London (1909).

4   NAM. 1968-07-293-9.

5   S Terrot, *Reminiscences of Scutari Hospitals in Winter 1854-55*, Edinburgh (1898).

6   British Library Add. Ms. 43397, f. 217.

7   NAM. 1978-08-90.

8   NAM. 1963-09-5-1.

9   NAM. 1978-08-90.

10   M Seacole, *Wonderful Adventures of Mrs Seacole in Many Lands*, London (1857), p143.

11   *Ibid*. p172.

12   *The Times,* London, 11 April 1857.

The Siege of Sevastopol

After the failure of the First Bombardment of Sevastopol (17–25 October 1854) and the Battle of Inkerman, the Allies were forced to wait until next spring before renewing their attack on the town. The Russian engineer Todleben, meanwhile, conducted an aggressive defence. Marksmen in rifle pits harassed the besiegers. Trench raids were launched. The British, exposed to the rigours of a Crimean winter and wasting away from disease and a lack of supplies, found it difficult to provide men to guard their trenches. On the night of 21 January 1855 only 290 were available. The French, now four times as numerous, agreed to take over some of the British trenches. This gave them the dominant role in prosecuting the siege. However, General François Canrobert, the French commander, felt constrained to await the arrival of the Emperor Napoleon III before taking Sevastopol. Much to the disgust of the British, the Russians took advantage of French hesitancy by seizing and constructing outworks on the tactically important feature called the Mamelon. The Second Bombardment of Sevastopol (9–19 April) failed because Canrobert would not attack. When in May he was forced by orders from Paris to recall the Anglo-French expedition to the Crimean port of Kerch – the key to a vital Russian supply route across the Sea of Azov – a humiliated Canrobert resigned. Thereafter, the siege of Sevastopol moved into a new and more decisive phase.

The Emperor Napoleon III

Photograph, 15.7cm. h x 10cm. w

Generously donated by the Royal United Service Institution

NAM. 1968-06-351-19

Napoleon III (1808-73), a nephew of the Emperor Napoleon I, assumed dictatorial power in France following the *coup d'état* of December 1851. Although by nature a conspirator rather than a man of action, as a Bonaparte he felt that a bellicose trait was expected of him; the initial spark for the Crimean War was ignited by his calculated intervention in the Holy Places dispute. Once war began, he was forced to rely upon those generals who had acquiesced in his seizure of power, which in view of their mixed quality was unfortunate. For example, General François Canrobert, while personally brave, showed himself temperamentally unsuited to exercise the supreme command which devolved to him following the death of Marshal St Arnaud. Knowing that Napoleon III wished to come to the Crimea and win a pitched battle against the Russians, Canrobert's commitment to the Siege of Sevastopol proved less than whole-hearted; it was only after he was succeeded by General Aimable Pélissier in May 1855 that the siege was prosecuted with vigour. Although Napoleon III, disliking the heavy casualties that Pélissier's strategy entailed, would have liked to dismiss him, the emperor's bluff was in effect called: he dared not offend the French Army, which was the basis of his régime's power, and consequently Pélissier survived.

Sevastopol. Sketch of the Mamelon and New Russian Defences, with the Siege Works of the Allies: By Lt. Col. Vaughan. March 20th 1855

Published in London by James Wyld, 14 April 1855, 30cm. h x 43cm. w

Generously donated by Mr G Boynton Williams

NAM. 1975-03-7-99

At the end of January 1855 the British, short of troops, handed over their trenches facing the Malakhov to the French. All that remained opposite the reduced British frontage was the Redan. To British annoyance, however, on the night of 10 March the French allowed the Russians to take the initiative by constructing a defensive outwork known as the Mamelon in front of the Malakhov. Mutterings in the British camp questioning French courage and inveighing against General Canrobert ('Bob Can't', as the British called him) grew louder.

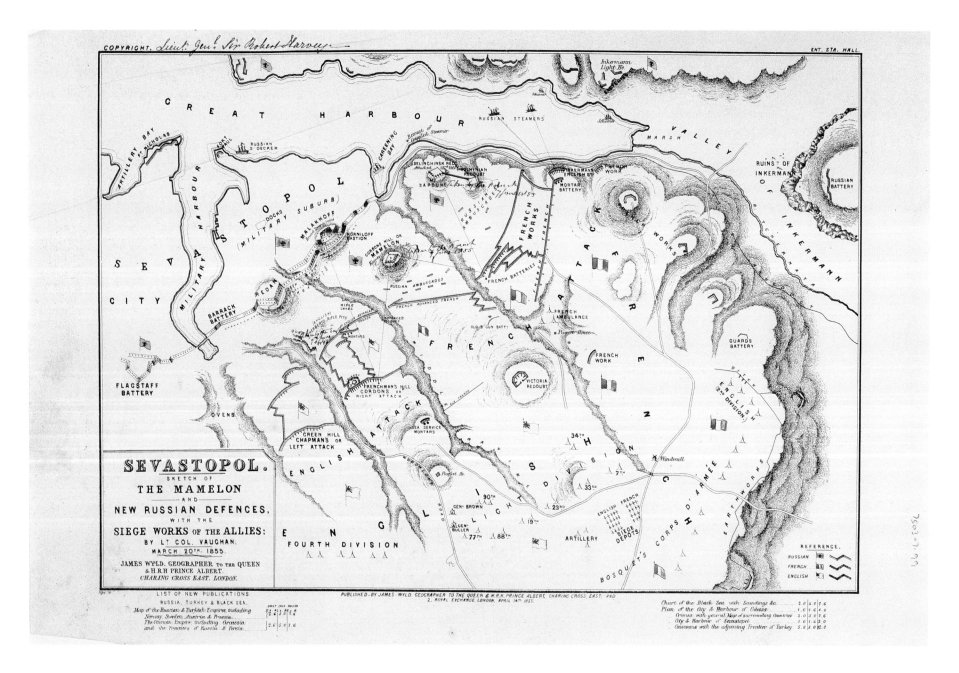

A 13-inch mortar of the Royal Artillery in action, c1855

Watercolour and pencil, signed lower left 'HJA', by Lieutenant (later Major-General Sir) Henry James Alderson (d. 1909), Royal Artillery, c1855, 26.7cm. h x 36.4cm. w

Generously donated by Mr R E Alderson

NAM. 1955-01-4-8

In the spring of 1855 the British brought up to the batteries before Sevastopol a number of 13-inch mortars. With their high trajectory they seemed ideal for lobbing bombs at buildings within the town. Major-General William Codrington, writing home on 19 April, was unconvinced:

These big mortars have not been of half the power which was anticipated - the weight and recoil is so heavy that the platforms are very much shaken, and thus destroy the correctness of fire; and the buildings are so large that even a hole made by a shell is like a pin in appearance. It is better to send them at the Works.

'Rifle Brigade parading in the Crimea', c1855

Watercolour, artist unknown, c1855, 26.6cm. h x 37cm. w

NAM. 1972-07-37

By the spring of 1855 the British soldier barely resembled the troops who had gone to war a year previously. The men of the Rifle Brigade depicted here – although they retain their rifle green jackets – wear trousers of various shades of khaki. Their Albert shakos or caps have long since been discarded and consequently, even on parade, they wear their soft Kilmarnock forage caps. Lieutenant-General Sir George Brown, resolutely orthodox on questions of dress as on so much else, blamed the Rifle

Brigade for setting a bad example. 'The practice of throwing away their Caps', he complained to Lord Raglan,

commenced at the Alma with Norcott's Riflemen, who very foolishly allowed the men to do so in imitation of the French & the ground was accordingly covered with Rifle Caps as Airey will assure you. Since then nearly all the Army have followed their example & the troops newly arrived don't wait to ask whether all this is right or wrong. By & by they will find out their mistake & that they may just as well walk about with a wet sponge on their heads as a woolen forage Cap!

The Rifle Screw.

'The Rifle Screen', c1855

Watercolour by Captain (later Colonel) Henry John Wilkinson (1829-1911), 1st Battalion, 9th (The East Norfolk) Regiment of Foot, c1855, 18.2cm. h x 13.2cm. w

Generously donated by the Royal United Service Institution

NAM. 1972-07-6-18

The purpose of the rifle screen was to keep Russian sharpshooters at a distance and prevent them picking off British artillerymen manning the siege guns. On 12 April 1855 John Fisher, a non-commissioned officer with the 1st Battalion of the Rifle Brigade, was performing this task in front of Number 7 Battery:

> We were all in good spirits and had been in the trench about an hour popping away at the Russians when we caught sight of one or two close together. Now for a volley, there they are boys. There were five of us to fire having taken cover under a part of the trench or the embankment higher than the rest [which] formed a better cover, the Russians having battered some parts level to the ground. No sooner said than we all took aim; whether we did any execution or not it is hard for me to say. All I know is that we had no sooner fired than whack! came a shot from a Great gun knocking the bank away, smashing two of my comrades all to a mortar, laying two others prostrate on the earth one of them loosing an arm, the other very much bruised and smothered in dirt, myself only left standing out of five.

'Truce for burial of the dead before Sebastopol 24th March 1855'

Watercolour and pencil, signed lower right 'H.J.W.', by Captain (later Colonel) Henry John Wilkinson (1829-1911), 1st Battalion, 9th (The East Norfolk) Regiment of Foot, 1855, the original for a wood engraving published by *The Illustrated London News*, 21 April 1855, 18.1cm. h x 23.6cm. w

Generously donated by the Royal United Service Institution

NAM. 1972-07-6-62-1

A comparison between this watercolour and the print that reproduces it reveals how the engravers of *The Illustrated London News* altered and combined images to suit the publisher's purposes, whilst carefully retaining the salient features referred to in the accompanying description of the scene written by the artist. On 22 March, the Russian Army had made a concerted attack on the Allied entrenchments, at a cost of considerable loss of life on both sides. Consequently, two days later on 24 March, a two-hour ceasefire was agreed to enable both sides to bury their dead. In the event, all parties also took advantage of the opportunity to survey the battlefield and to converse with each other on the progress of the war. According to Wilkinson, writing in the camp before Sevastopol, 30 March 1855:

> The flags of truce continued flying long after the appointed hour; but at length, as the last of the burying party withdrew within our respective lines of defences, they were lowered; and the immediate crack of the rifle and boom of heavy artillery proclaimed that peace was at an end.

'The Siege of Sebastopol – Burial of the dead in front of the Malakoff Tower', 24 March 1855

Wood engraving after Captain (later Colonel) Henry John Wilkinson (1829-1911), 1st Battalion, 9th (The East Norfolk) Regiment of Foot, published by *The Illustrated London News*, 21 April 1855, 24.4cm. h x 36.6cm. w

Generously donated by the Royal United Service Institution

NAM. 1972-07-6-62-2

In the text that accompanied this print in *The Illustrated London News,* the artist described the scene:

> On the right is the body of a gallant officer of Zouaves, which had been extricated from the ruins of a parapet thrown down by the

enemy during their temporary success. On the left is seen part of this parapet, still occupied by the French covering party. In the centre of the picture is the Mamelon, its sides thronged with parties carrying the ghastly and distorted dead to a soldier's grave; and, in the distance, on the left, may be observed the ruined Round Tower, formerly demolished by our Lancaster guns, but now surrounded by a most formidable earthwork, and yet further strengthened by a deep trench and abattis along its front. Conspicuous from his height amongst the group on the right, is a Russian officer of distinction, wearing a long black poncho over his uniform. In general, I may observe, the Russian officers were well and carefully dressed; so much so as to lead some to conclude that they were got up for the occasion – a thing which assuredly could not be laid to the charge of many in our own ranks.

Colonel (later Major-General) Philip McPherson, 17th (The Leicestershire) Regiment of Foot, 1855

Oil on canvas, signed and dated in pencil on the stretcher 'D. Cunliffe, Portsmouth 1855', by Daniel Cunliffe (*fl.* 1826-55), 1855, 55.9cm. h x 38.2cm. w

NAM. 1991-11-31

Philip McPherson (1790-1864) had served as a volunteer in the 52nd (or the Oxfordshire) Regiment of Foot in the Peninsula in 1809 before being commissioned ensign in the 43rd (or Monmouthshire) Regiment of Foot on 2 November of that year. He continued to serve with that regiment until the end of the Peninsular War in 1814, for which he received the Military General Service Medal with eight clasps. McPherson served as aide de camp to Sir Charles Napier throughout the operations in Scinde in 1843, was mentioned in dispatches twice, received the Scinde Medal and was nominated a Companion of the Order of the Bath.

Promoted lieutenant-colonel in the 17th (The Leicestershire) Regiment of Foot in 1852, McPherson commanded the regiment when it embarked at Cork for Gibraltar on 28 April 1854. There he was promoted brevet-colonel before accompanying the regiment to the Crimea on 2 December of that year. Appointed to the command of the 1st Brigade of the 4th Division on 18 December, McPherson served during the siege of Sevastopol until 15 June 1855, when he was invalided to England suffering from ill health brought on by 'over-fatigue' in the trenches.

It is believed that this portrait was painted in the artist's home town of Portsmouth shortly after McPherson's return from the Crimea.

Medals awarded to Major Maxwell Earle, 1854-56

Crimea War Medal 1854-56, with clasps: Balaklava, Inkermann, Sebastopol; Legion of Honour, France 5th class, *c*1856 ; Turkish Crimean War Medal 1855, Sardinian issue

Generously donated by the Trustees of the Middlesex Regiment Museum

NAM. 1992-09-108

Major Arthur Maxwell Earle (1832-63) was commissioned as an ensign into the 57th (The West Middlesex) Regiment of Foot in January 1850, rising to the rank of captain in December 1854. He served in the Crimea as aide de camp to Brigadier-General Thomas Goldie, and later as a Brigade Major in the 4th Division. In addition to the above awards, he was also appointed to the 5th Class of the Turkish Order of the Mejidie.

'Brigadier Genl. McPherson & Officers of the 4th Division'

Photograph by Roger Fenton, 18cm. h x 15.9cm. w

Generously donated by Lieutenant-Colonel N Lovett

NAM. 1964-12-151-9

Casualties among general officers were so heavy at the Battle of Inkerman that a man like Philip McPherson, who - through seniority alone - had risen to the command of a battalion at an advanced age, was given leadership of a brigade. The verdict on McPherson's capabilities delivered by his Brigade Major, Maxwell Earle, pictured here reading a dispatch (McPherson is the white-bearded figure standing to his left), was damning: 'Had I but a Goldie for a Brigadier instead of an old nonentity who, were I to put his own death warrant on his desk, he would sign it!'

Victoria Cross, Orders and medals awarded to General Sir Mark Walker, VC, 1854-93

Victoria Cross 1854; Order of the Bath, Badge and Star of a Knight Commander (KCB) 1893; Crimea War Medal 1854-56, with clasps; Alma, Inkermann, Sebastopol; 2nd China War Medal 1857-60, with clasps: Taku Forts 1860, Pekin 1860; Order of the Mejidie, Turkey, 5th Class; Turkish Crimean War Medal, Sardinian issue *(top to bottom, left to right)*

Generously donated by the Trustees of the Buffs Regimental Museum Trust

NAM. 2001-02-431

Born in Ireland, the son of Captain Alexander Walker who had distinguished himself in the Peninsula with the 38th Foot, Lieutenant Mark Walker was serving as Adjutant in the 30th (Cambridgeshire) Regiment of Foot when he earned the Victoria Cross for his gallantry at Inkerman on 5 November 1854. When the regiment was attacked and in imminent danger of being overwhelmed by two battalions of Russian Infantry, Walker jumped over the wall behind which his men were sheltering and led them forward in an inspired counter-attack that caused the enemy to flee, notwithstanding their superior numbers. In spite of subsequently losing an arm, Walker continued his military career as an officer in the 3rd (The East Kent) Regiment (The Buffs) and saw active service again as a Brigade Major in the Second China War of 1857-60, for which he was mentioned in despatches. He ended his 46-year army career as a general, receiving a knighthood in 1893, and died at Folkestone in 1902 at the age of 75.

'Capt. Walker, 30th Regt. Reading General Orders', 1855

Photograph by Roger Fenton, 15.9cm. h x 14.8cm. w

Generously donated by Lieutenant-Colonel N Lovett

NAM. 1964-12-151-17

'I got a Photographic portrait taken today of my home and myself,' noted Captain Mark Walker in his journal on Tuesday 1 May 1855.

Campaign Journal of Captain Mark Walker, 1854-55

Manuscript, 32cm. h x 42.5cm. w

Generously donated by the Royal United Service Institution

NAM. 1968-07-85

On Sunday 10 June 1855 the handwriting of Captain Mark Walker – who just a matter of days before had transferred from the 30th Regiment to the 3rd Buffs –alters dramatically. Walker's entry in his journal of that date explains why:

> Last night I went on with the reserve, just as I got into our approach which joins the trench on the right heavy firing commenced at the Mamelon. While I was in the act of hurrying the men up a howitzer shell dropped beside me and exploded. A peice struck me on the right elbow and smashed it. I immediately tied a large handkerchief above the fracture and walked to the rear untill I met some of the 55th who put me on a stretcher and carried me to Camp. I received great kindness from my new brother officers. After some time I was carried to a hut at the General Hospital where I now am. I was put under chloroform and on coming to consciousness I found my arm taken off above the elbow during the night and today I suffered a good deal of pain. The loss I have experienced is very great but I am very thankful that my life has been spared. The hut has been filled with sympathizing visitors particularly my old comrades of the 30th....

'Officers, Non-Commissioned-Officers and Privates. of the 88th (Connaught Rangers) Regiment', 1855

Photograph by Roger Fenton, 18cm. h x 25cm. w

Generously donated by Miss P N Steevens

NAM. 1977-10-10

On 26 April 1855 Roger Fenton took a photograph of officers and men of the 88th Regiment of Foot (Connaught Rangers). It was not one of his most successful efforts, as Captain Nathaniel Steevens (pictured, standing sixth from the left) admitted in a letter of 18 May: 'Our talbotype picture of the 'Rangers' proved a failure'. However, writing on 11 June - by which time the regiment's ranks had been sadly depleted following their part in the capture of the 'Quarries' four days before - Steevens' estimation of the photograph had changed:

I enclose a picture which I value much and wish to be mounted on Cardboard, and a Glass put over it, so that I may receive it in safety when we meet; the 4 poor comrades who fell the other Ev[enin]g are very clearly represented; poor Wray is next to me on my left; you remember him; on my right is *Capt Browne*, & then *Lt Colonel Maxwell, not distinct*; the figure with two Medals is our Quartermaster, a fine gallant soldier; my *chum Maxwell* is next to Wray's left, very like; our Brigadier *(Col. Shirley)* is indistinct as his horse unfortunately moved at the time; poor *Bayley* is standing with his left hand in his Belt, behind his right hand poor *Webb*, with his hands crossed; *Corbett* is lying down at my feet. I hope you may receive this (to me) most valuable talbotype, in safety. .. P.S. My likeness in the Talbotype shews I am not *starved*.

It was not only officers like Wray, Bayly, Webb and Corbett (the four killed on 7 June) who fell casualty. All four of the corporals – Hourigan, Connolly, Wrenn and Price – pictured standing on the right of the photograph at the back were either killed or died as a result of wounds received on 8 September 1855, during the second attack on the Redan.

Medals awarded to Lieutenant-Colonel Nathaniel Steevens, 1854-56

Crimea War Medal 1854-56, with clasps: Alma, Inkermann, Sebastopol;
Legion of Honour, France, 5th Class 1855; Order of the Mejidie, Turkey, 5th
Class; Turkish Crimean War Medal 1855, Sardinian issue

Generously donated by Miss P N Steevens

NAM. 1965-01-174

Nathaniel Steevens was commissioned ensign in the 20th (The East
Devonshire) Regiment of Foot on 19 December 1845, transferring to the
88th Regiment of Foot (Connaught Rangers) in 1850. Promoted captain on
27 October 1854, he served throughout the Crimean campaign, later
working up his letters (owned by the Museum, NAM. 1965-01-183) into the
book *The Crimean Campaign with "The Connaught Rangers".* This was
published in 1878, twelve years after Steevens' retirement from the Army
as a lieutenant-colonel.

Orders and Medals awarded to General Sir George Maxwell, 1854-81

Order of the Bath, Badge and Star of a Knight Commander (KCB) 1881; Crimea War Medal 1854-56, with clasps: Alma, Inkermann, Sebastopol; Indian Mutiny Medal 1857-58, with clasp: Central India; Legion of Honour, France, 5th class c1856; Order of the Mejidie, Turkey, 4th class c1856; Sardinian War Medal 1856; Turkish Crimean War Medal 1855, British issue

Generously donated by Major and Mrs G Goodliffe

NAM. 1954-07-17 and 1954-10-1

George Vaughan Maxwell (1818-92) was commissioned into the 88th Regiment of Foot (Connaught Rangers) in 1838, rising to the rank of lieutenant-colonel in 1855. He was severely wounded during the second attack on the Redan on 8 September 1855. In addition to his British and his foreign campaign awards he received the Companionship of the Order of the Bath in 1855 for his services in the Crimea. He retired as a general and Knight Commander of the Order of the Bath in 1881.

G V Maxwell (the *Lt Colonel Maxwell not distinct* in Steevens' photograph, p251) should not be confused with his namesake within the Regiment, Edward Herbert Maxwell (*my chum Maxwell*, as Steevens styles him). The War Department made this mistake in the Crimea by awarding a brevet promotion intended for one to the other.

Candelabrum, *c*1856

From the mess plate of the 88th Regiment of Foot (Connaught Rangers)

Silver, made by John S Hunt, hallmarked London 1856-57, 79.5cm. h x 56cm. w x 56cm. d

Generously donated by the Royal United Service Institution

NAM. 1962-08-84

Decorated with a relief scene of the 88th Regiment of Foot (Connaught Rangers) storming the Redan at Sevastopol, this candelabrum was purchased with money left in the will of Major Norton. It is inscribed, 'Bequeathed to the officers of the Connaught Rangers by Edward Norton late Major of the Regiment who died of cholera in camp before Sebastopol on the 19th of May 1855'.

Colonel Reynell Pack, 7th (Royal Fusiliers) Regiment of Foot wrote of the terrible loss of life from cholera in the Crimea:

> … men that had passed through the bullets of the enemy unharmed were suddenly cut off or smitten by this fell disease. Amongst those most lamented was Major Norton of the 88th Regiment…He had been the life and soul of the division races, loving the sport solely for its own sake, and his all but sudden death was much felt, casting gloom throughout the division.

Norton is included in Fenton's photograph of the Connaught Rangers reproduced on p251 standing in the middle of the picture with his head in profile.

Crimea War Medal, 1854-56

Awarded to Guiseppe Lucca,
Sardinian Artillery Train

NAM. 1982-11-58

On 26 January 1855, the Italian
state of Piedmont-Sardinia entered
the war against Russia. Britain,
which was in desperate need of
troops, had hoped to pay a
subsidy so that the 15,000
Sardinian soldiers sent to the
Crimea might be considered under
its control. However, the Sardinian
statesman, Camillo di Cavour,
wished his country to be seen as
an independent belligerent, and a
British loan of £2 million was all
that was accepted. Although the
Sardinian troops did not serve in
the trenches before Sevastopol,
they played a significant role in the victory of the Chernaya on 16 August
1855, and so earned the place at the peace conference which Cavour had
so much desired in order to increase the diplomatic pressure on Austria,
the occupying power in much of Italy. Some 15,000 British Crimea War
Medals were issued to Sardinian troops.

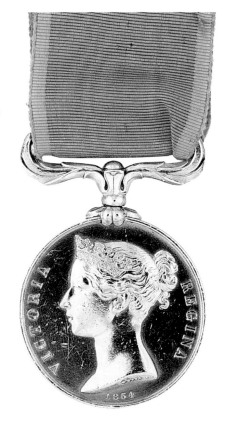

Reduced Bore, Experimental Minié Percussion Rifle Musket, .630in., 1853

Royal Small Arms Factory, Enfield

139 cm. l

Generously donated by the Ministry of Defence, Royal Army Ordnance Corps, Weedon

NAM. 1963-12-251-95

In 1852, a year after the introduction of the Pattern 1851 Minié Rifle
Musket, extensive trials began to develop a new, lighter firearm of smaller
calibre for the infantry. The aim was to reduce the weight of the Minié bullet
by effecting a reduction in the size of the rifle bore. Two rifle muskets were
initially produced, each modelled on the Minié with bores reduced from
.702in. to .530in. When Lord Hardinge succeeded the Marquess of
Anglesey as Master General of the Ordnance, the development became
more competitive and five gunmakers (Wilkinson, Lancaster, Purdey,
Greener and Westly Richards) were invited to produce firearms designed to
fire a lighter bullet. The resulting trials eventually led to the adoption of the
Pattern 1853 Enfield Rifle Musket.

This Minié has a reduced bore of .630in. and a lock dated 1853, suggesting
it is an experimental rifle musket from one of the trials. It was manufactured
at the Royal Small Arms Factory, Enfield and the barrel is rifled with four
grooves like the standard Minié. On closer inspection, the furniture is
revealed to be made of iron rather than of brass (a cheaper metal) which

was used for the Pattern
1851 Miniés. The sight
has not been engraved
and its condition, with
bluing visible on the sight
and barrel, remains as it
would have been when it
was manufactured,
indicating that it is a
prototype, which has
never been fired.

Pattern 1853 Enfield Percussion Rifle Musket, .577in., First Pattern, 1854

Royal Small Arms Factory, Enfield

140cm. l

Generously donated by the Museum of Artillery, Woolwich

NAM. 1979-07-60

Trials to produce a lighter, reduced bore firearm resulted in the adoption of the Enfield Rifle Musket as the new pattern for the infantry in 1853. Externally it can be identified by the barrel, which is held to the stock by three iron bands, instead of with pins, which were used for the Minié and the Pattern 1842 Musket. The Pattern 1853 Enfield was rifled with three grooves and sighted to 1,000 yards. It had an effective range of 800 to 1,000 yards (731 to 914 metres).

Due to demand for the Enfield a second pattern was produced, but there is no evidence that this reached British troops in the Crimea before the war ended. Some second pattern Enfield rifle muskets may have been waiting for them in store ready to be issued on their arrival back home.

Socket Bayonet, for Pattern 1853 Enfield Rifle Musket

53cm. l

NAM. 1979-07-70

This triangular tapered socket bayonet was the first universal issue British Army bayonet to have a locking ring, modelled on a French design. It was introduced with the new Pattern 1853 Enfield Rifle Musket and carried in a leather scabbard.

Three Pattern 1853 Enfield Cartridges

1.46cm. (.573in.) w x 8.64cm. l

Generously donated by Mr F Holroyd

NAM. 1972-03-37

The Pattern 1853 Enfield Rifle Musket fired a conical-shaped bullet, designed by the London gunmaker, Pritchett. It was contained with powder in a paper cartridge. The Pritchett bullet differed from the Minié bullet in that it had a hollow base, rather than an iron cup. It was expanded into the rifling grooves by the gasses from the exploding charge filling the hollow base. The bullets were issued in paper packets of ten.

The advantages of the Enfield over the Minié bullet were the simplicity of the design, which was easy to cast in a mould, and the cheapness with which it could be produced lacking as it did the iron cup.

Altered Pattern 1842 Percussion Rifle Musket, .758in., 1854 (bottom)

Manufacturer of lock, Tower; Contractor (conversion to rifling), Pritchett, 139cm. l

NAM. 1984-08-99

Although the introduction of the rifle musket and the expanding bullet rendered the smoothbore musket obsolete, it was possible to convert the smoothbore to the new system. During the early months of the Crimean War many Pattern 1842 Muskets which had remained in store in Britain were converted into rifle muskets, for issue to the Royal Navy and Royal Marines only. Rifling grooves were cut into the barrel, producing a new weapon that was designated the altered Pattern 1842 Rifle Musket. The process of rifling the bore enlarged the calibre from .753in. to .758in. and it fired a large conical-shaped bullet fitted with an iron cup, of Pritchett design. The bayonet for the Pattern 1842 Musket was also used for this rifle musket.

The first order for the conversion of 1,200 Pattern 1842 Muskets was made in April 1852; further orders were to follow. The conversions were rifled with either four grooves, like the Minié, or with three grooves, as with the Pattern 1853 Enfield. This example has three rifle grooves and is sighted to 1,000 yards (914m.). Externally the weapon is very similar to the Minié, but because the increased weight of the bullet (about twice as heavy as the Pattern 1842 Musket ball) gave it such a fierce recoil, it proved very unpopular.

Colt 1851 Navy Model Revolver, .36in., 1855 (top)

Colt, 34cm. l

NAM. 1979-05-3

The American six chamber Colt 1851 Navy revolver was invented by Samuel Colt. Five thousand were purchased for British Army use in the Crimea and distributed to officers and infantry sergeant-majors. A much larger number were purchased for issue to the Royal Navy. Although the term 'Navy' refers to the engraving on the cylinder and not to its specific use by naval forces, initial orders in 1854 were destined for the British Baltic fleet. Many officers also purchased Colts privately to take with them to the Crimea. Because of wartime pressures the War Department ownership and inspection marks usually stamped on the frame and grips of these weapons were not applied until after their return to England for refurbishment once the Crimean campaign was over.

Powder flask for Colt Navy and Adams revolvers, *c*1856

G & J W Hawkesley, Sheffield, 17.5cm. l x 5cm. w x 4cm. h

NAM. 1981-02-29

An example of the powder flask issued with the British service Colt Navy and Adams percussion revolvers. Early revolvers were loaded by pressing loose powder and a wadded ball into each of its chambers. The powder flask carries a War Department stamp.

Pattern 1822 Infantry Officer's Sword, 1836

James Wilkinson & Son, 96cm. l

Generously donated by Mrs D'Olier-Lees

NAM. 1961-06-26

Captain Archibald Rutherfoord joined the 4th (The King's Own) Regiment of Foot in November 1851 and served with it throughout the Crimean campaign. He had first joined the Army in 1836, which is when he would have purchased his sword. It has the cipher 'William IV' on the guard and 'Victoria' on the blade as swords were often re-bladed on a change of sovereign.

The sword has the early pipe-back blade, which was criticised for its flimsiness. It was produced by James Wilkinson and Son, later Wilkinson Sword.

Alarm Clock, *c*1854-56

13.5cm. w x 12cm. h x 5cm. d

Generously donated by Colonel C M McCleverty

NAM. 1966-07-8

This brass alarm clock on a stand accompanied Captain Frederic Anthony Trevor of the 4th (The King's Own) Regiment of Foot throughout the Crimean War. Trevor had first been commissioned in 1848 and retired from the Army as a major in 1862.

Major (later Colonel) Thomas Graham Egerton and a sentry of the 77th (The East Middlesex) Regiment of Foot, on the King's Bastion, Portsmouth, 1849

Over-painted photograph after Daniel Cunliffe (*fl.* 1826-55), 1849, 41.4cm. h x 47.4 cm. w

Generously donated by the Trustees of the
Middlesex Regimental Museum

NAM. 1994-01-1-108

Egerton was killed on the night of 19 April 1855 leading an attack against the defences of Sevastopol. Lord Raglan described his capture of the Russian rifle pits, known from then on as 'Egerton's Pit', as a 'brilliant achievement', which was 'dearly bought by the sacrifice of Colonel Egerton, who was one of the best officers in the army, and looked up to by all'.

The sentry is reputed to be Private Alexander Wright (1826-58), Egerton's soldier servant, who was later awarded the Victoria Cross:

> for conspicuous bravery through the whole Crimean War. Highly distinguished on the night of 22 March, 1855, in repelling a sortie. Highly distinguished at the taking of the Rifle Pits on the night of 19 April, 1855; remarked for the great encouragement he gave the men while holding the Pits under a terrible fire. He was wounded. Highly distinguished on 30 Aug. 1855.

Crimea War Medal 1854-56, with clasps: Alma, Inkermann, Sebastopol

Awarded to Colonel Thomas Graham Egerton, 77th (The East Middlesex) Regiment of Foot

Generously donated by the Trustees of the
Middlesex Regiment Museum

NAM. 1992-09-185

Thomas Graham Egerton was first commissioned into the 77th (The East Middlesex) Regiment of Foot in December 1829, taking over its command with the purchase of his lieutenant-colonelcy on 27 December 1850. He greatly distinguished himself at the Battle of Inkerman on 5 November 1854 by leading four companies of his regiment – just 259 men – in a successful attack against a Russian regiment 1500-strong. An unmistakable figure, six feet eight inches tall, Egerton was promoted colonel on 28 November 1854. He was killed on 19 April 1855 at the moment of victory during the attack led by him against the Russian rifle pits, the regimental history telling how, 'as Colonel Egerton was pointing out the flying Russians to Captain Chawner, he was struck in the mouth by a rifle bullet, which, carrying away four of his front teeth, passed through the spine at the back of his neck, and he fell dead.'

Medals awarded to Captain Audley Lemprière, 1854-56

Crimea War Medal 1854-56, with clasps: Alma, Inkermann, Sebastopol;
Turkish Crimean War Medal 1855, British issue

Generously donated by Miss E M Lempriere

NAM. 1974-09-48

Audley Lemprière was commissioned an ensign in the 77th (The East
Middlesex) Regiment of Foot on 10 December 1852 and promoted lieutenant
on 11 June 1854. The casualty rate among officers in the Crimea meant that
by the tender age of twenty, shortly before his death during the attack on the
Russian rifle pits on 19 April 1855, he had already been promoted captain.
His memorial tablet in Newton-Valence Church near Alton states that 'He
enjoyed in a remarkable degree the confidence of those above him in
command, and the esteem and affection of his brother officers and men; and,
from the excellence and amiability of his character, his loss is deeply
lamented by all who knew him.'

Officer's Coatee, Full Dress, *c*1848-55

77th (The East Middlesex) Regiment of Foot

Wool cloth, metal thread lace, waist lined with Morocco leather, gilt-metal
buttons

Generously donated by the Trustees of the
Middlesex Regimental Museum

NAM. 1992-09-53-1

Worn by Captain Audley Lemprière when he was killed on 19 April 1855. The
dimensions of the coatee – the chest measurement is only 31 inches, and
the length from nape to lower edge 30.5 inches - reveal how small of stature
he was.

Letter of Captain Nathaniel Steevens describing the attack on the Russian rifle pits, 19 April 1855

Manuscript, 20.2cm. h x 24.8cm. w

Generously donated by Miss P N Steevens

NAM. 1965-01-183-82

Captain Steevens, as he explained in this letter of 21 April 1855, had been positioned nearby when the attack was launched against the Russian rifle pits two nights before. He deplored the scale of the casualties:

Our loss was severe 60 men killed & wounded, & *seven Officers*, of whom Col. Egerton (a tall powerful man) & Capt Lempriere 77th were *killed;* the latter was very young, had just got his company and was about the *smallest* officer in the Army, a great *pet* of the Colonel's and termed by him his *child;* he was killed, poor fellow at the first attack in the rifle pit, the Colonel, *tho' wounded,* snatched him up in his arms & carried him off declaring "they shall never take my child"; the Colonel then returned and in the second attack was killed.

Russian bugle, *c*1855

26.5cm. l

Generously donated by the Royal United Service Institution

NAM. 1964-08-65

On the night of 19 April 1855, during the attack on the Russian rifle pits, fifteen year old Drummer Thomas McGill of the 77th (The East Middlesex) Regiment of Foot was orderly bugler to Colonel Egerton. His subsequent exploit came to the notice of William Howard Russell: 'A drummer boy of the

77th engaged in the melée with a young bugler of the enemy, took his bugle and made him prisoner – a little piece of juvenile gallantry for which he was well rewarded.' McGill received the French medal for valour and the captured bugle, bearing the Imperial Russian double-headed eagle, was presented to Lieutenant-General Sir George Brown.

'Part of the 77th Regiment's Cemetery with some of the Officers' tombstones, April 1856'

Photographed by James Robertson, 24cm. h x 29.4cm. w

Generously donated by the Trustees of the Middlesex Regimental Museum

NAM. 1994-01-1-417-24

On 21 April 1855, Colonel Egerton and Captain Lemprière were buried side by side in the 77th Regiment's graveyard on the left of the Vorontsov road, near the Picquet House. Lord Raglan and Lieutenant-General Sir George Brown both attended the interment. The graves are in the second row in this photograph.

Diary kept by Lieutenant William Stirling, Royal Artillery, 1855

Manuscript, 16.5cm. x 10.5cm. w

Generously donated by Major C R Stirling

NAM. 1986-06-96-1

The first of three home-made volumes in which Lieutenant (later General Sir) William Stirling (1835-1906) kept his Crimean War diary; this volume covers the period 9 January to 30 June 1855. In it Stirling, who served with 'E' Battery, Number 1 Company of the 3rd Battalion Royal Artillery, describes life in camp, the arrival of supplies, the weather, changes in command, visits to friends and the build-up of ammunition for the bombardment of Sevastopol. The cover is decorated with Stirling's doodles of French troops.

Lieutenant William Stirling, Royal Artillery, 1855

Photograph by Roger Fenton, 19.6cm. h x 14.8cm. w

Generously donated by Miss H Somervell

NAM. 2002-08-58-1

Stirling's photograph was taken before his transfer to the Royal Horse Artillery (RHA) in July 1855: he still wears the Royal Artillery shell jacket which lacks the gold braid at the edgings, collar and cuffs of the RHA version. Stirling subsequently saw action with 'C' Troop RHA and the British Cavalry Division at Eupatoria in October 1855. After the Crimean War he served in the suppression of the mutiny of the Bengal Army, the China Expedition of 1860 and the Afghan War of 1878-80. Knighted in 1893, Stirling attained the rank of general and was Lieutenant of the Tower of London between 1900 and 1902.

'Interior of Coll Warre's Hut', *c*1855

Coloured tinted lithograph by M & N Hanhart after Lieutenant-Colonel Henry James Warre CB, 57th (The West Middlesex) Regiment of Foot, plate 12 from 'Sketches in the Crimea', published by Dickinson Bros, London, 1856, 18.6cm. h x 27cm. w

NAM. 1984-04-116-12

In the spring of 1855, wooden huts began to replace the tents that had proved so inadequate against the elements during the preceding months. In this print, Lieutenant-Colonel (later General Sir) Henry James Warre (1819-98) depicts himself seated in his hut, surrounded by the equipment and accoutrements of a soldier in the field, with the regimental colours propped against the wall to the left.

Warre was first commissioned in 1837, transferring to the 57th (The West Middlesex) Regiment of Foot in 1847. He arrived in the Crimea in March 1855, Lieutenant Joshua Cunliffe Ingham of the 57th commenting:

> Warre has joined out here; he wrote to Col Shadforth to say that he could neither ride nor walk, but when he heard from the Horse Guards that he would not get his Lt. Colonelcy until he joined here he came out, and looks as well and strong as any one. This morning he tried to drill the Regiment but made a total failure, in fact I could have done it much better myself. If he commanded for 2 months we should be worse than a Militia; from what I have seen of him I like him very well as a man, but as a soldier he is worth nothing.

Warre however was subsequently mentioned in dispatches for his role in the attack on the Redan, 18 June 1855, and later rose to be Commander-in-Chief of the Bombay Army, 1878-81.

Miniature portable communion set, 1852-53

Silver, made by Henry Wilkinson & Co, hallmarked Sheffield 1852-53, 12cm. h x 11cm. w x 8cm. d (in closed case)

Generously donated by Miss Nancy Gallagher

NAM. 1996-10-9

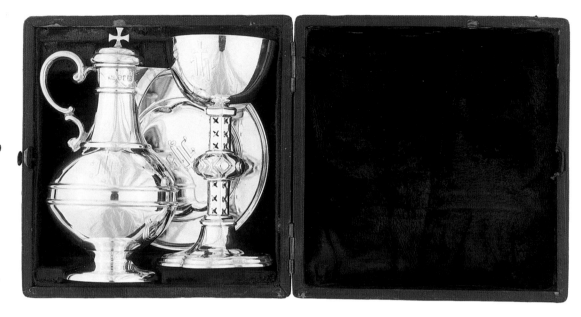

In February 1854, just one Presbyterian minister, two Roman Catholic priests and four Anglican chaplains accompanied the Army sent to the East, but by the end of the war the Government had sent over 100 clerics to the Crimea.

The Reverend William Whyatt, sometime curate of St Peter's in Leeds and then of the district of Crumpsall in Manchester, was appointed Chaplain to the Forces, attached to the 2nd Division of the Army of the East, by General Order No 6 of 9 January 1855. On 17 February that year, he was granted sick leave to go on board ship at Balaklava until 10 March. This leave was subsequently extended to 31 March on the recommendation of the Medical Board, and Whyatt was ordered to proceed to Scutari. However, on 17 March he died of Crimean Fever on board the *Herefordshire*. Whyatt was included on the medal roll as entitled to the Crimea War Medal with the clasp for Sevastopol.

The communion plate is inscribed underneath: 'This service was used by the Revd William Whyatt ... as Chaplain to the 2nd Division... in the Crimea ... presented as a mark of respect, by his Mother in Law, Mrs Sarah Lyon, to the Revd Richard Tonge MA, Curate of St Luke's, Cheetham, 7th March 1859. St Luke 11c.2v.'

Lieutenant-Colonel Robert Jocelyn Straton, 77th (The East Middlesex) Regiment of Foot, *c*1855

Oil on canvas, attributed to Alfred Frank de Prades (*fl.* 1844-83), *c*1855, 63cm. h x 76.3cm. w (canvas)

NAM. 2002-06-96

Commissioned an ensign in the 77th (The East Middlesex) Regiment of Foot on 10 January 1828, Straton served with the Regiment throughout his career. During the Crimean War, Straton fought at the Battle of the Alma and was

mentioned in dispatches for 'distinguished service in the field' at the Battle of Inkerman, in consequence of which he was promoted brevet lieutenant-colonel on 9 March 1855. On 21 April 1855, following the death of Colonel Egerton in the assault on the Russian rifle pits, Straton succeeded to the command of the Regiment, although he did not take over until his return from sick leave on 5 July. He is shown in this portrait wearing the badge of the Companion of the Order of the Bath and the Crimea War Medal with clasps, with a view of Sevastopol in the distance. Colonel Straton died of cholera on 16 June 1858, soon after his Regiment's arrival in India to combat the mutiny in the Bengal Army.

'Life in camp before Sebastopol No. 2. an unwelcome visitor', 1854

Coloured lithograph after artist unknown, number two in the series of six prints of life in camp before Sebastopol, published by Read & Co, London, 22 November 1854, 21.8cm. h x 29.1cm. w

NAM. 1981-10-110-1

The British encampment before Sevastopol was for the most part situated far enough away from the town to be out of range of the Russian guns. Occasionally, however, by 'supercharging' their artillery pieces, the Russians were capable of launching projectiles into the British camp.

Lieutenant-Colonel Sir James Alexander of the 14th Regiment testified to the effect of one such barrage in August 1855:

The long range guns have been sending hissing balls over our tents & dumping among us for the last 10 days. One Artillery man was struck at night whilst asleep among 9 others, and his leg carried off with a 40 lb shot - a fearful awakening. Another man, a servant (68th), boiling coffee at his master's tent at 7 a.m. had his leg carried off. Both men died.

Officer's Short Frogged Jacket, *c*1854; Officer's Vest, *c*1854

10th (Prince of Wales's Own) Royal Regiment of Light Dragoons (Hussars)

Wool cloth, gilt metal buttons, gold Russia braid, Vandyke pattern lace:
Scarlet wool cloth, gold Vandyke pattern lace, gilt metal buttons

Generously donated by Mrs E A W Renner

NAM. 1980-03-1 -1, -3

To replace the cavalry lost in the Charge of the Light Brigade, two regiments were ordered to the Crimea from India, the 10th Hussars and the 12th (The Prince of Wales's) Royal Regiment of Lancers. The 10th Hussars arrived on 17 April 1855, the regimental history commenting that:

> The landing of the Tenth in the Crimea excited a good deal of interest, not only in the Cavalry Division, whose ranks it came to reinforce, but in the army generally. Crowds of officers of all ranks and men came down from the front to witness the disembarkation. The beautiful Arab horses were objects of special admiration, and the smart and soldierlike appearance of the men seemed to meet with much approval.

Among the 10th Hussars' ranks was Lieutenant-Colonel (later General) John Wilkie (1817-82), who had joined the regiment as a cornet in 1838. His short-frogged jacket, of which the style – reflecting the Hungarian origins of the hussar - was *de rigueur*, is luxuriantly decorated with Vandyke pattern lace and Russia braid. To the centre front are twenty-one large gilt metal plain ball buttons for fastening the jacket; the other four rows of ornamental buttons are plain gilt metal half domed patterned. The jacket is lined with white silk to the body, while to the waist there is a lining of buff coloured leather. The officer's vest is also decorated in the distinctive hussar fashion, with the same pattern lace and braid as the jacket and fastened with sixteen gilded brass, plain ball buttons. The lining is of a drab fine woollen fabric.

Officer's Shako, 1855 Pattern

34th (The Cumberland) Regiment of Foot

Black felt, patent leather, metal buckle

Generously donated by Mrs B M Bale

NAM 1965-03-61-5, -6, -7

Suppliers of the new-style shako began to arrive in the Crimea in the spring of 1855 and there are photographs of men wearing it in conjunction with old-style coatees. Superficially it was similar to the obsolete 'Albert' Shako, with black-patented leather peaks both front and back and the same ball-tuft. However, unlike the 'Albert' it was deeper at the back than at the front, with the top being 2.5cm. less in diameter at the top than the bottom; the 'tilted' effect achieved was in the French style. Whether Captain Henry Bale of the 34th (The Cumberland) regiment of Foot received this, his new shako - with

its changed shako plate and bronze gorgon's head motif at the back – while in the Crimea is unclear; after a trench fight on the night of 5 April 1855 he had to have his left forefinger amputated. He nevertheless continued to serve in the Army and died in India in 1858 as a major.

Officer's Shako Plate, 1844-55 Pattern

Generously donated by Mrs B M Bale

NAM. 1965-03-61-8

When the 1844 'Albert' Shako was superseded by the smaller 'French Pattern' Shako, Captain Henry Bale of the 34th (The Cumberland) Regiment of Foot appears to have retained his original shako plate as a keepsake. Made of gilt metal and silver, it consists of an eight-pointed star, the topmost point displaced by a crown, bearing on its rays the battle honours of the regiment, clockwise from top: PYRENEES, NIVE, ORTHES, PENINSULA, NIVELLE, VITTORIA, ALBUHERA, and on the central scroll, the battle honour: ARROYO DOS MOLINOS.

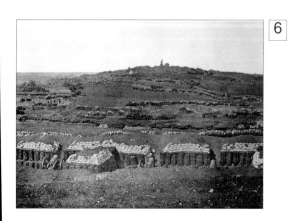

'Rout of the English from the town of Taganrog, 22nd May 1855'

Woodcut by A Vasuleva, published in Russia, 1855, 39.5cm. h x 53cm. w

NAM. 1969-08-26

The capture at the end of May 1855 of the strategically vital port of Kerch (situated at the eastern tip of the Crimea) by a joint Anglo-French expedition commanded by Sir George Brown opened the Sea of Azov to the depredations of British gunboats. On 3 June 1855 (Modern Calendar; 22 May 1855 Old Style), the Royal Navy bombarded the Russian port of Taganrog in order to check the supply of provisions to Sevastopol across the Sea of Azov.

According to the historian Kinglake, the town was garrisoned by '... from three to four thousand soldiers which had feebly resisted the landing, and had hardly, if at all, interfered with the steady work of destruction effected under their eyes'. Contrary to the bombastic and self-deluding title of this print, the Allies achieved their aims at Taganrog. By mid-afternoon, all the Russian stores of grain, wood and tar and a number of government buildings and ships had been set ablaze, without the loss of a single Allied life.

The Siege of Sevastopol

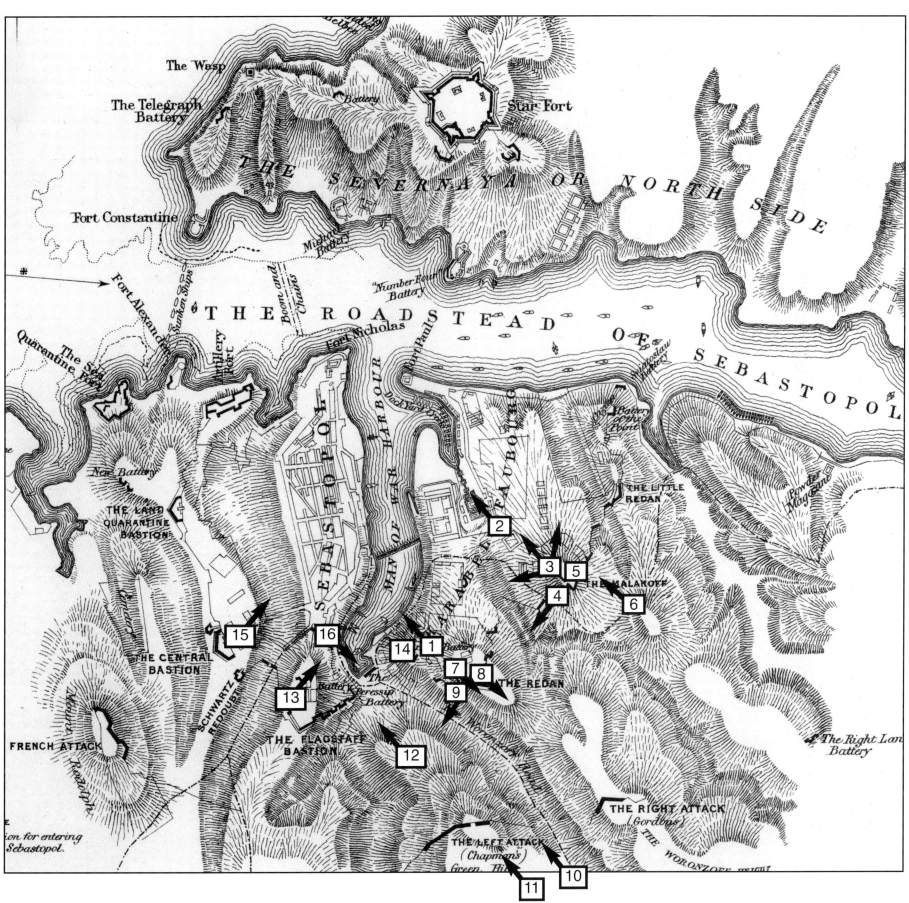

All photographs are by James Robertson except numbers 4 and 9 which are by George Shaw Lefevre

1. Man of War Harbour from the Redan
2. Sevastopol's dry docks before (left) and (right) after demolition
3. Sevastopol from the Malakhov
4. The glacis of the Redan from the curtain of the Malakhov
5. Interior of the Malakhov
6. View from the Mamelon towards the Malakhov
7. View from the Russian barricade at the rear of the Redan, looking towards the salient angle
8. Interior of the Redan looking towards the British Right Attack

9. View from the Redan, looking towards the Vorontsov Ravine
10. The Vorontsov Ravine: 'The Valley of Death'
11. The Green Hill Battery, British Left Attack
12. Sevastopol from the western slope of the Vorontsov Ravine
13. Sevastopol from the Flagstaff Bastion
14. Interior of the Barrack Battery
15. Sevastopol from the Central Bastion
16. View from Sevastopol towards the Vorontsov Ravine

Britain's French and Sardinian Allies

Michael Ball

> 'The organization of the French is beautiful, ours a perfect disgrace...' [1]
>
> Lieutenant-General Sir Charles Ash Windham

The British and French armies had last met in 1815, as enemies on the battlefield of Waterloo. Now they were to be allies, and for both parties the experience was to prove a difficult and unhappy one.

By the 1850s, the French Army was widely regarded as the best in Europe, but its character was very different to that of its new British ally. The rank and file, numbering around a third of a million men, were long-service conscripts. Most of its officer corps, about 20,000 strong, came from relatively humble backgrounds and, unlike their British counterparts, most had to live on their pay.

In the years after Waterloo, French forces were involved in limited operations in Spain, Belgium, Greece, and Italy, but their greatest military commitment was in Algeria. What began as limited French intervention in the 1830s ended as full-scale military occupation which, by 1846, required 118,000 troops, a third of the entire army. It was there that most French troops gained their combat experience, and there too that the French commanders who were to figure prominently in the Crimea made their military reputations. Indeed, nearly all the significant military figures of the French Second Empire [2] had first met in Algeria as junior officers. Algeria demanded tacticians, not strategists; operations usually involved small French columns operating against mobile and relatively lightly-armed tribesmen, an experience which greatly influenced French military thinking. [3] By 1854, both officers and men regarded themselves as 'battle-hardened', but none had ever fought in a war against a major European power, and the experience was to test them severely.

The French Emperor Napoleon III had come to supreme power in 1851 with the active assistance, or at least the acquiescence, of a number of senior figures in the French Army, and was anxious to enhance the prestige of his new dynasty by means of successful military action. The Emperor originally envisaged the Crimean enterprise as no more than a large colonial expedition, requiring perhaps 10,000 troops but, by the end of the war, over 120,000 Frenchmen were involved, a commitment as large as Algeria. As the French Army provided by far the largest force in the Crimea, French commanders naturally expected to dictate the course of the campaign, a position which was to cause considerable difficulties with their British ally.

Several of France's most experienced generals had refused to command the expeditionary force because they had political objections to Napoleon III. The choice fell, therefore, on Marshal Jacques St Arnaud (1798-1854). As Minister of War in Paris, he had played an important part in the coup which brought Napoleon III to power, and had been rewarded for his services with a marshal's baton. A protégé of the legendary Marshal Bugeaud, St Arnaud had served in Algeria from 1836. He was not in good health, suffering from a recurring intestinal infection, but his loyalty was unquestioned and he spoke English well, an important consideration in an Allied operation. Three of St Arnaud's divisional commanders, Generals Canrobert, Bosquet, and Forey, had either supported or acquiesced in the coup of 1851. The fourth, Prince Napoleon, was the Emperor's cousin and heir.

Marshal Jacques Leroy de St Arnaud.
NAM. Negative 98118

In the spring of 1854, French forces began their embarkation from Toulon, Marseilles and Algiers. In Malta, where elements of the expeditionary force were first assembled, St Arnaud made a good impression with his command of English and friendly enthusiasm. It was here, and later in camp at Gallipoli, that British troops encountered their new allies for the first time, and a rapport was rapidly established between the rank and file of the two armies. Two features of the French army made a particular impact on the British – its organisational skills and its exotic appearance.

The development of France's Army of Africa had given it some of its most colourful troops, who made a deep impression on military and civilian observers alike. William Russell, *The Times* correspondent, remarked at length on the appearance of the *Tirailleurs Indigènes*, recruited from Berber tribesmen, and the Zouaves, whose ranks, despite their exotic appearance, were filled with Frenchmen. They maintained a ferocious fighting reputation and were amongst the first drafts of troops for the Crimea, where they would figure prominently throughout the campaign. Russell concluded: 'He [the British soldier] cuts a sorry figure beside a great Gaul in his blazing red pantaloons and padded frock, epaulettes, beard *d'Afrique*, and well-twisted moustache.'[4] St Arnaud even had his own bodyguard of *spahis* (Algerian cavalry), which reinforced the exotic aspect of French forces.

French military administration was undeniably better than that of the British, mainly as a result of their experience of organising men and supplies through Marseilles for Algeria. The French had sophisticated systems to handle mail, pay, casualties, and supplies, and were skilled in achieving the correct balance between mobility and logistic support. The sharp contrast with British arrangements did not go unremarked.

Throughout the war, mutual suspicion of motives and intentions dogged the Allies' attempts at co-operation. Friction was apparent from the outset, in the arrangements for quartering in Malta, and again in Gallipoli. A Turkish proposal to put Omar Pasha's troops under French authority caused further difficulties with the British, who feared the erosion of their own influence if 'French' forces were increased in this way. In the interests of Allied harmony, the plan was dropped, as was a French proposal to allow the senior officer (which would always be St Arnaud) to command on the day of battle.

By the time that the Allies moved from Gallipoli to Varna, the French, now 60,000 strong, were experiencing supply shortages – the men had come east by steam, but their provisions by sail. More seriously, cholera, which may have come with the troops from Marseilles, was on the increase. A French expedition to the Dobrudja, north of Varna, to relieve pressure on the Turks, set out on 22 July 1854; it returned to Varna on 22 August, having achieved nothing except many more cases of cholera. Canrobert's 1st Division alone lost 5-6,000 men in this fruitless enterprise. The Russian retreat north of the Danube removed the immediate threat, but left the Allies without a definite objective. For Napoleon III, the Crimea offered the opportunity to restore French prestige after the Dobrudja fiasco. Like their British allies however, the French were largely lacking in adequate military or topographical information about their intended destination.

The Battle of the Alma

After an unopposed landing where the French, as expected, made a better job of getting ashore, the Allies fought their first action in the Crimea, at the River Alma, on 20 September 1854. Some 25,000 French occupied the right of the Allied line. Their attack was led by General Pierre Bosquet (1810-61), who was to prove perhaps the most able of any of the Allied generals in the Crimea. Like many of his contemporaries, Bosquet had spent most of his military service in Algeria.

The French were delayed by waiting for the British to close up on their left. A major difference in tactics between the two armies was apparent from the outset – the French troops scurried forward, the British marched in lines, and incurred heavier casualties. The French admired British stoicism, but were not inclined to emulate it. Bosquet's Zouaves rapidly scaled the heights in open order, coping well with their first

General Pierre Bosquet and staff, photographed by Roger Fenton. NAM. 1964-12-151-6-48

exposure to artillery fire. St Arnaud reported to Napoleon III, 'Your Majesty can be proud of his soldiers; they have not degenerated; these are the soldiers of Austerlitz and Jena.'[5]

Raglan favoured an immediate pursuit, but St Arnaud objected. He was hampered by lack of cavalry (most of the French cavalry had not yet arrived), shortage of ammunition, and the need to tend the wounded. In addition, the French soldiers needed to retrieve their knapsacks – put down immediately before going into action. The French were ready to move by the following morning, but now it was the British who were reluctant, requiring two days to tend to their wounded before they were ready to advance. 'Heaven is with us', wrote an exasperated St Arnaud to his wife, 'but the English always hold me back.'[6]

An immediate follow-up would probably have taken Sevastopol, and both Allies (with the advantage of hindsight) recognized this. General Todleben, the defender of the city, later declared that an immediate assault would have taken it. With some mutual recrimination, St Arnaud

and Raglan agreed to march their troops south of Sevastopol, to take up positions for a siege. This was barely completed before St Arnaud's failing health finally collapsed, and he died on 29 September.

Although he had often disagreed with Raglan, St Arnaud had proved an effective French leader. He was succeeded by General François Canrobert (1809-95), who had served in Algeria from 1835. Canrobert was a friend of St Arnaud; a courageous soldier, popular with the troops, and reportedly a good administrator, he was to prove sadly lacking in the qualities required for high command. Nevertheless, both Allies had high expectations and few doubted that the war would be over by Christmas.

Now faced with the need to maintain his forces in a protracted campaign, Canrobert reorganized the French army into two corps, the first, under the command of General Forey, to carry on the work of the siege, and the second, under General Bosquet, to prevent the Russian field army from aiding Sevastopol. The Allied bombardment of the city began on 17 October, but the French quickly ceased fire after the explosion of a powder magazine and all thought of an assault was abandoned. French 'excuses' further weakened relations between the Allies.

French Zouaves come to the assistance of the British Guards at Inkerman. A watercolour by Colonel The Honourable George Cadogan, Grenadier Guards, an eye-witness to this very scene.
NAM. 1998-06-128-87

Balaklava and Inkerman
Canrobert planned to concentrate on reducing Sevastopol and to ignore the Russian field forces. On 25 October 1854, the Allies were forcibly reminded of this threat by a Russian thrust at Balaklava, to cut off the British from their supplies. The French played little part in the battle, and are remembered chiefly for General's Bosquet's succinct comment on the Charge of the Light Brigade; 'C'est magnifique, mais ce n'est pas la guerre'. The remnants of the Brigade were saved by the intervention of the 4th Regiment of Chasseurs d'Afrique.

The Allied assault on Sevastopol, now scheduled for 7 November, was pre-empted two days earlier by a Russian attack on British positions at Inkerman. Misjudging the scale of the attack, the British at first declined Bosquet's offer of assistance, but were soon requesting French help. As a consequence, the French engaged late, but their intervention turned the tide of the battle. A Russian general, observing the arrival of the Bosquet's reinforcements, remarked to his staff, 'The French are saving the English at Inkerman, as the Prussians did at Waterloo.'[7]

Although Bosquet and Raglan were warm in their expressions of friendship, the French refusal to follow up without British support aggravated tensions between the Allies.

The First Winter

The Russian attack at Inkerman was followed by a hurricane on 14 November which destroyed many French and British supply ships. This removed any chance of an Allied assault before the onset of winter, which was to prove a stern test for the French as well as the British. The British press exaggerated differences between the French and

British supply situations – the French were, in reality, not that much better off, and their food supplies remained critical throughout. Coupled with bad weather, this drastically reduced their effectiveness. However, the French were on the whole much better organised, and French officers were perceived by their men to share their hardships in a way that British officers did not. The French harbour at Kamiesch was more suitable for landing supplies than Balaklava (which the British had chosen), and they were able to construct warehouses and medical facilities there. Perhaps most importantly, supplies reached the troops because the French built paved roads from the harbour to their siege lines, and used transport animals cared for by properly trained men.

British medical opinion identified a number of other factors which enabled the French to survive the first winter better than the British. The French administrative services within each regiment were better. The troops had shelter tents and, for the treatment of their wounded, a good ambulance-mule corps. Every regiment had a baker who distributed fresh bread daily. French food was prepared collectively, and included

French mule ambulance, a watercolour by Cadogan.
NAM. 1998-06-128-85

supplies of dried vegetables. Thus the French were able to maintain their health on one third of the British meat ration. The British did not adopt techniques of mass food preparation until mid-winter, after which their situation improved. French soldiers were also better acquainted with the importance of looking after their own health than their British counterparts, for example, using local wild plants as a salad to supplement their rations.[8] For Charles Windham, the difference between the Allies could be summed up very simply: 'The English soldier, I admit, has not the *savoir faire* of the French…'[9]

By January 1855, the French contingent mustered about 90,000 men.[10] Raglan estimated the French force to be four times the size of the British. In addition to maintaining their own forces, the French also assisted their ally, putting parts of their ambulance train at British disposal, supplying men to carry shells and work on the road from Balaklava, and taking over more of the siege lines. The French soldiers' view of the British was that, although they were brave on the battlefield, they were afraid of getting their hands dirty. The British appeared to take French assistance for granted, and Raglan even went so far as to complain that the French might have done more.[11] Bosquet, for his part, criticised the inability of the British to help themselves. Although there was still cordiality and good faith between French and British troops, little remained between their senior officers or politicians.

With the Allied force effectively immobilised by winter and no signs of progress, an inertia gripped the French senior command. Canrobert's leadership began to be questioned, and Bosquet in particular began to hint that something would have to be done about it. Napoleon III felt that his presence might be required in the Crimea to restore the situation, and despatched as his special representative General Adolphe Niel (1802-69). An engineer and administrator, Niel attended all high-level meetings, and his direct channel of communication with the Emperor made Canrobert's position very difficult. Niel estimated that the French could lose 25,000 men in an assault; the British forces he regarded as little more than an embarrassment.

The cost of war was now making heavy inroads on the French economy. Voices in Paris were suggesting peace, and that continuation of the war served only British interests. Canrobert's position was becoming more difficult by the day. He could not initiate any major operation without permission from Napoleon III and, as it was not known whether or not the Emperor would come in person (Napoleon III had intended to go to the Crimea, but decided it was politically too dangerous to leave Paris), very little action was taken. Late in April 1855 contact by submarine telegraph would bring Paris still closer.

The need for top-level unity between the Allies was now imperative if anything was to be salvaged from the campaign, but there was little sign of it. On 20 February 1855 an Allied attack on Chorgoum was aborted due to bad weather, providing yet another source of friction. An assault on Sevastopol was at last agreed for 28 April, then abandoned on the prospect of Napoleon III's arrival.

The Sardinians

In the spring of 1855, the Allies received a welcome reinforcement in the shape of the Sardinian contingent. The Kingdom of Piedmont and Sardinia was one of the few Italian states to retain its independence after the Congress of Vienna in 1815, when much of Northern Italy

General François Canrobert.
NAM. 1968-06-57

came under Austrian control. Its king, Victor Emmanuel II, entertained ambitions to lead a united Italy, but recognised that to throw off the Austrian yoke he would require the military assistance of another European power. Support for the Allies in the Crimea was a political gamble which might bring him such assistance. Although obliged by treaty to provide only 15,000 men, the Sardinians actually supplied nearly 17,000, well equipped and organised in three divisions.[12] As the peacetime strength of the Sardinian army was only some 45,000, this represented a serious commitment. The contingent was financed by the British, who hoped that this would give them more political leverage with the French. Predictably, wrangling over 'control' of the Sardinians simply caused more friction between the Allies.[13]

The quality of the Sardinian contingent deeply impressed observers. A British officer, writing anonymously in 1856, noted that 'The interior discipline of the Piedmontese army could not be surpassed'; and that

'They manoeuvred with the quickness of the French, and at the same time with the accuracy and solidity of our troops.'[14] He noted particularly the quality of their Land Transport Corps *(Corpo del Treno)*,[15] considering these services superior to their British equivalents. As for their officers, '…I never met a more gentlemanlike, frank, and hospitable set of men, nor did I ever see regiments in which more harmony existed amongst the officers.' He also noted that, as a means of maintaining morale, the Sardinians entertained themselves with musical soirées, operas and comic songs. The Sardinians, however, keen to be seen as more than just the stuff of comic opera, were anxious to be employed in field operations, not merely as labour at Balaklava.

Canrobert Resigns

Canrobert and Raglan continued to blame each other for delays in the preparations for an assault. The Russians were now carrying out

Sardinian staff officers, an unfinished study by Colonel The Honourable George Cadogan, their British liaison officer. NAM. 1998-06-128-3

numerous attacks against the French sectors of the line, and succeeded in reclaiming some ground. The French took heavy casualties contesting the Russian possession of rifle pits and the cemetery in front of the Central Bastion; they retook the cemetery on the night of 1-2 May 1855, in an action described by Raglan as 'very brilliant'.

On 3 May 1855 an Allied naval expedition was mounted against the Russian port of Kerch, to cut off Russian supplies to Sevastopol. British and French admirals were in favour, and so was Raglan, but not Canrobert. The expedition was recalled when only two hours from its target at Canrobert's insistence, following a telegram from Napoleon III. This incident caused great bitterness in Anglo-French relations, and ruined Canrobert's effectiveness as French Commander-in-Chief in the Crimea, a fact which he himself recognised. Although capable of getting on personally with Raglan, Canrobert had found it impossible to cooperate fully with his allies when his authority was so restricted by Paris (and by the presence of General Niel). On 16 May he asked to be relieved of overall command.

Pélissier takes Command

Canrobert's successor as French Commander-in-Chief was General Aimable Pélissier (1794-1864), who had arrived in February to take command of the 1st Corps. Pélissier had spent most of the 1840s in Algeria and had served as Chief of Staff of the Algerian province of Oran. He inherited a French force of some 120,000 men, supported by 32,000 British, 17,000 Sardinians, and 55,000 Turks.

Pélissier's tenure of command was characterized by an implacable determination to conduct military operations without interference from Paris. From the outset, he made his presence felt, demanding much greater freedom of action from Napoleon III, and preparing for a major assault. With his approval, the Kerch expedition was renewed (22 May) and proved a resounding success, Pélissier naturally taking the credit.

Pélissier was determined to press the siege strongly from the south side; the advantage was now back with the Allies, who had been reinforced, whereas the garrison was weakening daily. The first step was to take the Mamelon Vert, a heavily fortified position facing the right of the French lines. Pélissier was fiercely opposed to the yielding of ground, and counterattacked immediately when the Russians sought to establish outworks. He would brook no opposition; his legendary rudeness extended to giving General Niel a dressing down in front of British officers, and exchanging very strongly worded telegrams with Napoleon III. One British observer referred to him as '…a grand and overpowering example of bad manners and bad language.'[16] But

progress was at last being made – on 7 June, the French took the Mamelon Vert, and the British the Quarries in front of the Redan.

The First Assault on Sevastopol

The Allies' first attack on the Redan and the Malakhov, on 18 June 1855, was badly coordinated, and hampered by Pélissier's removal of Bosquet from a critical command only hours before the attack. Its failure produced more heated exchanges between Napoleon III and Pélissier; the Emperor was ready to replace him, but eventually changed his mind. Pélissier's evident grief at the death of Raglan (28 June 1855) did much to heal the growing rift between the Allies. Napoleon III was now determined that siege must continue come what may, even if Sevastopol held out until winter.

The Battle of the Chernaya

The food situation in Sevastopol was now becoming critical. On 16 August 1855, in an attempt to relieve the city, General Gorchakov's Russian field army attacked French and Sardinian positions on the River Chernaya. Warned in advance that an attack was imminent, the Allies put up a spirited resistance, and the much larger Russian force was repulsed with heavy casualties. Pélissier, who commanded the battle, received considerable credit. For the Sardinians, it was their only real action of the entire war, and although their losses were very small compared to those of the French and the Russians,[17] the political consequences of the Chernaya were incalculable. In his Order of the Day, Lieutenant-General Sir James Simpson wrote that: 'The Sardinian army has shown itself worthy to fight by the side of the greatest military nations of Europe.'[18] The Sardinian Prime Minister, Cavour, wrote to General Alfonso La Marmora, the commander of the Sardinian contingent: 'The news has raised the spirit of the nation and reconciled everyone to the policy of the alliance.'[19] The Chernaya would earn Sardinia, represented by Cavour, a seat at the peace table in Paris in 1856.

The Second Assault and the Fall of Sevastopol

The victory of the Chernaya transformed the strategic situation. Sevastopol no longer had any hope of relief, and 8 September 1855 the French, commanded by Bosquet, made their second attack on the Malakhov. A massive artillery bombardment was followed by direct assault, led by MacMahon's Division.[20] The French achieved complete surprise and the Malakhov was taken in ten minutes, whilst the British failed for the second time to take the Redan. After their counter-attacks failed, the Russians evacuated the southern sector of Sevastopol the same night. Once again the British failure led to recriminations; the French attached little importance to the fact that the British had had to cross 200 metres of open ground, the French only 25 metres.

Cadogan's watercolour of General Pélissier (in the white cape) observing the French capture of the Mamelon, 7 June 1855. The Malakhov, which the French assault columns spontaneously but unwisely attempted to storm at the same time, lies beyond, crowned with fire.
NAM. 1998-06-128-22

With the end of the war apparently now in sight, Pélissier was made a Marshal of France, followed somewhat belatedly by Canrobert and Bosquet. French troops under the command of General Bazaine were despatched to Kinburn, but in general French thinking now became more defensive, whereas the British, conscious that the French had so far won all the laurels in the Crimea, still wanted more action. The British had begun to feel that they were losing control of the war, and were particularly concerned about the status of the Sardinian contingent, which they were financing. When the Allies met in Paris to

discuss the further prosecution of the war, General La Marmora, for the Sardinians, did not feel bound to side with the British, having already identified France as the most likely source of support against Austria. The French were now keen for peace, as they could no longer sustain the vast expense of continued operations.

The Second Winter
The winter of 1855-56 proved tragic for the French army. Sanitation got out of hand and typhus took a high toll of French troops, a situation similar to that faced by the British in the winter of 1854-55. The French

had started the war with high standards of hygiene and medical treatment, but these had not adapted to the increasing numbers of French troops.[21] By the spring of 1856, the death rate in the French army was nearly four times what it had been in the autumn of 1854. At least 24,000 died of disease in the first three months of 1856 alone, mostly from typhus and cholera. Jean Baudens, the Medical Inspector to the French Army in the Crimea, identified a lack of cleanliness as a principal factor in the spread of disease. 'The habits of cleanliness which distinguished the English army, should have been followed in our camps', he wrote; 'Our quarters for troops shine with the greasy filth of daily neglect.'[22] He also identified the inadequacy of the French diet (the soldiers got only two meals a day; it was recommended that this should be increased to three), the lack of anti-scorbutics (the British drew rations of lemon juice preserved in casks) and the vast influx of young soldiers, not as hardy as the seasoned Algerian veterans with which France had started the war. Moreover, many medical officers succumbed to disease, leaving the survivors with an impossibly large workload. He found the medical services of the Sardinians better managed: 'General Marmora invited me to visit the field hospitals of the Piedmontese army, whose management and attendance deserved nothing but praise.'[23] In these circumstances the armistice, finally signed on 14 March 1856, came not a moment too soon, and the last French troops had left the Crimea by 5 July. The whole campaign had cost the French Army over 95,000 casualties.

Aftermath

The shared hardships of the Crimea did not improve Anglo-French relations. The British had not enjoyed the experience of being the junior partner in the alliance, and an atmosphere of mutual suspicion persisted for the rest of the century. In 1859, renewed fears of a French invasion of Britain gave birth to the Rifle Volunteer movement.

The Crimea was a turning point in the histories of France and Sardinia. Partly as a result of her participation in the war, Sardinia obtained French assistance to recover much of northern Italy from Austria in 1859, a critical step towards a united Italy. France, which had gained the laurels in the Crimea, was not so fortunate. Diplomatically, she had become the greatest power in Europe, but her success encouraged an aggressive stance which incurred the enmity of other powers. The generals of the Crimea – Canrobert, MacMahon and Bazaine – would be remembered not as heroes, but as the men who led France to humiliating defeat in the Franco-Prussian War of 1870-71, when the French regular army, confident of victory, collapsed in the space of just six weeks, taking with it the dynasty of Napoleon III. That defeat was to haunt the French Army for a generation.

Notes

1   Major Hugh Pearse, *The Crimean Diary and letters of Lieut.-General Sir Charles Ash Windham*, London (1897) p98.

2   Napoleon III assumed dictatorial powers in 1851, and ruled as Emperor from 1852 to 1870.

3   For a useful summary of these campaigns and their influence on French military thinking, see Paddy Griffith, *Military thought in the French Army, 1815-51,* Manchester (1989).

4   William Howard Russell, *The British Expedition to the Crimea*, London (1858) p37.

5   Leroy de St Arnaud, *Lettres du Maréchal Saint-Arnaud 1832-1854*, Vol II, Paris (1858) p577.

6   *Ibid.* p498.

7   James Henry Skene, *With Lord Stratford in the Crimean War,* London (1883) p155.

8   Surgeon-General Sir Thomas Longmore, *The sanitary contrasts of the British and French Armies during the Crimean War*, London (1883).

9   Pearse, *op. cit.* p94.

10 Longmore, *op. cit.* The average effective strength of the French army from January to April 1855 was 88,250.

11 Brison D Gooch, *The New Bonapartist Generals in the Crimean War*, The Hague (1959) p161.

12 Cristoforo Manfredi, *La spedizione Sarda in Crimea Nel 1855-56*, Rome (1896) p295. The official strength of the contingent as at 31 July 1855 was 16,946 all ranks plus 36 guns.

13 The Sardinians were financed by a British loan, not a subsidy, giving them the status of Allies rather than merely hired troops. The British were thus forced to concede equal control to the French.

14 *Colburn's United Service Magazine* 1856 Part III pp205-207. The writer was probably Colonel The Hon. George Cadogan, the Queen's Commissioner at Sardinian Headquarters.

15 Manfredi, *op. cit.* p295. *The Corpo del Treno* was organised in three companies totalling 994 all ranks, a very high proportion of the total force.

16 Pearse, *op. cit.* p158.

17 Manfredi, *op. cit.* p179. French casualties were 1,451, Sardinian 186, Russian 6-8,000.

18 Patrick Turnbull, *Solferino: the Birth of a Nation*, London (1985) p45.

19 *Ibid.* p46.

20   MacMahon, another career 'Algerian', had taken over command of the
        1st Division in August 1855.

21   Approximately two and a half times the number at the start of the war.

22   Jean Baptiste Lucien Baudens, *On military and camp hospitals, and
        the health of troops in the field, being the results of a commission to
        inspect the sanitary arrangements of the French Army, and incidentally
        of other armies in the Crimean War*, translated by Franklin B Hough,
        New York (1862), p45.

23   *Ibid.* p20.

Photography in the Crimea

Kate Wood

> The dimly allusive information, which alone the conventional works of the painter can convey, is powerless in attempting to describe what occurs in such operations, whilst a photographic picture brings the thing itself before us.[1]

The first known war photographs date from the American-Mexican War of 1846-47, but these amount to images captured by photographers who happened to be present; the Crimean War was the first campaign subject to systematic photographic documentation. Though compromised by political, commercial, technical and artistic considerations, its photographic legacy offers a tantalising and unprecedented glimpse of a conflict poised between traditional and modern warfare.

When the Crimean War broke out, photography was still very young. The first photographs, daguerreotypes, had appeared as recently as 1839, and their accurate and apparently magical mimicry of views and people aroused considerable public interest.

Yet by the 1850s the development of the art form in Britain had already stagnated, restricted by the monopolistic approach of Henry Fox Talbot (1800-77), the inventor of the calotype. In common with the daguerreotype, this process had been patented in England, and photographers were accordingly obliged to apply to Talbot for a licence even if they wished to use apparently dissimilar processes such as the new albumen on glass and waxed paper processes originated by Claude Felix Abel Niépce de Saint Victor (1805-70) and Gustave Le Gray (1820-84) respectively, and freely published in France.

The situation began to change in 1851, when the Great Exhibition showed Britain's first important display of photographs, providing public access to the technically experimental work of US and continental photographers, and thus highlighting the insularity of the domestic photographic scene. Further momentum was provided by English sculptor and calotype photographer Frederick Scott Archer's (1813-57) publication in *The Chemist* that March of a new photographic process, the collodion, or wet-plate method. This was not only a great improvement on previous processes, but was the first considered sufficiently distinct from Fox Talbot's to merit an exemption from his draconian patent restrictions.

A collodion negative could record fine detail and subtle tones and had the great advantage of being much more sensitive than either the daguerreotype or the calotype. Exposure times were reduced to a matter of a few seconds, enabling the photographer to experiment with less static subject matter and produce more naturalistic images. Scott Archer applied no patent, which contributed significantly to the popularisation and development of photography but also led to his financial ruin.

The Crimean photographs of Roger Fenton (1819-69) and James Robertson (c1813-88) were taken by this wet-plate or wet collodion method. The recently discovered substance collodion (made by dissolving gun-cotton[2] in ether and containing potassium iodide) was poured onto a thoroughly clean glass plate, which was tilted to achieve even coverage. When the ether had practically evaporated, leaving a tacky coating, the plate was plunged into a bath of silver nitrate to sensitise it. The plate, still wet, was then loaded into a plate holder and exposed in the camera; if left to dry almost all its sensitivity was lost. Immediately after exposure it was developed, fixed and washed. The technique's major drawback, notwithstanding its many advantages, was that due to the need to expose the glass plate while it was still wet, the itinerant photographer was obliged to take with him his darkroom and a large quantity of cumbersome equipment.

For Fenton, a converted wine merchant's van provided the answer, serving as a mobile darkroom and a caravan in which to live, cook and sleep. The chemicals used in photographic processing would have produced lingering and pungent fumes in such a small space, and

**Roger Fenton's photographic van.
NAM. Negative 98121**

neither was the process entirely safe: instances were reported of explosions occurring in collodion darkrooms as a result of using open flames in a dense ether atmosphere.

The weather added a further dimension to these practical challenges. The arid heat of the Crimean summer was so intense that Fenton reported that one of his gutta-percha (a type of rubber) funnels, on exposure to the sun's rays, 'became blistered all over, as if it had been laid upon the heated bars of a fireplace'.[3] It became necessary to thin the collodion much more than was usual in England, to allow it to spread evenly over the plate before drying, and even then the glass slides would often dry before they could be inserted into the camera to be exposed.

Bearing in mind the considerable technical, practical and financial challenges of photography during the 1850s, we are fortunate indeed that, due to the skill and enthusiasm of these early practitioners, so many photographs survive.

The Romanian amateur painter and photographer Carol Popp de Szathmari (1812-87) is held to be the first 'war photographer'. He was on the Danube as early as April 1854, when his van was targeted by the Turkish artillery, who suspected that it belonged to a Russian spy. De Szathmari's photographs record scenes of battlefields, landscapes and fortifications, as well as Turkish and Russian troops with their commanding officers. A display of his photographs, exhibited at the Paris World Exposition of 1855, was very well received.

When France and Britain entered the war at the end of March, the British Government attached a small photographic unit to the Army. Captain (later Major) John Hackett, of the 77th (The East Middlesex) Regiment of Foot, who held the appointment of Deputy Assistant Quartermaster-General of the expeditionary forces, was charged with employing a suitable photographer. On 29 May he contracted the civilian Richard Nicklin, an employee of the commercial New Bond Street photographic studio of Dickinson and Company. Nicklin was offered a six-month contract (with the possibility of a subsequent extension) at a salary of six shillings per day, plus rations and other allowances, and a free passage to Turkey. Corporal John Pendered and Lance-Corporal John Hammond of the Royal Sappers and Miners were selected to accompany him. They received a few days' training in photography and, on 11 June, embarked with Nicklin for Varna aboard the *Hecla* with 16 cases of photographic equipment. We can assume that Nicklin, accompanying the Army, took photographs at Varna and then at Balaklava after its occupation by the British on 26 September. Sadly, nothing is known of what must have been a unique record of the

early months of the war. The photographer and his assistants were on board the *Rip Van Winkle* when it foundered, along with 20 other transport and supply ships, during the hurricane of 14 November 1854.

Unaware that they had drowned in the *Rip Van Winkle* nearly two months before, the Deputy-Secretary of State for War, Benjamin Hawes, enquires for news of Richard Nicklin and his assistants from Lord Raglan's Military Secretary, Lieutenant-Colonel T M Steele.
NAM. 1968-07-377-2

Nicklin's replacements, sent to the Crimea in the early spring of 1855, were military personnel: Ensigns Brandon and Dawson. The pair received a month's instruction in photography from J E Mayall, one of London's leading portrait photographers, and took a large number of pictures, which this time were successfully returned home. However, as early as May 1869 the photographs, which, like Nickin's are assumed to have been produced from paper negatives, were reported to be held 'in a deplorable condition' at the War Office. Whether this was due to poor storage conditions or lack of technical expertise on the part of the photographer it is impossible to ascertain.

A letter of 29 September 1855 from Lieutenant-General Sir William Codrington points to another little-known 'official' photographer, Captain Edward Augustus Inglefield (1820-94) of the *Firebrand*. Writing to his wife Lady Mary, Codrington recounts that Inglefield left his photographic equipment in charge of 'Artillery people in one of the magazines of the Redan', only to find, on his return three days later, that it has been 'plundered, broke to pieces, his glasses and sketches lost'. Codrington assisted Inglefield in his investigations and discovered that soldiers of the 46th (The South Devonshire) Regiment of Foot were seen taking the cases away (the camera lens was later found to have been purchased by a newspaper correspondent). 'It is too provoking', Codrington continued,

> to find that English soldiers have been the cause of this destruction not only of valuable property - but of the power of perpetuating in exactness - the state of ruin and appearance of destruction of the works and buildings. This would be most curious. I believe several have been done, but this was for the Admiralty and Govt., and the apparatus was the best London could make.[4]

Inglefield was an interesting and adventurous character who, in 1852, commanded Lady Franklin's private steamer *Isabel* in an Arctic expedition in search of Sir John Franklin, and who as captain of the *Phoenix* commanded the Arctic relief expedition of 1853-54. On arrival in the Crimea, he was already a practised photographer; an engraving based on one of his polar photographs was printed in *The Illustrated London News* in October 1854.[5] Knighted in 1877, he attained the rank of admiral two years later. He was accomplished in both arts and sciences, and invented the hydraulic steering gear and the Inglefield anchor. His paintings, including, in 1865, portraits of the Queen and Princess Royal, were exhibited at the Royal Academy,[6] and a set of his lithographs of ships and shipwrecks in the Arctic are held in the collections of the National Archives of Canada.

The photographic career of Roger Fenton, in contrast, is well documented. He trained as a painter, and it is likely that Paul Delaroche (1797-1856), with whom he studied in Paris in the early 1840s, provided his first introduction to photography. He returned to London in about 1844 to study law and practised as a solicitor in the City of London. He did not abandon his interest in painting and photography, however, and exhibited 'genre' paintings on sentimental themes at the Royal Academy as well as, more significantly, playing an instrumental role in the establishment of the Royal Photographic Society.

Fenton and his two assistants arrived in the Crimea on 8 March 1855, shortly after Lord Aberdeen's government announced its resignation, its credibility irretrievably damaged by William Howard Russell's reports in *The Times* of the squalid conditions suffered by British troops and

Roger Fenton, dressed as a French Zouave.
NAM. Negative 46981

allegations of gross incompetence on the part of the government. The timing of Fenton's expedition, it has been suggested, points to the possibility of a political agenda. The privileged and well-connected son of Member of Parliament John Fenton, he travelled to the Crimea with the patronage of Queen Victoria and Prince Albert, with whom he was on friendly terms, having been commissioned to take portraits of the royal family. Whilst working in the Crimea, he often lodged with the high-ranking French and English officers that he photographed, including General Bosquet and Lieutenant-Colonel Colin Frederick Campbell of the 46th (The South Devonshire) Regiment of Foot, who treated him as an honoured guest. The fact that luminaries such as Prince Albert, the Duke of Newcastle (Secretary of State for War until his resignation on 30 January 1855) and Lord Raglan provided him with letters of introduction no doubt eased his path.

Although the exposure times of wet-plate photography were still too long to make practicable the depiction of the 'live action' battle scenes to which we are now accustomed, Fenton had ample opportunity to photograph the scenes of horror and destruction that his letters testify he witnessed. Instead he concentrated on views of camps and staged tableaux such as 'The cookhouse of the 8th Hussars' and a convivial party of French and English officers entitled *L'Entente Cordiale*. A letter written on 2 April 1855 by Lieutenant-Colonel Anthony Sterling of the Highland Brigade from the camp at Balaklava offers an insight into Fenton's selective approach:

L'Entente Cordiale by Roger Fenton.
NAM. 1964-12-151-6-41

There has been a photographer too, who took a few camp-views and suddenly went off: I scarcely know how to explain his difficulty. Too much truth. What is called decency, and the natural wants of the animal man, exist here in antagonistic position, and all his pictures presented such peculiar and unusual details, that he concluded to abandon the enterprise of communicating the naked truth to the British public.[7]

Fenton's self-censorship may well have been commercially motivated: his financial backer was Manchester publisher Thomas Agnew and Sons, who required from him the exotic views and picturesque 'types' demanded by the Victorian commercial market.

Fenton also took a large number of portraits. Although he was keen to capture the likenesses of high-ranking officers and the great diversity of 'exotically' uniformed and accoutred foreign troops, as soon as he arrived at Balaklava he was pestered by the many ordinary soldiers who wanted photographs of themselves to send home to their loved ones. For Fenton, these portraits constituted a form of barter in exchange for having his van transported from one locality to another; in a turn of events symbolic of the organisational chaos that typified his stay in the Crimea, the three horses that he had purchased for the purpose were discovered on arrival to be riding horses unbroken for draught.

Fenton observed the French storming the Mamelon Vert on 7 June, and on 18 June watched from Cathcart's Hill the progress of the assaults on the Malakhov and the Redan, during which many of his friends were killed. Depressed and in ill health, he left the Crimea on 26 June.

There is evidence that, before he left, Fenton met James Robertson, who arrived in the Crimea in mid-June. Robertson, who was employed as superintendent and chief engraver at the Imperial Mint in Constantinople, was also a well-known and successful amateur photographer, having published in London a number of albums of views of locations such as Constantinople and Athens. Many details of his early life remain unconfirmed, although he is thought to have been born in Middlesex, perhaps of Scottish ancestry, and to have studied at Edinburgh University.

Lieutenant-Colonel Colin Frederick Campbell of the 46th (The South Devonshire) Regiment of Foot wrote of him in a letter to the artist Lowes Dickenson, after the fall of Sevastopol on 8 September 1855:

Since Mr Fenton was here a man of the name of Robertson, who has an establishment in Constantinople, has taken a great many views, superior, I think to Fenton's. He went to Constantinople, about a month ago to have them printed off, and promised to let me have £5 worth, but I have heard no more of them. He had the great advantage of being able to take the interior of the Malakoff, Redan and other places almost immediately after their capture.[8]

Robertson's striking photographs of the Malakhov and the Redan certainly document the chaos and destruction of a savage fight. If they were taken immediately after the forts' capture, however, they must have been very carefully framed, for there are no dead bodies to be seen. Like those of his predecessor (though to a lesser extent), Robertson's photographs are sanitised, although whether this is through

**The interior of the Redan after its capture, photographed by James Robertson.
NAM. Negative 4447**

respect for Victorian propriety, or with an eye on the commercial print market, is open to interpretation.

In reading accounts of Robertson's life and work one certainly gains the impression of an ambitious and acutely commercially aware entrepreneur. Campbell's comment quoted above implies that he may have touted a selection of photographs to tempt potential customers, returning periodically to his studio in Constantinople to make prints. He also appears to have taken photographs (such as the 'Grave of Captain The Honourable Cavendish Browne, 7th Fusiliers'[9] in response to orders from relatives.

Robertson's first 'Crimean' photographs were taken at Scutari, a short ferry ride across the Bosphorus from his base in Constantinople, between April and June 1854. He photographed the British troops assembled there awaiting orders to sail to Varna, and engravings based on these prints appeared in *The Illustrated London News* soon afterwards. On arrival in the Crimea, his subjects included panoramas of Sevastopol, encampments, fortifications, trenches, mortar batteries and burial grounds, but it was his depictions of the aftermath of the fall of Sevastopol that made his name and provided him with an 'angle' distinct from Fenton's.

During the spring and summer of 1856 Robertson made efforts to fill gaps in his pictorial coverage of the Crimea, photographing parts of Sevastopol which had been inaccessible before the allied victory, such as the forts guarding the north shore of Sevastopol harbour, and views of renowned locations such as the battlefields of Balaklava, Inkerman and the Chernaya, as well as 'Lord Raglan's House', and 'Miss Nightingale's Tower'.[10] These images were intended for sale as mementos or in souvenir albums. During this busy period he also continued to develop other strands of his business, adding to his portfolio of Constantinople views and even mounting a photographic expedition to Malta.

When Robertson left the Crimea for the last time in June 1856, his brother-in-law, associate and future business partner Felice Beato (1825-*c*1908) was despatched in his stead to continue taking souvenir photographs. Beato went on to attain great success in his own right, particularly for his unflinching photographs of the suppression of the mutiny of the Bengal Army (1857-59) (including pictures of gibbeted corpses) and it is possible that he was responsible for some of the Crimean photographs attributed to Robertson.

Fenton and Robertson both exhibited their work in London. Fenton showed 312 of his 360 photographs at the Gallery of the Water Colour

Society in Pall Mall in October 1855 and 58 of Robertson's 60 views went on display at the Regent Street studio of well-known daguerreotypist W E Kilburn the following February. Throughout 1856 their photographs were displayed nationwide, at times as a joint exhibition and on other occasions separately. But after the war drew to a close public interest quickly waned. Print sales were very slow and as early as December 1856 Robertson and Fenton jointly auctioned off their unsold stock.

The portfolio cover for Shaw Lefevre's collection of photographs. NAM. 1986-04-101

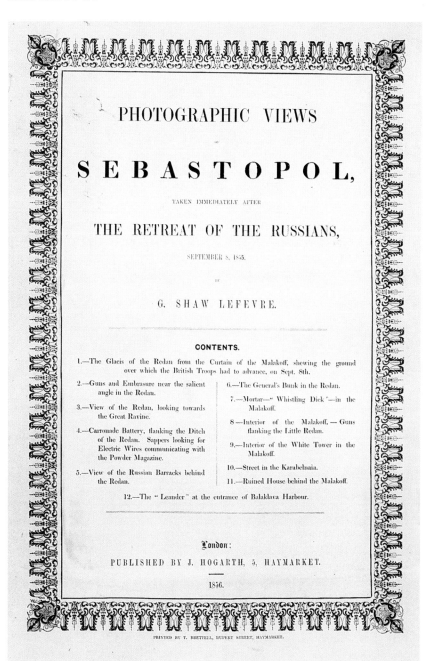

The album *Views of Sebastopol taken immediately after the retreat of the Russians, September 8, 1855*, and published by Hogarth in 1856, was taken by a keen amateur photographer, George Shaw Lefevre (later Baron Eversley) (1831-1928).[11] Lefevre shared with Fenton a background in politics and the law and inherited from his father, John George Shaw Lefevre, an interest in politics and travel. Educated at Eton and Trinity College Cambridge, he was called to the Bar of the Inner Temple the year after his graduation. In 1863 he was elected Liberal Member of Parliament for Reading.

Lefevre embarked for the Crimea aboard Sir Edward Colebrooke's yacht in September 1855. Very little is known of his career as a photographer, but his photographs often cover the same ground as Robertson's, including the Redan, the Malakhov and the ruined suburbs of the town, and as a result they have sometimes been mistakenly

attributed to him.[12] Like Robertson and Fenton before him he carefully ensured that no corpses were visible in his compositions, although in view of Lefevre's intention to donate the proceeds of his photographic sales to the Florence Nightingale Fund, this is understandable.

While Lefevre's compositions are not as accomplished as Robertson's, he showed some originality in his choice of subject matter, and his photographs of the glacis of the Redan, the Russian General's bunker in the fort and the search for wires laid by the Russians to explode the magazines, are useful contributions to the pictorial record of the Crimean War.

Space does not permit of an exhaustive account of photography in the Crimea, but no treatment of the subject would be complete without mentioning the French contribution to the photographic history of the War.

Sappers in the Redan after its capture looking for electric wires connecting to the powder magazine. Photograph by George Shaw Lefevre. NAM. 1986-04-101-4

Colonel (Jean-)Charles Langlois (1789-1870) arrived in the Crimea on 13 November 1855. Commissioned by the French Minister for War with the creation of a panorama commemorating the fall of Sevastopol, he had already painted a series of popular panoramas celebrating French military engagements. Langlois was assisted by the young calotypist Léon-Eugène Méhédin (1828-1905), with whom he had an antagonistic relationship. Together they made a series of preparatory photographs from the top of the ruined Malakhov, although the fact that the military installations there were already being demolished meant that Langlois was obliged to use some of Robertson's earlier views for reference (he nevertheless opined that they were devoid of artistic merit). The completed panorama, 'The Taking of Sebastopol', did not open to the public in Paris until 1860.

Méhédin, who had trained in photography with Le Gray, created independently his own series of 'picturesque' photographic panoramas of the ruined city. A firm supporter of the Emperor Napoleon III, he was one of the first to see the potential of photography as a means of propaganda, but his technical ineptitude (incapable of mastering wet-plate photography, he was still using the calotype as late as 1875) put an end to his career as 'chroniqueur' du Second Empire.

In September 1855, after the fall of Sevastopol, Jean-Baptiste-Henri Durand-Brager (1814-70), along with the professional photographer Lassimone (dates unavailable), accompanied the expedition to Kinburn. The resulting photographs, which include the fort at the mouth of the Dniepr and atmospheric shots of ships of the French blockade frozen in the ice, were published by Gambart & Co in London and Bisson Frères in Paris.

The Crimean War marked a watershed in terms of the pictorial representation of conflict; from this time onwards the war artist was gradually marginalised, his perceived role as the recorder of documentary reality transformed into that of a purveyor of 'artistic impressions' and general abstract truths. Of course the 'realities' communicated by the Crimean photographer remain mediated, views carefully chosen and framed. Nevertheless, few would counter the assertion that these images are more immediate, more 'real' than any of the war artist Simpson's conventional depictions of heroism.

Notes

1   *The Practical Mechanics Journal*, January 1854, quoted in H and A Gernsheim, *Roger Fenton: Photographer of the Crimean War*, London (1954) p11.

2   An explosive substance made by immersing cleaned and dried cotton waste in a mixture of strong nitric and sulphuric acids.

3   Fenton, in a lecture to the Photographic Society, quoted in J Hannavy, *The Camera goes to War: photographs from the Crimean War 1854-56,* Edinburgh, (c1974) p15.

4   NAM. 1978-08-90-1 typescript of letters of Major-Gen Sir William Codrington.

5   'Captain M'Clure in his Arctic dress – from a photograph by Captain Inglefield', *The Illustrated London News* supplement, 7 October 1854, p348.

6   Frederic Boase, *Modern English Biography*, supplement to Vol II, London (1965 reprint) p746.

7   NAM. 1968-07-270 bound manuscript volume, 1854-1856, compiled by Lt-Col A C Sterling, Brigade Major to Sir Colin Campbell.

8   Letter of Nov 1855 to Lowes Dickenson, from Col Colin Frederick Campbell, *Letters from camp to his relatives during the siege of Sebastopol*, London (1894) pp357-58.

9   This photograph is held in the Royal Collection at Windsor.

10   Both images are held in the Royal Collection at Windsor.

11   NAM. 1986-04-101 folio of twelve photographs taken by G Shaw Lefevre.

12   For example, 'Glacis of the Redan' and 'Shipping in Balaklava Harbour', Lawrence James, *Crimea 1854-56: the war with Russia from contemporary photographs*, Thame (1981) pp156, 172.

Assault on the Redan

With General Aimable Pélissier having succeeded Canrobert in command of the French, preparations to assault Sevastopol were pursued with greater vigour. On 7 June 1855 the British captured the Russian outworks at the Quarries, and the French those at the Mamelon. This cleared the way to attack the key fortifications of the Redan and Malakhov respectively. On 18 June, the anniversary of the Battle of Waterloo, the onslaught was unleashed. The French, however, moved prematurely and were repulsed from the Malakhov; the British, attempting to support them, were bloodily defeated at the Redan. A disappointed Lord Raglan died ten days later and was succeeded by Lieutenant-General James Simpson. Siege operations against the town continued. The Russians' final effort to break the siege of Sevastopol was defeated on 16 August by the French and Sardinians at the Battle of the Chernaya. On 8 September, a second attempt to take the Malakhov and Redan was made. The French captured the Malakhov but the British, with many of their army's young recruits performing badly, once again failed at the Redan. Nevertheless, Sevastopol without the Malakhov was untenable and the same night the Russians evacuated the south of the town. After a siege lasting almost a year, Sevastopol had fallen.

'The Council of War held on the morning of the taking of the Mamelon', 7 June 1855

Photograph by Roger Fenton, 17.8cm. h x 15.5cm. w

Generously donated by the Royal United Service Institution

NAM. 1968-06-348-7

The three commanders-in-chief of the principal Allied contingents in the Crimea – Lord Raglan, the Turk Omar Pasha (1806-71) and the Frenchman, General Aimable Jean-Jacques Pélissier (1794-1864) - photographed in conference. Although Pélissier had the utmost respect for Raglan he treated Omar Pasha so contemptuously that the Turkish commander, a Croatian Moslem convert born Michael Lattas, was increasingly eager to remove his army from the Crimea to the alternative theatre of war in the Caucasus.

Major-General (later Lieutenant-General Sir) Charles Ash Windham (1810-70) standing in front of the Redan, Sevastopol, *c*1855

Oil on canvas, indistinctly signed and possibly dated lower right, by Charles Couzens (*c*1821-89), *c*1858, exhibited at the Royal Academy 1858 No. 463, 92.2cm. h x 71.3cm. w

NAM. 1966-03-70

Following active service with the Coldstream Guards in Canada from 1838 to 1842, Windham retired on half-pay in 1849 with the rank of lieutenant-colonel. However, on the outbreak of the Crimean War he was promoted colonel and appointed Assistant Quartermaster-General of the 4th Division.

Windham distinguished himself at the Battle of Inkerman (5 November 1854), having succeeded to the command of the 4th Division at an early stage of the action. He was then selected to lead the final, abortive, attack by the 2nd Division on the Redan on 8 September 1855. For 'his distinguished conduct in having with the greatest intrepidity and coolness headed the column of attack which assaulted the enemy's defences', he was promoted major-general. He was also an outspoken critic of the management of the War and, during the terrible winter of 1854, did all that he could to alleviate the sufferings of his starving and frozen men.

Windham went on to serve during the suppression of the mutiny of the Bengal Army (1857-59), where he commanded a division throughout the operations at Kanpur (Cawnpore). Promoted lieutenant-general in 1863, he received a KCB in 1865. His last appointment was in 1867 as Commander of the British forces in Canada.

'The Cemetery taken 18th June 1855'

Watercolour by Captain (later Colonel) Henry John Wilkinson (1829-1911), 1st Battalion, 9th (The East Norfolk) Regiment of Foot, 1855, 13.2cm. h x 20.3cm. w

Generously donated by the Royal United Service Institution

NAM. 1972-07-6-8

At the same time as the British launched their main assault against the Redan, a subsidiary attack was made on the Russian defences at the head of the Man of War Harbour by the 1st Brigade of the 3rd Division, commanded by Major-General William Eyre (1805-59). Forcing their way into a suburb of Sevastopol, the troops suffered the highest rate of loss – 650 out of 1800 – of any British formation committed to action on 18 June. When in the evening a withdrawal was made, the small cemetery at the corner of the defile leading to the Man of War Harbour was retained, even though the Russians commanded it with their guns.

'Wounded Officers carried to the rear 18th June 1855'

Watercolour and pencil by Captain (later Colonel) Henry John Wilkinson (1829-1911), 1st Battalion, 9th (The East Norfolk) Regiment of Foot, 1855, 13.3cm. h x 21cm. w

Generously donated by the Royal United Service Institution

NAM. 1972-07-6-23

Wilkinson's watercolour is inscribed in pencil verso, 'Entrance to the Cemetery - Incident of the attack on Sebastopol 18th June 1855 Capt Agar Ellis 44th (?) Regt mortally wounded'; it shows the wounded officer - Captain The Honourable Charles Welbore Herbert Agar (1824-55), 44th (The East Essex) Regiment of Foot - lying on a litter addressing a colleague as he is carried from the field of battle. Although 'Ellis Agar' was one of the family surnames of the Earls of Normanton, The Honourable Charles Agar clearly did not assume it. Agar had joined the 44th Regiment as an ensign on 30 March 1844, purchased a lieutenancy on 27 February 1846 and his captaincy on 25 March 1853.

Minié Bullet, found in the cemetery outside Sevastopol, 1855

5.6cm. l x 3cm. w

Generously donated by Mr C C P Lawson

NAM. 1959-03-86

This 'splashed' lead Minié bullet has been flattened upon hitting an object after being fired. It was picked up by a J B Robert in the cemetery outside Sevastopol captured by Major-General William Eyre's Brigade on 18 June 1855. Robert sent it home in an envelope to his sister, but being made of lead and so heavy he commented in the accompanying note that he could only send one bullet on account of the expense of postage.

'18th Royal Irish Regt. Camp Sebastopol. May 1856'

Photograph by James Robertson, 18.5cm. h x 27cm. w

Generously donated by the Royal Irish Regiment Old Comrades Association

NAM. 1962-08-57

The 18th (Royal Irish) Regiment of Foot, part of Eyre's Brigade during the assault on Sevastopol of 18 June, was said to have run amok upon first breaking into the town. Certainly, Lieutenant-Colonel Clement Alexander Edwards (1812-82), pictured sitting towards the right with his cap on his knee, had felt that discipline needed to be improved upon taking command of the Regiment in March 1855: 'I am much afraid that it will be a long time before I can see the results of my endeavours for the improvement of the Regiment: the malady was too deep & of too long a standing to hope for any great sign of amendment, or any substantial change for the better, till the whole system is restored.'

Orders and Medals of General William Inglis, 1854-56

Order of the Bath, Badge of a Companion (CB) 1868; Crimea War Medal 1854-56, with clasps: Balaklava, Inkermann, Sebastopol; Legion of Honour, France, Badge of a Chevalier (5th Class) 1859; Order of the Mejidieh, Turkey, Badge of the 5th Class; Turkish Crimean War Medal 1855, Sardinian issue

Generously donated by the Inglis Family

NAM. 1965-02-163

William Inglis (1823-88), the son of the General Sir William Inglis who so memorably commanded the 57th (The West Middlesex) Regiment of Foot at Albuhera in 1811, was commissioned an ensign in his father's old regiment on 6 March 1840. Promoted captain in 1849, he served during the Crimean War at Balaklava, Inkerman, the Assault on the Redan (18 June 1855) and in the expedition to Kinburn. While in the Crimea he received the brevet ranks of major (1854) and lieutenant-colonel (1855) and was later created a Companion of the Order of the Bath. He retired with the rank of general in 1882.

'Lieut. Col. Shadforth & Officers of the 57th'

Photograph by Roger Fenton, 15cm. h x 20cm. w

Generally donated by Lieutenant-Colonel N Lovett

NAM. 1964-12-151-22

Among this group, Major William Inglis is seated far left and Lieutenant-Colonel Thomas Shadforth is standing third from the right. During the attack on the Redan on 18 June 1855, command of the left column of assault fell to Shadforth almost immediately, Major-General Sir John Campbell having been killed as soon as he left the trenches. Shadforth himself had barely time to give the order: 'Colonel Warre, you mind the right, I will take the left, and Major Inglis the centre', when he too fell dead. The attack quickly degenerated into a dismal failure.

'Sebastopol', *c*1855

Watercolour, signed lower right 'F Norie', by Frederick Norie, *c*1855, 16cm. h x 22.5cm. w

Generously donated by Group Captain L F Sealey

NAM. 1960-07-224-3

A watercolour showing British infantry advancing to the attack. The artist Frederick Norie is believed to have accompanied the Sardinian Army to the Crimea, painting a number of military scenes there in 1855.

Travelling medicine chest, *c*1854-55

32cm. h x 24cm. w x 20.5cm. d

Generously donated by Mrs E H Graham

NAM. 1964-11-2

Used by Surgeon Henry Fowle Smith of the Medical Staff in the Crimea.

Henry Fowle Smith (1823-1906) was born at Weyhill, Andover and qualified as a doctor at King's College, Aberdeen in 1850. Appointed Assistant Surgeon of the 16th (The Bedfordshire) Regiment of Foot in 1847, he became a Surgeon on the Staff on 12 January 1855, having been present at the battles of Alma, Balaklava and Inkerman. He was doctor to Major-General James Estcourt and was consulted during Lord Raglan's final illness. Although Alexander Kinglake in the later editions of his history *The Invasion of the Crimea* referred to it only indirectly, Smith had in 1877 provided him with his own explanation for Raglan's demise, which occurred on 28 June 1855:

The last sorrow which broke the heart of Lord Raglan, was General Estcourt's death. General Estcourt loved Lord Raglan, as one Brother loves another, and I have every reason to know that, that love was reciprocated. It is probable that if on the morning of the 24th June, Lord Raglan had heard that General Estcourt was better & likely to recover, the attack of depression with painless diarrhoea would not have come on, or would have passed off without any outward symptom.

Henry Fowle Smith retired with the honorary rank of Deputy Surgeon General in 1875.

Letter of Major-General Richard Airey on the death of Lord Raglan, 1855

Manuscript, 18.4cm. h x 11cm. w

NAM. 1962-10-94-1

Richard Airey, Raglan's Quartermaster-General, writing to Major-General George Wetherall on 4 July 1855, gave another explanation for his Commander-in-Chief's death. He could not forgive the persecution of Lord Raglan by two successive secretaries of state for war:

> To me Lord Raglan had always been all that confidence and affection could picture! He died of a broken Heart. Altho' he kept *it hid,* to me his mind was opened, and at night he spoke of nothing, [our rooms communicating with each other, but the shameful treatment he had experienced. ... The tone of both the Duke of Newcastle and Ld. Panmure, but most especially the latter, was not to be borne.]

Fragment from the wreath of immortelles (everlasting flowers) placed by General Pélissier on Field Marshal Lord Raglan's coffin during his funeral, 1855

Wreath of dried flowers on a lace-covered silk pad over a blue velvet cushion; contained in a red velvet-lined, domed-glass display case, maker unknown, *c*1855, 14.5cm. h x 18cm. w x 14cm. d

Generously donated by the Royal United Service Institution

NAM. 1963-10-276

Lord Raglan's coffin was draped with a Union Flag, upon which was placed his plumed hat and sword as well as a garland of immortelles, put there by General Pélissier, his French counterpart. Pélissier, ordinarily considered a brutal man, was strangely affected by Raglan's passing and wept copiously at his deathbed. In a General Order issued the day after, he paid tribute to the Commander-in-Chief of the Army of the East:

> The history of his life - so pure, so noble, so replete with service rendered to his country – those who witnessed his fearless demeanour at Alma and Inkerman, who recall the calm and stoic greatness of his character throughout this rude and memorable campaign, every generous heart indeed, will deplore the loss of such a man.

Medal commemorating the Death of Lord Raglan, 1855

Gilded-pewter, 41mm. diam

The obverse depicts a funerary plinth, upon which rests a heavy cavalry helmet, with a portrait of Raglan at the centre and battle honours: PENINSULA WATERLOO and CRIMEA. Raglan's name surrounds the plinth and at the base it is inscribed: BORN A.D. 1788. The reverse of the medal depicts an Army encampment in the Crimea, with the inscription: DIED IN THE SERVICE OF HIS COUNTRY AT HEAD QUARTERS BEFORE SEBASTOPOL JUNE 23RD 1855.

NAM. 1982-03-40

The incorrect date given for Raglan's death – which actually occurred on 28 June - is likely to be an error on the part of the engraver.

'Departure of the cortege for Lord Raglan's funeral', 1855

Pen and ink and watercolour, from an album of paintings, sketches and ephemera by Colonel (later General Sir) The Honourable George Cadogan (1814-80), 1st (or Grenadier) Regiment of Foot Guards, 1854-56, 17.7cm. h x 25.3cm. w

NAM. 1998-06-128-33

Following his death on 28 June 1855, Lord Raglan's body was returned to Britain on the *Caradoc*, attended with full military honours. According to the historian, Kinglake:

> The Allied commanders provided that before 4 o'clock on the afternoon of the 3rd July, the whole road from the English Headquarters to the port of Kazatch – a distance of about seven miles – should be lined on each side by double ranks of infantry… From the English to the French Headquarters the infantry lining the road was to be furnished by a contingent of officers and men told off for this honour from every one of our regiments, and beyond, along the remaining distance of six miles, by the Imperial Guard of the French and the troops of their First Corps. In the courtyard of what had been Lord Raglan's house there stood the Guard of Honour, one furnished by the Grenadier Guards, with the drums and regimental colours. In the vineyards adjoining were placed the bands of three regiments.

Lord Raglan was interred at the family home, Badminton House in Gloucestershire, on 26 July 1855.

'Lord Stratford distributing the Order of the Bath - at English Headquarters', 27 August 1855

Watercolour, pen and ink and pencil, from an album of paintings, sketches and ephemera by Colonel (later General Sir) The Honourable George Cadogan (1814-80), 1st (or Grenadier) Regiment of Foot Guards, 1854-56, 22.5cm. h x 35.2cm. w

NAM. 1998-06-128-43

The ceremony was held with the British Ambassador at Constantinople, Stratford Canning, First Viscount Stratford de Redcliffe (1786-1880), presiding. Rear-Admiral Sir Edmund Lyons (who prided himself on his physical resemblance to Nelson) is first in line to be invested a Knight Grand Cross of the Order of the Bath, followed by Major-General Sir Colin Campbell. Generals James Scarlett, William Eyre, Richard Airey and Henry Bentinck await their turn to become Knights Commander of the Order.

Orders and medals of Field Marshal Sir Colin Campbell, Lord Clyde, 1842-58

Order of the Bath, Star of a Knight Grand Cross (GCB) 1855; Military General Service Medal 1793-1814, with clasps: Vimiera, Corunna, Barrosa, Vittoria, St Sebastian; 1st China War Medal 1842; Punjab Campaign Medal 1848-49, with clasps: Goojerat, Chilianwala; Crimea War Medal 1854-56, with clasps: Alma, Balaklava, Sebastopol; Indian Mutiny Medal 1857-58, with clasps: Lucknow, Relief of Lucknow; Legion of Honour, France 1856, miniature badge of the 2nd Class (Grand Officer); Order of St Maurice and St Lazarus, Italy, Star of the First Class 1856; Order of the Mejidie, Turkey, Badge and Star of the First Class 1856; Turkish Crimean War Medal 1855, Sardinian issue

Generously donated by the Royal United Service Institution

NAM. 1964-01-9

The orders and medals of Field Marshal Sir Colin Campbell, Lord Clyde (1792-1863) include the GCB with which he was invested by Lord Stratford de Redcliffe in the Crimea on 27 August 1855. Campbell's medals bear testimony to his long and varied military service. He had first been commissioned in 1808 into the 9th (or the East Norfolk) Regiment of Foot with which he performed distinguished service during the Peninsular War.

By 1837 he was lieutenant-colonel of the 98th Regiment of Foot, which he commanded during the First China War (1842), before going to India as a brigadier-general in 1846. He remained there until 1853, having gained distinction in the 2nd Sikh War (1848-49). In the Crimea, having been promoted major-general on 20 June 1854, he commanded the Highland Brigade with notable success at the battles of the Alma and Balaklava; he later commanded a division. His career was crowned by his appointment as Commander-in-Chief in India for the suppression of the mutiny of the Bengal Army, 1858-59. He was ennobled as Lord Clyde in 1858 and promoted field marshal in 1862.

Major-General Sir Colin Campbell

Photograph by Roger Fenton

NAM. Negative 46937

In spite of his vast experience and his battlefield successes in the Crimea, Sir Colin Campbell never achieved command of the Army of the East, even though the list of alternative candidates to replace General Simpson in November 1855 was so short that the Government had to turn to Major-General Sir William Codrington, a man who had never heard a shot fired in anger until the Alma. Campbell was considered unfortunate to have been overlooked, and his case was pressed by Queen Victoria herself, but both the Commander-in-Chief of the Army, Lord Hardinge, and Lord Raglan before his death considered him unsuitable, either from a lack of subordination or for being too excitable. Indeed, Campbell could be intractable and the suspicion that he would find it difficult to cooperate with the French also told against him.

View of Sevastopol from the British Siegeworks, the Sailor's Battery and the Lancaster Gun Battery, 1855

Colour lithograph by and after Thomas Packer, number 13 in the series 'Packer's Panoramic Views of the Crimea', published by Stannard and Dixon, London, 13 August 1855, 44.2cm. h x 68.2cm. w

Generously donated by Mr Boris Mollo

NAM. 1974-01-71

The scale of the most important features in this panoramic view – the Russian defences of the Redan and the Malakhov, and the British and French advanced works at the Quarries and the Mamelon respectively – have of course been exaggerated, but the depiction nevertheless conveys a sense of the siege's impending climax as the long summer of 1855 wore on.

Letter of Lieutenant Thomas Harvey, 1855 (right)

Manuscript, 17.6cm. h x 22.5cm. w

NAM. 1997-07-47-44-4

Lieutenant (later Major) Thomas Peter Harvey (1837-73) was typical of the young officers who arrived as replacements as the Crimean War progressed. He was only sixteen years old when he was given a commission without purchase in the 77th (The East Middlesex) Regiment of Foot on 27 October 1854 and not quite seventeen and a half when he arrived in the Crimea as a lieutenant on 7 June 1855. His letter, written in July, betrays the confidence of youth in its recounting of narrow escapes and gruesome deaths.

'Charges preferred against Lieut. A W Kirby 19th Regt.', 1855 (left)

Manuscript, 33.8cm. h x 21cm. w

Generously donated by the Royal United Service Institution

NAM. 1968-07-376-4

Drunkenness amongst the troops was of widespread concern in the Crimea, but it was all the more shocking when an officer succumbed to inebriation. Lieutenant Arthur Wellesley Kirby had enlisted in the 19th (The 1st Yorkshire North Riding) Regiment of Foot under the name Frederick Arthur before being commissioned from the ranks on 5 November 1854. He was cashiered on 30 August 1855. In a letter commenting on the case, Major-General William Codrington noted that at the same time Lieutenant The Honourable Nathaniel Fiennes of the 23rd (Royal Welsh Fusiliers) Regiment of Foot had been arrested for suspected drunkenness, but had managed to escape being court-martialled:

> No doubt, he was not really sober at the time, but the scrape he was in sobered him well. Of course this will be put in the papers as sacrificing the man who rose from the ranks, Lt. Kirwan [sic], and saving the Honorable. ... Brownrigg told me that he heard of Lt. Kirwan saying, that if Queen Victoria did not do him justice, the Emperor of Russia should – meaning that he would desert!

Medals awarded to Private John Fahey, 3rd (East Kent) Regiment of Foot (The Buffs), 1854-56

Crimea War Medal 1854-56, with clasp: Sebastopol; Sardinian War Medal 1856; Turkish Crimean War Medal, British issue; Regimental Medal for Merit 1855, in silver

Generously donated by the Trustees of the Buffs Regimental Museum Trust

NAM. 2001-08-94

On 6 June 1856 the King of Piedmont-Sardinia authorised a silver medal to be awarded to 450 specially selected officers and men of the British naval and military forces who had fought in the Crimea. Some 400 of these went to the Army, and the first awards were made on 18 July to the Royal Artillery at Woolwich. Private John Fahey was one of only three members of the Buffs to receive the medal, the others being Colonel C T Van Straubenzee and Major G J Ambrose. The medal's design is similar to the Medal for Military Valour, instituted in 1833.

Medals awarded to Private John Connors VC, 3rd (The East Kent) Regiment of Foot (The Buffs), 1854-56

Crimea War Medal 1854-56, with clasp: Sebastopol; Médaille Militaire, France; Turkish Crimean War Medal, Sardinian issue; Silver Regimental Medal 1855, inscribed on the reverse 'FROM HIS COMRADES to Pte. J. Connors In recognition of his remarkable Gallantry during the assault on the Redan SEPT.8TH. 1855'

Generously donated by the Trustees of the Buffs Regimental Museum Trust

NAM. 2001-08-210

Private John Connors, 3rd (The East Kent) Regiment of Foot (The Buffs)

Daguerreotype

Generously donated by the Trustees of the
Buffs Regimental Museum Trust

NAM. 2001-08-480-1

John Connors, who is erroneously referred to as Joseph Connors in some sources, was born in County Kerry and enlisted on 8 January 1849, when he was described as a labourer. He earned the Victoria Cross for 'conspicuous courage and devotion during the assault on the Redan' on 8 September 1855. According to the citation, published in *The London Gazette* of 24 February 1857, Private Connors 'got inside the Redan at great personal risk, and seeing an officer of the 30th Regiment surrounded by the enemy, he rushed to his assistance. He immediately shot one of the Russians, ran his bayonet through another, and then for some time carried on a hand-to-hand encounter against great odds until support came.'

Before he could receive his Victoria Cross, Connors tragically died. It is believed he fell to his death from the battlements of Port Neuf, on the island of Corfu, where the Buffs were then garrisoned, on 29 January 1857. Connors is buried on the island. The whereabouts of his VC is not known and it is possible that his widow, then living in County Galway, never received it. This photograph is said to be of him.

Distinguished Conduct Medal, awarded to Corporal Michael Lynch, 3rd (East Kent) Regiment of Foot (The Buffs), 1855

Generously donated by the Trustees of the
Buffs Regimental Museum Trust

NAM. 2001-08-248

On the night of 31 August 1855, outside Sevastopol, a patrol of the Buffs under Captain Charles C Ross encountered a Russian picket. Michael Lynch carried back the mortally wounded Sergeant McCabe under heavy fire and for his gallantry was promoted corporal and awarded the Meritorious Service Medal (MSM) with an annuity of £5. He was subsequently awarded the Distinguished Conduct Medal (DCM) with a £5 gratuity for gallant conduct during the Second Assault on the Redan on 8 September, during which he was slightly wounded. It has been surmised that, in the event, Lynch received the DCM instead of, rather than in addition to, the MSM, although his name remained on the MSM Annuity Roll.

Report submitted by Lieutenant H D Radcliffe, 1 September 1855

Manuscript, 32.4cm. h x 20.8cm. w

Generously donated by the Royal United Service Institution

NAM. 1968-07-376-15

Herbert Delmé Radcliffe had been given a commission without purchase in the 23rd (Royal Welsh Fusiliers) Regiment of Foot by the Commander-in-Chief Lord Hardinge in recognition of the bravery of his elder brother, Lieutenant Frederick Peter Delmé Radcliffe, who had been killed while serving with the 23rd at the Alma. He was complimented for coolness of his own after submitting this report of a Russian sortie against the British trenches before Sevastopol on 30 August 1855. For others, however, what had happened provided an ominous foretaste of what might be expected of the inexperienced soldiers now filling the British ranks when the Redan was next assaulted. Captain Maxwell Earle of the 57th (The West Middlesex) Regiment of Foot was forthright in his condemnation: 'The sortie I mentioned was a disgraceful business. The 23rd threw down their arms and ran! The enemy was in our trench nearly an hour, took 100 gabions and filled our new trench. We lost 1off[icer] killed & 51 men K[illed] & W[ounded].'

'Charge of the 23rd at the Assault of the Redan September 8th 1855'

Pen and ink, from an album of Crimean and other sketches, by Lieutenant Herbert Delmé Radcliffe, 23rd (Royal Welsh Fusiliers) Regiment of Foot, 1855-58, 12.2cm. h x 18cm. w

NAM. 1992-07-18-21

The attack against the Redan had already stalled when, as a last desperate throw of the dice, Major-General Sir William Codrington sent forward a wing of the 23rd (Royal Welsh Fusiliers) Regiment of Foot. It was hoped that the 23rd might be able enter the Redan by its right face and get behind the Russian defenders, but when this attempt failed the rout of the British troops desperately trying to cling on inside the salient angle and along the outer slope of the Redan became inevitable. Among the wounded who managed to make their way back to the British trenches was the executor of this sketch, Lieutenant Delmé Radcliffe.

Letts Diary for 1855 of Lieutenant Fitzhardinge Kingscote

Print and Manuscript, 15.2cm. h x 21cm. w

Generously donated by Miss Katharine and Miss Dorothy Potter

NAM. 1973-11-170-3

Lieutenant (later Captain) Fitzhardinge Kingscote (1837-1900), a half-brother of the Major Nigel Kingscote who had been on Lord Raglan's personal staff, was first commissioned in the 41st (The Welsh) Regiment of Foot on 7 April 1854 and was promoted lieutenant on 6 November, nine days before he arrived in the Crimea. As the entry in his diary vividly illustrates, during the attack on the Redan on 8 September 1855 he was so badly wounded in the right arm that it had to be amputated. He nevertheless remained in the Army, transferring to the Rifle Brigade with which he served until his retirement in 1867.

Mameluke-hilted presentation sword, 1857

Landon, Morland and Landon, 92 cm. l

Generously donated by the Trustees of the
Buffs Regimental Museum Trust

NAM. 2001-04-270

Major (later General Sir) Frederick Francis Maude (1821-97) commanded the Buffs in the assault on the Redan on 8 September 1855. When the storming parties broke into the fortification, he and a small party penetrated the farthest, taking up an advanced position down the left side of the Redan. Only when dangerously wounded and all hope of support had receded did he retire. On its institution Maude was awarded the Victoria Cross (*London Gazette*, 24 February 1857). He later became a general, serving in India before retiring in 1885.

Although Maude was born in Armagh, his father was Rector of Enniskillen from 1825 to 1860. On his return to Ireland, and following his promotion to lieutenant-colonel, he was presented with this sword by the town of Enniskillen. Such swords were often presented by towns to famous sons and were usually supplied by military tailors or sometimes jewellers. The Mameluke hilt and curved blade was a favourite-style for presentation swords.

Spirit flask, *c*1855

Used by Lieutenant-Colonel (later General Sir) Frederick Francis Maude VC

11cm. l x 7cm. w x 14cm. h

Generously donated by the Trustees of the
Buffs Regimental Museum Trust

NAM. 2001-04-85

Sandwich case, *c*1855

James Dixon and Sons, 11cm. l x 7cm. w x 14cm. h

Generously donated by the Trustees of the
Buffs Regimental Museum Trust

NAM. 2001-04-86

Used by General Sir Frederick Francis Maude VC, this sandwich case is
not one of the canteens issued to the troops but was privately purchased.

Report of Captain Robert Grove, 1855

Manuscript, dated 9 September 1855, 18cm. h x
20.3cm. w

Generously donated by the Royal United Service Institution

NAM. 1968-07-376-18

Captain Robert Grove was with the storming party of the
90th Regiment of Foot (Perthshire Volunteers) (Light
Infantry) during the attack on the Redan, 8 September
1855. His report hints at the fact (which others made
more explicit) that not all the raw young troops behaved
well, taking advantage of any excuse to shelter in an
advanced trench. The failure to bring forward sufficient
scaling ladders meant that the men trying to get into the
Redan could only do so on too narrow a frontage:

> Some of the storming party of my left, seeing
> themselves in advance of ladders, took shelter
> awhile under the new sap, and my acting Major,
> (Capn Smith) begged for ladders to be brought
> & put down, but ladders were left in the new sap
> and never were taken to the front, excepting
> about 7 or 8 (and of this number I sent one
> chiefly with men of the 90th). At no time was
> there more than three ladders on the ennemy's
> side of the ditch.

'Brigadier Genl. Van Straubenzee & Officers of the Buffs', 1855

Photograph by Roger Fenton, 17.1cm. w x 16.9cm. h

Generously donated by Lieutenant-Colonel N Lovett

NAM. 1964-12-151-6-14

The 3rd (East Kent) Regiment of Foot (The Buffs) had arrived in the Crimea in May 1855. It took part in the attack on the Quarries on 7 June and was also heavily involved in the second attack on the Redan on 8 September. Brigadier-General (later General Sir) Charles Thomas Van Straubenzee (1812-92), seated in the centre and wearing the regulation undress frock coat, initially commanded the so-called 'Separate Brigade' and later the 1st Brigade of the Light Division.

'Tête d'Armée or how the British Generals stormed the Great Redan', 8 September 1855

Coloured tinted lithograph after Touchstone, published by Charles Moon and E Gambart and Co, London, October 1855, 29.1cm. h x 38.8cm. w

NAM. 1981-03-57

This caricature depicts General Sir James Simpson, Commander-in-Chief of the Army of the East following the death of Lord Raglan, Major-General Sir Henry David Jones, Royal Engineers, and Major-General Sir Richard Airey, Quartermaster-General. The attack on the Redan on 8 September was conducted during a high wind and the print reproduces an extract from *The Times* 'special' correspondent describing how the first subject drew his cloak up around his ears, the second was ill and sat in a litter wearing a red nightcap, whilst the third had a handkerchief tied over his cap.

'Dr Duigan attending the Wounded. Hospital in Sebastopol', 1855

Watercolour and pencil by Edward Angelo Goodall (1819-1908), 'special' artist for *The Illustrated London News, c*1855, published in *The Illustrated London News*, 6 October 1855 as 'Hospital in Sebastopol – Dr Durgan [*sic*] attending the wounded', 25cm. h x 35.2cm. w

NAM. 1991-12-107

As a Naval Assistant-Surgeon, David Duigan was amongst a group of medical officers in the bombardment of Bomarsund commended to the Commander-in-Chief as having 'evinced the greatest willingness and promptitude in the execution of the work of their duties'. Promoted surgeon in 1854, Duigan's reports record the close co-operation which existed between Army and Navy medical officers in the field.

Upon the fall of Sevastopol, Dr Duigan was one of the doctors who attended some of the patients in the Russian hospital in the long-besieged town. According to Nathaniel Steevens of the 88th Regiment of Foot (Connaught Rangers), the patients in the hospital by the Dockyard Creek were not discovered until the day after the Allies occupied the town:

> The scene that presented itself is too horrible to describe; there was a flag of truce, and the Russian wounded were removed. Captain Hutton (97th Regiment) was found among the dead in this hospital, in an emaciated condition; and Captain Vaughan of the same regiment was discovered, badly wounded, trying to crawl downstairs to get water, being, poor fellow, quite delirious from privation and exhaustion, having been stripped of almost everything.

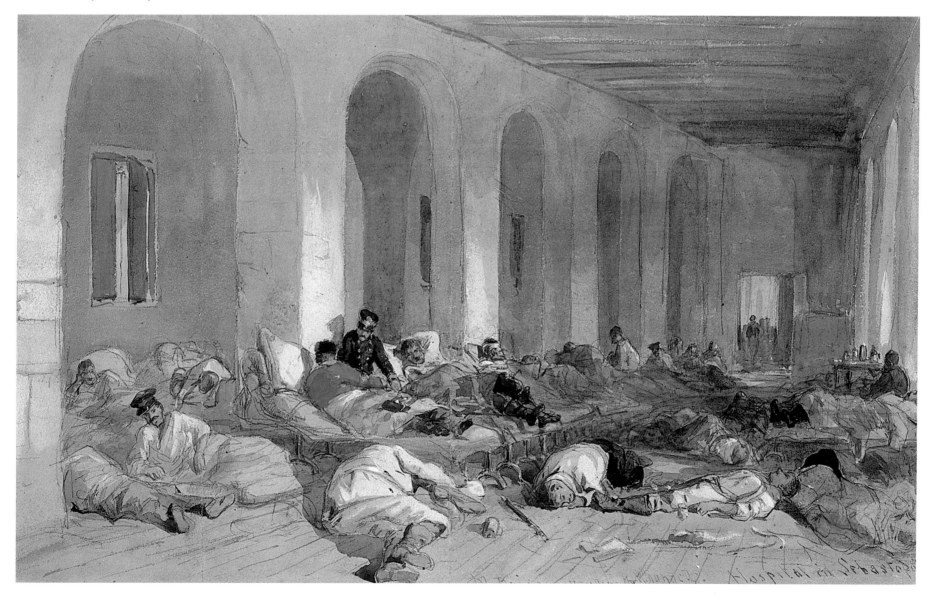

'Sebastopol (Storming of the Great Redan)' 8 September 1855

Coloured tinted lithograph after artist unknown, from 'The Officers' Portfolio of the Striking Reminiscences of the War from Drawings, Photographs and Notes, taken on the spot, made into Complete Pictures by Eminent Artists', published by Dickinson Brothers, London, *c*1855, 29.8cm. h x 79.9cm. w

Crookshank Collection, transferred from the British Museum

NAM. 1971-02-33-360

After the French had captured the Malakhov, the British attacked the Redan. Although they managed to break into the fortification, the British were pinned down by Russian troops firing from behind a barricade at the rear of the Redan. In spite of the efforts made by Major-General (later Lieutenant-General Sir) Charles Ash Windham (1810-70) to encourage his men to advance, they were unable to do so and eventually had to retreat. Windham is shown towards the rear of the picture, dressed in blue and waving his hat.

Officer's Coatee, Full Dress, *c*1831-55 and Officer's Epaulettes, *c*1850

3rd (The East Kent) Regiment of Foot (The Buffs)

Wool cloth, gilt-metal buttons; gilt-metal

Generously donated by the Trustees of the
Buffs Regimental Museum Trust

NAM. 2001-10-134, -1, -4,

John Lewes, whose items of uniform these were, was first commissioned into the Buffs in 1847 and was a captain when he went out to the Crimea in 1855. During the assault on the Redan on 8 September he commanded the Buffs covering party, comprising the best shots in the Regiment. He was anxious that his services should be recognised, writing to Major William Fyers of the Rifle Brigade the day afterwards: 'With respect to my covering party, it is I think needless to say they did their duty well, as you must have seen them yourself and I trust in your report on the subject you will do us the justice to say we did our duty.' He signed off with the words 'Hoping that the conduct of my party has merited the approbation of the General Commanding.' Placed on half pay as a major on 1 February 1856, the following year Lewes joined the 2nd West India Regiment of Foot, purchasing his lieutenant-colonelcy in the 3rd West India Regiment on 7 May 1858. He returned to half pay in 1859, finally retiring in 1860.

'The Fall of Sebastopol, 1856'

Watercolour by William Simpson (1823-99), 1856, 53.8cm. h x 99.1cm. w

Bequeathed by Henry Edward Hugh, 9th Duke of Newcastle

NAM. 1992-01-130

This atmospheric watercolour shows Russian soldiers evacuating Sevastopol either across an overcrowded pontoon bridge or by boat to the north side of the harbour on the night of 8-9 September 1855. The heavens above Sevastopol are lit-up by the burning city, put to the torch by the retreating Russian forces. Measuring 53.8 x 99.1cm., this is the largest known example of the artist's work and was purchased directly from him for the considerable sum of £60 by Henry Pelham Pelham-Clinton, 5th Duke of Newcastle (1811-64) and Secretary of State for War in the Government of Lord Aberdeen. The watercolour was subsequently reproduced as a chromolithograph by Day and Son and published by Colnaghi's on 28 January 1857, with a dedication to the Duke.

Joseph Archer Crowe, 'special' artist for *The Illustrated London News*, included a vivid description of the evacuation of the naval base in his autobiography. He noted that the Russians:

> being convinced that they had lost the key of the position, they set to work under cover of the darkness and moved the whole garrison of Sebastopol from the south to the north side, only breaking up their bridge at Fort Paul at daybreak when nothing was left but a number of wounded who were afterwards taken away under a flag of truce. For some hours the work of retreat was carried on with as little noise and as much speed as possible. The ships in harbour were sunk, and then the torch was applied to the buildings and everything inflammable began to burn… Flames were rising or bursting in every direction. The ships which had floated so long in our sight within the harbour had disappeared, and their mastheads were to be seen above the water.

'A Welcome Arrival', c1855

Oil on canvas, signed and dated lower right 'J D Luard 1857', by John Dalbiac Luard (1830-60), 1857, exhibited at the Royal Academy 1857 No. 133, 76.2cm. h x 100cm. w

Generously donated by Mrs Dulci Luard

NAM. 1958-08-18

Born into a military family, the artist John Dalbiac Luard had passed through Sandhurst and served with the 63rd (The West Suffolk) Regiment of Foot and then the 82nd (The Prince of Wales's Volunteers) Regiment of Foot before selling his commission as a lieutenant in January 1854 in order to take up painting as his profession. In the winter of 1855-56 Luard travelled to the Crimea in order to produce sketches of the war and to visit his brother, Captain Richard Amherst Luard (b. 1827) of the 77th (The East Middlesex) Regiment of Foot, who is believed to be the central figure in the painting. The figure on the right has never been positively identified, but may be a self-portrait of the artist, who in a letter to his father recounted how he had witnessed the unpacking of a box of supplies while visiting his former regiment, the 82nd Regiment of Foot.

For officers at least, the arrival of parcels from home was a welcome relief from the monotony and privations of life in camp. Those depicted here can be seen unpacking bottles and tins as well as articles of warm clothing. The walls of their hut are decorated with pages from *The Illustrated London News*, an indication of an attempt to make it more homely.

In the centre of the painting, asleep on a table behind the stove, is a cat, long popularly identified as 'Crimean Tom', the pet rescued from the ruins of Sevastopol and brought back to England by Deputy Assistant Commissary William Gair. Extrapolating from the uncertain to the unknown, it was posited in turn that Gair was the officer on the left of the painting examining a miniature or photographic image of loved-ones at home. However, there is no evidence to substantiate either of these claims.

Door-knob taken from a house in Sevastopol, 1855

6.5cm. w x 3cm. h

Generously donated by the Reverend Penelope Rundle

NAM. 1998-06-16

After the Russian evacuation of the south side of Sevastopol on the night of 8-9 September, parties of men were seen streaming towards the abandoned town. As Captain Maxwell Earle of the 57th (The West Middlesex) Regiment of Foot put it:

> Then came the pillaging parties, the burying parties, the police and provost parties, the picquet parties and in fact every kind of party which was ever formed. Plunder soon arrived - horses, dogs, cats, men, carriages, sacerdotal robes, plain clothes, military *do,* cloth, furniture of every description, muskets and accoutrements, in fact every thing which you might expect to find in a town like Sebastopol.

William Smith Rodway of the Naval Brigade helped himself to this decorative glass door-knob.

Padlock, taken from Sevastopol's Arsenal Gate, 1855

Cast iron, 18cm. l x 10cm. w

Generously donated by the Royal United Service Institution

NAM. 1959-07-152

This padlock secured the Arsenal's gate at Sevastopol. It was taken as a trophy after the fall of the town on 8-9 September 1855.

Officer's Epaulette, *c*1854

Russian 44th Infantry Regiment

Cloth, gold wire and gold bullion

Generously donated by the Royal United Service Institution

NAM.1960-09-123

This epaulette was reputedly retrieved from the Redan after the fall of Sevastopol.

Sights from a Russian gun captured at the Redan, 1855

10cm. l x 6cm. w x 5.5cm. h (front sight, -1); 8cm. l x 6.2cm. w x 3.8cm. h (back sight, -2)

Generously donated by the Royal United Service Institution

NAM. 1963-10-220-1 & -2

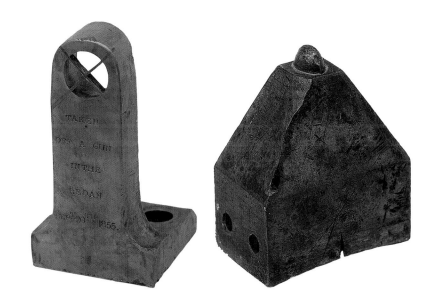

Russian Pioneer Sword, Pattern 1827

71cm. l

Generously donated by Miss P N Steevens

NAM 1965-01-184-1

Typical of pioneer swords carried by most European armies during the nineteenth century, the sword is more of a tool than a weapon. The heavy saw-backed blade was used for cutting down small trees and shrubs. The weapon was brought home by Captain (later Lieutenant-Colonel) Nathaniel Steevens, 88th Regiment of Foot (Connaught Rangers), who was appointed a town major after the fall of Sevastopol.

Russian Other Rank's Helmet Plate, *c*1855 (below)

Russian, 26th Infantry Regiment

Generously donated by Lieutenant-Colonel H F N Jourdain

NAM. 1960-05-73-2

Full-dress for Russian infantry entailed wearing the tall *pickelhaube*-style leather helmet, although most Russian soldiers in the Crimea wore the soft fatigue cap instead. The brass helmet plate, with the Russian double-headed eagle perched on an Amazon shield, the edging lined and beaded, and two decorative curls to each side, was common to all infantry regiments; only the regimental number, which in the case of officers was picked out in silver, was subject to change.

Helmet Plate, *c*1855 (left)

42nd Russian Naval Detachment

NAM. 1963-10-335

The pair of anchors, situated behind the double-headed eagle to either side, identify this helmet plate as belonging to a naval detachment.

Russian ammunition pouch, *c*1854

25.5cm. l x 15.5cm. w x 7cm. d

Generously donated by Lieutenant-Colonel A Blunt

NAM. 1961-12-28-1

Russian infantry ammunition pouch with a brass grenade badge, which is likely to indicate a Fusilier regiment. The pouch would be carried slung by a cross belt over the left shoulder and would normally contain 40 paper wrapped cartridges fitted in a drilled wooden block. A tool pouch, which contained a screwdriver and cleaning rags, is sewn on the front of the pouch.

Russian cartouche box captured at Sevastopol, *c*1855

25cm. l x 9cm. w x 9cm. h

Generously donated by Lieutenant-Colonel H F N Jourdain

NAM. 1960-05-73

A brass Russian naval cartouche, or cartridge, box captured by Lieutenant George Priestly, 88th Regiment of Foot (Connaught Rangers) at Sevastopol in 1855.

Priestly served in the Crimea from the 17 June 1855. The day after his arrival in the Crimea, he took part in the first assault on the Redan and on the 8 September 1855 he commanded the Grenadier Company in the second assault. He was awarded the Crimea War Medal with the clasp for Sevastopol and also the Sardinian and Turkish Crimea Medals. He later served in the suppression of the mutiny of the Bengal Army, 1857-58.

Dispatch pouch, 1855

33.5cm. l x 21.8cm. w

Generously donated by the Royal United Service Institution

NAM. 1959-07-151

Russian chair from Sevastopol, *c*1855

152cm. h x 70cm. w x 75cm. d

Generously donated by the Royal United Service Institution

NAM. 1978-12-15

Russian chair taken from Sevastopol by men of the 88th Regiment of Foot (Connaught Rangers) as a trophy after the capture of the town in 1855. The chair, a piece of travelling furniture which can be dismantled (without the need for tools) by removal of the bosses holding it together, was later part of the Officer's Mess furniture of the 88th Regiment. The original leather back (NAM. 1956-02-955) was removed in 1906 by H F N Jourdain.

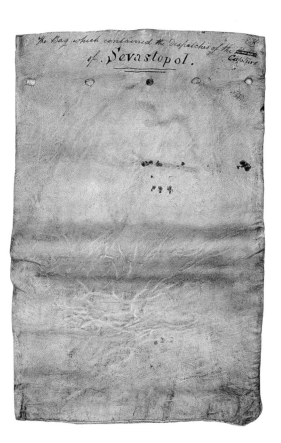

Almost a year after the opening of the siege and with heavy loss of life on both sides, Sevastopol fell into the hands of the Allies. This pouch, which belonged to Lieutenant-General Sir James Simpson, contained the dispatches announcing the capture of the town on 8-9 September 1855. The dispatches were brought home by his Assistant Military Secretary, Major The Honourable Leicester Curzon of the Rifle Brigade.

Pass allowing entry to Sevastopol, 1855

Printed and manuscript, 10.2cm. h x 19.2cm. w

Bequeathed by Mr R E Balfour

NAM. 1973-06-11-1

To prevent a continuation of looting, admission to Sevastopol was regulated by pass within a week of the fall of the town. There were a large number of Warrens in the Army in 1855 and it has not been possible to identify which of them was the recipient of this pass.

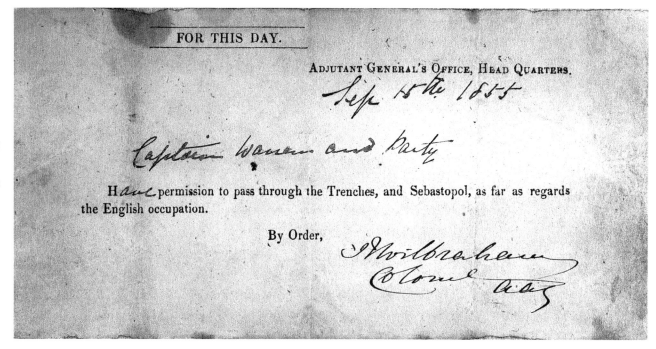

French pass allowing admission to Sevastopol, 1855

Printed and manuscript, 11.3cm. h x 15.8cm. w

Generously donated by Lieutenant-Colonel A Monro

NAM. 1958-04-32-13

The French had been more tolerant of looting in Sevastopol at the outset but jealously guarded entry to their own sector of the town.

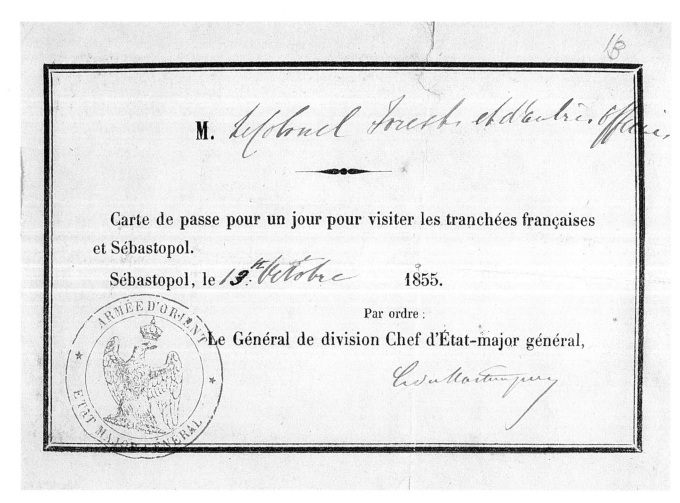

Order in Council for Prayers, 24 September 1855

Printed, 39.2cm. h x 31.3cm. w

NAM. 1994-09-124-1

'A Form of Prayer and Thanksgiving to Almighty God .. for the Capture of the Town of Sebastopol', 1855

Printed, 21.5cm. h x 17cm. w

NAM. 1968-07-394-2

Events during the Crimean War had already been the subject of Days of Prayer even before the fall of Sevastopol. The Proclamation of a Fast in April 1854 had been well-observed, but when in March 1855 a 'Public Day of Solemn Fast, Humiliation and Prayer' was announced 'in order to obtain pardon of our sins' the response of the populace was one of indignation: if the War was going badly, it was the Government's fault, not that of the people. Thereafter, the reception afforded Days of Prayer was more jaundiced, *The Reasoner* newspaper commenting with heavy irony how: 'Instead of a new prayer by the Archbishop of Canterbury for the success of our failing arms in the Crimea, we had a Committee of Inquiry.'

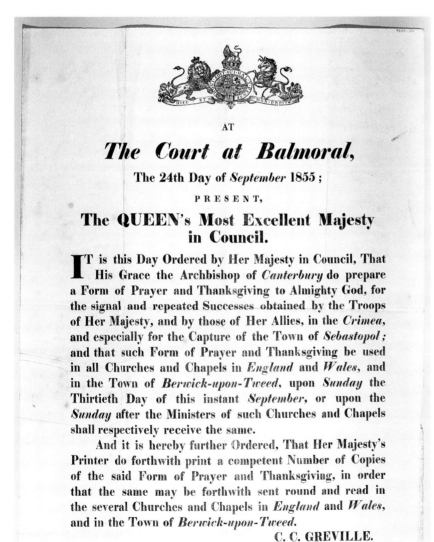

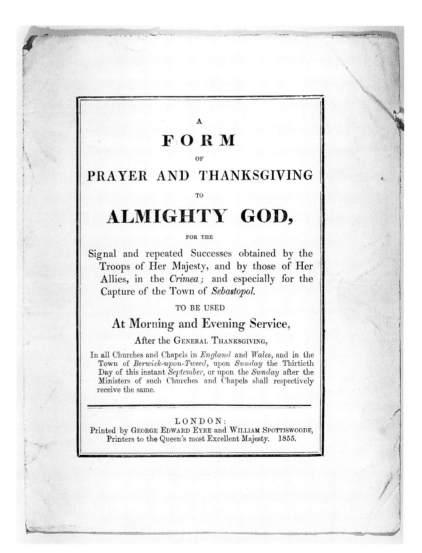

Stuffed cat, 'Crimean Tom', *c*1855

54cm. l x 13cm. w x 22cm. h

Generously donated by Lady Compton MacKenzie

NAM. 1958-02-27

This tabby cat, known as 'Crimean Tom', was one of the survivors of the fall of Sevastopol. He was rescued from the ruins by Deputy Assistant Commissary William Gair, who brought him back to England as a pet. When Tom died on 31 December 1856, his skin was stuffed and mounted.

Medals awarded to Deputy Assistant Commissary William Gair, 1854-58

Crimea War Medal 1854-56, with clasps: Alma, Balaklava, Inkermann, Sebastopol; Indian Mutiny Medal 1857-58; Turkish Crimean War Medal 1855, Sardinian issue

Generously donated by Mrs C A McDowall

NAM. 1973-02-24

William Gair served as a Deputy Assistant Commissary, Field Train Department in the Crimea. In 1857 he was commissioned an ensign into the 3rd West India Regiment, transferring as a cornet in 1858 to the 6th Regiment of Dragoon Guards (Carabineers), with which he served in India during the suppression of the mutiny of the Bengal Army. In 1864, as a captain, he joined the 77th (The East Middlesex) Regiment of Foot and remained in service until his death on 30 July 1867.

Art and War Reportage in the Crimean War II:
William Simpson, Carlo Bossoli and recreational artists of the Crimean War

Emma Armstrong

> At dinner Lord Clarence[1] explained the difference between his going into action and my doing the same thing. He would be doing his duty, and if a shell struck him he would be a "hero", whereas, as I had no business there, if a shell struck me I would be called a "fool".
>
> (from William Simpson's autobiography)[2]

While special correspondents sent to the Crimea for the illustrated journals produced the bulk of images of the conflict, they were not by any means the only artists to make visual records of the war in the east. A number of publishers followed the newspapers' lead, employing professional artists such as William Simpson and Carlo Bossoli to make drawings on the spot which would satisfy the public demand for pictures of the war. Furthermore, serving officers who, until the advent of illustrated press in the 1840s, had produced nearly all the eyewitness illustrations of the Army on campaign, continued to sketch in the field.

Within a year of its foundation in 1741, the Royal Military Academy, Woolwich employed drawing-masters to instruct officers so that they could make topographical sketches and maps while on reconnaissance. When the Military College at Great Marlow opened in 1802, it too included drawing as part of its military training. This practice was continued when the College moved to Sandhurst in 1812, and was introduced at the East India Company's Military Seminary at Addiscombe from 1813. The key skill taught was the ability to simplify a landscape to its significant features and express them in two dimensions, to scale, as part of a training in topographical reconnaissance. The majority of the officers who kept sketchbooks did so for their own amusement, or as visual records of their experiences for their families; but a number realised that their drawings might have commercial possibilities.

The invention of lithography at the very end of the eighteenth-century, which enabled print-makers to produce near-faithful facsimile copies of paintings and drawings quickly and economically, precipitated an enormous expansion in the print trade. More versatile than traditional relief or intaglio printing techniques such as engraving, lithography could reproduce the qualities of a variety of media such as ink, pencil or chalk, with the minimum of alteration. By this process, artists draw or paint in a greasy lithographic crayon or ink directly onto a smooth porous printing surface such as stone. The stone is then treated with acid, gum arabic and water so that the printing ink, when applied, is drawn to the greasy lines of the drawing, but repelled by the wet stone. By the mid-1830s, a new type of lithographic process had been developed which enabled printers to suggest the delicate and subtly graded washes of watercolour by printing in coloured tints. Tinted lithography employed separate printing stones inked with pale colours such as fawn, grey and blue to construct the image using tone in addition to line. However, other colours still had to be added in watercolour, if required.

The speed of the lithographic technique enabled high quality prints of sketches drawn in the Crimea to be published within a month of the events depicted. In view of the fact that newspaper reports often took about three weeks to publish, this meant that print publishers could keep up with them and exploit the news value of their subjects. The majority of these cheap lithographic prints were designed to cater to the same middle-class market as the illustrated press. Lithography, in addition, was used in conjunction with hand colouring to produce more exclusive print editions, which were usually sold in bound sets incorporating explanatory text with the images. These more elaborate productions did not need to rely on the news-worthiness of their subjects, but had a greater longevity as souvenirs of the war.

On 1 September 1856, Thomas McLean published one such volume entitled, 'A Series of Views in Turkey and the Crimea from The Embarkation at Gallipoli to the Fall of Sebastopol, from the original sketches taken on the spot by Lieut: Col: Andrews, late 28th Regiment'. It was marketed as a superior product through its dedication to the Duke of Newcastle and by the list of subscribers who had supported its publication, a quarter of whom were members of the aristocracy, and a half army officers. Indeed, officers returning from the Crimea and their families at home accounted for an important part of the market for prints reproducing the work of military personnel. Many of these prints in the National Army Museum have such a provenance. For instance, the copy of a panoramic view of Sevastopol after Lieutenant (later Captain) Ernest Augustus Perceval, 88th Regiment of Foot (Connaught Rangers) was owned by Captain (later Lieutenant-Colonel) Nathaniel Steevens, a fellow-officer of Perceval's regiment.[3] This bound lithograph, which folds out to a staggering length of 504.2cms., published by M & N Hanhart on 10 March 1857, is of a military topographical style which would have appealed to officers who had spent so many months besieging the city. Both men had served at the Siege of Sevastopol, the attack on the Quarries on 7 June, and in the two attacks on the Redan on the 18 June and 8 September 1855.

Those officers who drew for publication usually worked up sketches on the spot into watercolours which they later bound into albums to make visual diaries of their life on campaign. Captain (later General Sir) Michael Anthony Shrapnel Biddulph (1823-1904), Royal Artillery, who was described in an article in *Vanity Fair* as 'an ardent admirer of

Nature, whom he truthfully paints with water colours and much appreciative skill',[4] compiled one such album.[5] Inscribed 'From Trewarren (Pembrokeshire)/ Milford Haven/ to Corsica/ to the Crimea via Gibraltar/ to/ Corfu + India/ 1854 to 1861', the volume is filled with pages from his sketchbooks and annotated with comments and recollections of scenes that he had witnessed on his travels. However, apart from an accomplished portrait of a fellow officer by another hand, most of Biddulph's sketches remain characteristic examples of military draughtsmanship, informative but lacking in detail or atmosphere.

In contrast, the topographical studies after Biddulph's drawings, published as small volumes by Edward Stanford and Chapman & Hall and priced at four shillings, display a little more vibrancy. In one such volume entitled, 'Assault of Sevastopol. Two topographical & panoramic sketches, representing the advanced lines of attack, and the Russian defences, in front of Sevastopol, with a description and remarks', the publisher acknowledges the technical rather than decorative nature of the illustrations, commenting that they '… were drawn, as we are assured, with the most rigid faithfulness, no sacrifice being made to picturesque effect; and they have been accurately copied by the lithographer.'[6] The authenticity of the illustrations as on-the-spot records of the conflict, is reinforced by reference to Biddulph's journal in the text, recording such incidents as when '… a Minié ball passed through my plaid, making four holes in the folds, and through my pocket, a cigar-case, and a pair of gloves; and then, alas! struck Martin, who was just behind me'.[7] Biddulph also submitted sketches to Paul and Dominic

Colnaghi, the well-known London art dealers, who published his work with astonishing rapidity. The caption to 'Siege of Sevastopol from the new 32 Pounder Battery above the left attack Picquet House', published on 17 November 1854, refers to a letter enclosed with the sketch which Biddulph dated just 15 days prior to publication.[8] Moreover, some of his work received official sanction, for example his 'View of the Country in front of Balaklava. Representing the scene of the memorable Light Cavalry Charge, 25th October, 1854, with the Russian Outposts at Kamara' which was lithographed and printed at the Topographical and Statistical Depot of the War Department.[9]

Another artist who achieved a degree of commercial success with his illustrations of the Crimean War was Lieutenant (later Colonel) Henry John Wilkinson (1829-1911), 1st Battalion, 9th (The East Norfolk) Regiment of Foot. *The Illustrated London News* reproduced a number of Wilkinson's drawings, including 'The Siege of Sebastopol – Burial of the dead in front of the Malakoff Tower', published on 21 April 1855,[10] while Paul and Dominic Colnaghi published one of his panoramas of Sevastopol on 21 August 1855.[11] Wilkinson was a prolific amateur artist, whose legacy includes a number of drawings and watercolours in the Collection of the National Maritime Museum in Greenwich and 98 in the National Army Museum, all of the latter Crimean subjects. These sketches are of variable technical ability and range from quick, well-observed studies drawn on small sketchbook pages in pencil or pen and ink, to larger, detailed scenes such as the gardens and architecture of Malta rendered by a delicate use of watercolour over pencil. One

'Looking down the Ravine which divides the right and left attacks'.
Lithograph by Day & Son after Captain (later General Sir) Michael Anthony Shrapnel Biddulph (1823-1904),
published by Chapman & Hall, London, 1855.
NAM. 1972-03-8-2-2

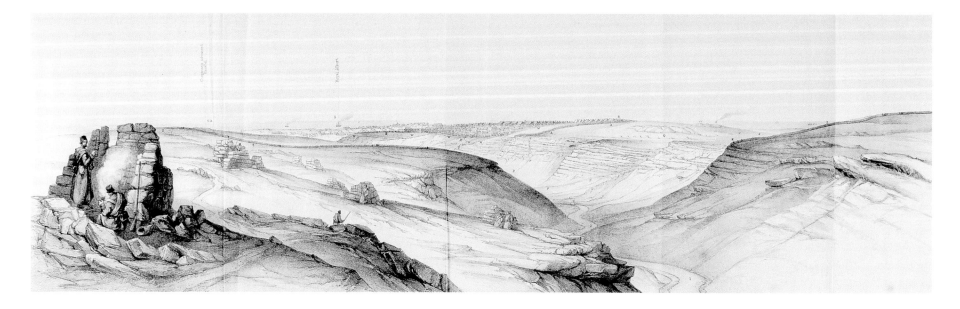

such study, which appears to be a frontispiece design for a collection of illustrations, suggests that Wilkinson intended to publish a volume of Crimean prints.[12] However, the project was never realised.

'Sketches in the Crimea Sebastopol by Capt H.J.Wilkinson.ix Regt.'
Watercolour and pen and ink by Captain (later Colonel) Henry John Wilkinson (1829-1911), 1st Battalion, 9th (The East Norfolk) Regiment of Foot, c1855. NAM. 1972-07-6-74

Although a number of soldiers in the Crimea were ambitious to get themselves published, many others drew for their own pleasure and that of their friends and families. These recreational artists generally chose panoramic landscapes or light-hearted scenes of camp life as their subject matter, recording their studies in small, portable sketchbooks. Pasted into one such album are the drawings of Lieutenant (later Captain) Herbert (also referred to as Hubert) Delmé Radcliffe, 23rd (Royal Welsh Fusiliers) Regiment of Foot, who served in the Crimea at the Siege of Sevastopol from February 1855.[13] The small pages of drawings, torn from a pocket notebook, give a charming insight into the more humorous aspects to life in the Crimea. In drawing such light-hearted scenes, officers might achieve a cathartic escape from the dangers and privations of war. A sketch entitled, 'Assault by the 2nd Brigade, my capture by the Connaught Rangers' shows a snowball fight, during which the unfortunate artist was carried off by the 'enemy', whilst in another captioned 'Nobbling the thief', a surprised Radcliffe is shown entering his tent to find a cat in the act of stealing his food.

Although most of the studies executed by officers in the Crimea were essentially diagrammatic and topographical rather than decorative, several military men were particularly skilful in their sketching. Indeed, some of their drawings appear more finished than those of the special correspondents, whose work needed to be hurriedly completed before dispatch to publishers in London. One such amateur was Captain (later General Sir) The Honourable George Cadogan (1814-80), 1st (or Grenadier) Regiment of Foot Guards. Educated at Eton College, Cadogan would have received instruction from the college drawing master William Evans (1798-1877), a talented watercolourist who exhibited 264 paintings at the Society of Painters in Water Colours. A scrapbook of Cadogan's work in the National Army Museum Collection contains over 100 watercolours by this prolific artist.[14] A visual journal of his service in the Crimea, the volume includes the Battles of the Alma, Balaklava and Inkerman, in the last of which he took a prominent part, followed by an insight into his military service as Queen's Commissioner to the Sardinian Army in the Crimea from 2 April 1855, until its withdrawal in May 1856. The studies are mostly figurative rather than topographical, including portraits of such notable figures as Florence Nightingale, Major-General Sir William Codrington, Major-General Charles Ash Windham and Major-General Sir Colin Campbell. Although Cadogan's work was comparable to that of many professional artists and of a higher standard than that of any of the officers whose work was reproduced, it appears that he neither exhibited nor published his work. As a member of the aristocracy and an officer in an elite regiment, such a commercial venture may not have been thought appropriate. Nevertheless, the album stands as one of the most accomplished visual descriptions of the campaign.

Undoubtedly the most celebrated of the civilian artists who recorded the war was William Simpson (1823-99). As a lithographer working in London, Simpson constructed his first illustrations of the Crimean War from newspaper accounts. However, when commissioned to produce an image of the Fall of Sevastopol in anticipation of the event, he found it an impossible task since there were no images of the city to be had in London on which to base his illustration. Similarly, he noted that even the language of war used by the newspapers was unfamiliar to the general public, 'Here they are making "gabions", "fascines", "traverses", &c. What are these? No one knows. If I were there I could send sketches of them, so that every one would understand'.[15] Thus, in response to the growing demand for authentic images of the conflict, the print publishers, Colnaghi's, commissioned Simpson to undertake the journey to the Crimea in October 1854.

'The artist's room at the Sardinian Head Quarters, Kadikoi'.
Watercolour by Captain (later General Sir) The Honorable George Cadogan (1814-80),
1st (or Grenadier) Regiment of Foot Guards, c1855.
NAM. 1998-06-128-73

As a special artist, Simpson found himself in a different category from the special correspondents for the press. His work was viewed by the military administration as documentary rather than political. He commented in his autobiography that, while special correspondents were 'much courted and much hated. I escaped all this. Everyone was friendly to me, and I was welcomed wherever I went.[16] Since the authorities controlled every aspect of life on campaign, including access to food and shelter, as well as movement round the battlefields, this official sanction was enormously valuable.

In return for submitting his drawings to Lord Raglan and his staff for approval, the artist was permitted to send his work to his publishers in

Raglan's official letter-bag, which ensured their prompt and safe delivery to London. On their arrival, Simpson's drawings were examined by the Secretary of State for War, Henry Pelham Pelham-Clinton, 5th Duke of Newcastle (1811-64), and then Queen Victoria, before being lithographed. This official scrutiny did not deter Simpson from depicting the appalling conditions under which the army in the east laboured, nor were his illustrations of such subjects as 'Commissariat Difficulties. The Road from Balaklava to Sebastopol, at Kadikoi, during the wet weather' and 'Embarkation of the Sick at Balaclava' subject to censorship.

In an effort to achieve verisimilitude in his depictions of battles which had taken place prior to his arrival, Simpson was frustrated by the

'Light Cavalry Charge 25th Octr 1854'.
Watercolour, pen and ink and pencil, signed lower left 'Wm Simpson', by William Simpson (1823-99), 1854.
NAM. 1961-08-4-1

inconsistencies in eyewitness accounts of battles, recalling in his autobiography, 'I had my first experience as to how men who have been actors in an event will differ in their descriptions'.[17] However, for Simpson, 'Accuracy was a point I aimed at'.[18] To this end, when Lord Cardigan said of the artist's sketch for the print 'Charge of the Light Cavalry Brigade. 25th Oct. 1854 under Major General The Earl of Cardigan', 'It is all wrong,'[19] Simpson submitted two more versions before gaining his approval. When this was achieved, the artist, '… was rewarded with the warmest praise, and was able to send it home with the expression of Lord Cardigan's highest admiration. The real truth was that in the last sketch I had taken greater care than in the first two to make his lordship conspicuous in the front of the Brigade'.[20] The watercolour of this scene in the National Army Museum is thought to be one of those rejected by Cardigan, since the finished print shows the angle of the line of cavalry altered to make him more prominent.[21]

Although originally commissioned to produce 32 plates for Colnaghi's, the prolongation of the war led to the publication of 80 of Simpson's watercolours in two volumes under the title 'The Seat of War in the East'. The initial series of 40 prints was published in parts in the spring of 1855 and as a folio edition in June of that year, while the folio of the second set of 40 was published in March 1856.[22] The folios were priced at ten pounds and twelve shillings coloured, or six pounds and twelve shillings plain. This was an enormous sum considering that Simpson recorded, 'I think I was paid £20 for each drawing, but paid my own expenses of travelling, etc'.[23] The project was an enormous commercial success for Colnaghi's, realising a clear profit of £12,000.[24] The publishers retained the originals which they later sold and, according to Simpson, they 'no doubt received as much as they gave me for them, so that they had the copyright for nothing'.[25]

Charge of the Light Brigade. 25th Oct. 1854. under Major General the Earl of Cardigan'.
Coloured tinted lithograph by E Walker after William Simpson (1823-99),
published by Paul & Dominic Colnaghi in the first series of 'The Seat of War in the East', London, 1855.
NAM. 1971-02-33-490-15

In his account of the war, William Howard Russell of *The Times* referred to 'the admirable sketches of Mr Simpson, which form, perhaps, the best history of the Crimean expedition in its picturesque aspect'.[26] The high regard in which Simpson's work was held is reflected in Francis Wemyss, Lord Elcho's attempt to secure them for the nation. That he failed to do so was due to the antipathy felt towards watercolour as a medium employed by amateur artists, which moreover had the propensity to fade over time. Besides, the common view was that the originals of these works had been devalued by having been reproduced.[27] Nevertheless, with this print series, Simpson made his name as a pioneering war reporter, and was known henceforth as 'Crimean Simpson'.

On 1 August 1856, Day & Son, the lithographers of Simpson's print series, published a lavish print series of the Crimean War. This production, after the work of the Italian artist Carlo Bossoli (1815-84), was entitled 'The Beautiful Scenery and Chief Places of Interest throughout the Crimea'.[28] Bossoli was a professional artist who was born in Lugano and had spent much of his life travelling in Europe, painting in the Crimea *circa* 1839 and in London in the 1850s. From

'Sebastopol from the Northern Forts'.
Tinted lithograph by R M Bryson after Carlo Bossoli (1815-84), published in
'The Beautiful Scenery and Chief Places of Interest throughout the Crimea' by Day & Son, London, 1856.
NAM. 1972-11-13-7

1852-55, he was on the staff of Prince Mikhail Vorontsov, Governor-General of New Russia, Bessarabia and the Crimea,[29] before returning to London where he exhibited at the Royal Academy in 1855 and 1859. The content of the series is in marked contrast to Simpson's, making no apparent reference to the conflict. His 'View of the Valley of Inkermann' shows civilians and goats roaming in a pastoral setting. Instead, Bossoli's approach is altogether more anthropological, including illustrations of the 'Tartar Children's School' and 'Dance of Tartars'. In their printing of Bossoli's illustrations, Day and Son demonstrated their mastery of the lithographic process. The 52 lithographs in the series were tinted in up to five colours, as opposed to the two used to lithograph Simpson's work, thereby removing the need for hand colouring.

In addition to the officers and professional artists in the Crimea, there was a number of other civilians involved in the war who drew scenes that were reproduced as prints. Lady Alicia Blackwood had accompanied her husband, the Reverend Dr Henry Blackwood, to the Crimea following the news of the Battle of Inkerman on 5 November 1854. Once in Scutari, Lady Alicia offered her assistance to Florence Nightingale stating, '… we came out here with no other wish than to help where we could, and to be useful if possible'.[30] Tasked with looking after the soldiers' wives, she distributed gifts and funds to them and helped to establish a hospital for the women.

An amateur artist and lithographer, Lady Alicia drew and lithographed two volumes of views entitled 'Scutari. Bosphorus. Crimea', which she dedicated to Florence Nightingale, stating that 'these sketches, though simple and without artistic pretension, are yet true and faithful delineations, of some deeply-interesting localities with which we have both been so singularly connected'. These charmingly naïve prints or 'trifles', as Lady Alicia called them, were published by John Lavars of Bridge Street, Bristol, and sold in aid of a number of charities - The Irish Church Missions, The Moravian Church Missions, The Vaudois Schools and The Turkish Missions. Lady Alicia also published a memoir, *A Narrative of Personal Experiences and Impression During a Residence on the Bosphorus throughout the Crimean War*, London (1881), which she illustrated with ten pages of vignettes, simple line drawings of places of interest such as the Barrack Hospital at Scutari.

The development of the swift and economical lithographic processes such as tinted lithography encouraged print producers to exploit the demand for visual records of the war. In competition with each other, publishers provided the public with a miscellany of illustrations of the Crimea drawn from a variety of sources, military and civilian. While the illustrated press published scenes of camp life, military manoeuvres, battles and marine views, the newspapers' medium of wood engraving was not suited to the reproduction of the exquisite watercolours of landscapes by artists such as Simpson. Since the illustrated papers relied on the news-worthiness of their subjects, they curtailed their production of images of the conflict after the Fall of Sevastopol on 9 September 1855. However, lithographs of the Crimea had a greater longevity, and demand for them continued until 1857, when the mutiny in the Bengal Army diverted public attention away from the Black Sea.

Notes

1 Captain (later Admiral) Lord Clarence Paget (1811-95), Royal Navy, commanded the *Princess Royal* in the Baltic in 1854 and during the blockade and bombardment of Sevastopol in 1855.

2 G Eyre-Todd (ed.), *The autobiography of William Simpson RI, (Crimean Simpson)*, London (1903) p46.

3 NAM. 1965-01-160.

4 *Vanity Fair,* 21 November 1891.

5 NAM. 1972-03-8-1. Biddulph's work is discussed at length by G C Swinden, 'The Sketchbook of General Sir Michael Anthony Shrapnel Biddulph KCB' *National Army Museum Annual Report*, 1971-72 pp32-34.

6 NAM. 1972-03-8-2. These sketches by Biddulph were made whilst he was acting as Assistant Engineer Officer in the trenches.

7 Quoting his journal entry of 24 Nov 1854.

8 NAM. 1957-10-11.

9 NAM. 1970-06-10-1.

10 NAM. 1972-07-6-62-2.

11 NAM. 1964-10-106-1.

12 NAM. 1972-07-6-74.

13 NAM. 1992-07-18.

14 NAM. 1998-06-128. The volume is discussed by J Spencer-Smith 'The Crimean Sketchbook of Captain the Hon George Cadogan' *National Army Museum Annual Report*, 1976-77 pp29-32.

15 G Eyre-Todd (ed.), *The autobiography of William Simpson RI, (Crimean Simpson)*, London (1903) pp19-20.

16 *Ibid*. p36.

17 *Ibid*. p33.

18 *Ibid*. p80.

19 *Ibid*. p34.

20 *Ibid*. p35.

21 The watercolour is NAM. 1961-08-4-1, whilst the print is NAM. 1969-07-27-21.

22 There are 41 prints in some examples of the second volume of Simpson's 'The Seat of War in the East'.

23 G Eyre-Todd (ed.), *The autobiography of William Simpson RI, (Crimean Simpson)*, London (1903) p81.

24 Colnaghi's also re-printed the drawings in octavo size (11 x 18cm.) in George Brackenbury's *Campaign in the Crimea*, London (1855 & 1856).

25 G Eyre-Todd (ed.), *The autobiography of William Simpson RI, (Crimean Simpson)*, London (1903) p81.

26 W H Russell, *The Great War with Russia*, London (1895) p236.

27 It is ironic that six of the original drawings for the series are now in the Government Art Collection.

28 NAM. 1972-11-13.

29 D Miller, *Victorian Watercolours and Drawings in the Collection of Her Majesty The Queen*, London (1995) pp101-102.

30 Lady Alicia Blackwood, *A Narrative of Personal Experiences and Impression During a Residence on the Bosphorus throughout the Crimean War*, London (1881) p49.

Peace and Aftermath

Following the capture of Sevastopol the Allies mounted an expedition to the Black Sea fortress of Kinburn and skirmished in the Crimea against the Russians at Eupatoria. In the Caucasus, the Russians finally captured the city of Kars after prolonged Turkish resistance. Austria then threatened to intervene in the war on the Allied side and the so-called Four Points, long under negotiation between the warring powers, were accepted by Russia. Under the Treaty of Paris (27 April 1856), Russia lost territory on the Danube and the Black Sea was declared neutral. Although Britain, which had not only strengthened its army with German, Swiss and Italian mercenaries, but had a major naval expedition to the Baltic under preparation, would have liked to continue the war to make victory more decisive, Napoleon III of France wanted peace and his view prevailed.

The British Army of 1856 had in some respects changed rapidly. Newly introduced uniforms were already being superseded. The revolutionary Minié Rifle had given way by the war's end to the Enfield. Administrative reform had seen the Board of Ordnance swept away and the Commissariat removed from Treasury control. But the investigation of the Roebuck Committee into military administration (1855) and the McNeill and Tulloch Commission's 1856 report on the Commissariat generated more heat than light. The lessons of the Crimean War were soon forgotten. Only with the Cardwell reforms a decade later would the process of change in the British Army be recommenced.

'The Turkish Contingent'

Coloured aquatint by J Harris after Henry Martens (*fl.* 1828-54), after uniform designs by Landon, Morland & Landon, number 11 in the series 'R. Ackermann's Costumes of the British Army', published by Rudolph Ackermann, London, 1 February 1856, 46cm. h x 35.1cm. w

NAM. 1964-02-4-2

On 3 February a convention was concluded with the Sultan of Turkey to take into British pay a contingent of 20,000 Ottoman troops. 'The colour of their uniform shall be left to the discretion of the commander-in-chief of the British army,' the second article laid down, 'but its general style and appearance shall be similar to those of the regular Turkish army.' For the British officers of the Turkish contingent, however, review order consisted of the latest in military fashion: tunics both double and single-breasted, and *pickelhaube* helmets similar to those worn by the British heavy cavalry.

British Swiss Legion Flag, 1855-56

Regimental Colour of the 2nd Battalion, 1st Regiment of Light Infantry,
1.75m. h x 1.88m. w

Generously donated by the Royal United Service Institution

NAM. 1959-12-80

To address the problem of the British Army's shortage of men, in December 1854 Parliament passed the Foreign Enlistment Act authorising the raising of troops abroad. One such body of troops was the British Swiss Legion, of which the 1st Regiment of Light Infantry (of two battalions) was formed by August 1855. Although sent to the East in November 1855 it was realised that it would be impossible to hut them in the Crimea and so they wintered in Turkey at Smyrna (Izmir), where they remained until peace was declared in April 1856. The entire Swiss Legion, which numbered 3,150 officers and men, was then disbanded.

The Regimental Colour is a painted design with a red cross on a black ground; in the centre is a wreath of rose, thistle and shamrock, and within it the title British Swiss Legion, with underneath the wreath a white cross. In the upper canton is the Union Flag with the number of the battalion in roman numerals in gold.

Lieutenant Thomas Murphy in the undress uniform of the Turkish Contingent, 1857

Oil on canvas, signed with a monogram symbol and dated lower left '1857', artist unknown, 1857, 89.8cm. h x 71.5cm. w

Generously donated by Mr D C Murphy

NAM. 1972-05-10-1

Thomas Murphy (1833-1922) was a gunner in the Royal Artillery and served throughout the Crimean War, being present at the Battle of Inkerman and the six bombardments of the Siege of Sevastopol. In fact, *Hart's Army List* noted that he was 'not absent from regular trench duty for a single day from the first breaking ground to the end of the siege' and that he was 'recommended for distinguished conduct', although there is no record of his having received the Distinguished Conduct Medal.

From January 1856 until the end of the war, Murphy, newly commissioned, served as a lieutenant with the Turkish Contingent which formed the garrison at Kerch. This force of 20,000 Turkish troops provided by the Sultan was paid by Britain and many of its British officers were on leave from the armies of the East India Company.

Murphy sat for this portrait wearing the undress uniform of the Turkish Contingent and his Crimea War Medal, showing the reverse of the medal with two clasps, lacking their inscriptions. He went on to serve with the 46th (The South Devonshire) Regiment of Foot and afterwards the 66th (The Berkshire) Regiment of Foot. Murphy retired as an honorary lieutenant-colonel in 1883.

Full Dress Tunic, *c*1855

Turkish Contingent

Blue cloth, gold lace, gilt metal buttons

NAM. 1962-11-204-1

Worn by Major (later Lieutenant-Colonel) Dawson Cornelius Greene whilst serving with the Turkish Contingent during the Crimean War. Greene had joined the 43rd (The Monmouthshire) Regiment of Foot (Light Infantry) as an ensign on 3 July 1840, gaining his lieutenantcy on 14 January 1842. Promoted captain on 11 December 1849, he served in Cape Colony in the Eighth Frontier War 1850-53 before receiving his majority on 7 November 1855. Greene served with one of the sixteen regiments of infantry belonging to the Turkish Contingent and his uniform, blue with red piping, reflects the French inspiration behind the Turks' newly westernised military dress.

Fez, *c*1855-56

Turkish Contingent

Worn by Major Dawson Cornelius Greene

Made of thick red wool felt with silk tassel.

NAM. 1962-11-204-2

Overalls, *c*1855

Turkish Contingent

Worn by Major Dawson Cornelius Greene

Blue cloth with bone buttons at the waist. The two bone buttons at each ankle edge were for attaching a leather foot strap.

NAM. 1962-11-204-3

Turkish Contingent Commission, 1856

Print and Manuscript, 24cm. h x 34cm. w

Generously donated by Mr Barton

NAM. 1974-10-168

Although Charles Howarth, Gentleman, was granted a commission as a lieutenant in the Osmanli Horse Artillery (part of the British-paid Turkish Contingent) on 5 March 1856, his name does not appear in the *Monthly Army List* as one of its officers, and with the imminence of peace one suspects that Howarth never had the opportunity of taking up his post.

Royal Artillery Officer's Sword, *c*1855

Turkish Contingent

Manufacturer, Meyer

102cm. l

NAM 1985-07-55

In the mid-1840s the Royal Artillery adopted the Pattern 1821 Light Cavalry Sword already carried by the Royal Horse Artillery. When the Turkish Contingent, officered by the British, was formed in 1855 it included six battalions of artillery and swords of the appropriate type would have been carried by its British officers.

However, this sword, marked to the Turkish Contingent, has a much heavier blade than the standard pattern; indeed, its unfullered blade is similar to those found on weapons carried by East India Company army officers whose expectation of being engaged in close fighting was greater.

The Capitulation of Kars, 26 November 1855

Oil on canvas by Thomas Jones Barker (1815-82), *c*1860, 252cm. h x 440cm. w

Generously donated by the St Stephen's Club

NAM. 1963-07-3

Fighting had continued since 1853 on the north-eastern frontier of Turkey. When a Russian army 25,000 strong laid siege to the city of Kars in June 1855, Brevet Colonel (later General Sir) William Fenwick Williams (1800-83), the British commissioner with the Ottoman army in Anatolia, undertook its defence. Through his brilliant organisation, the garrison was able to repulse three major Russian attacks, but eventually cold, famine and an outbreak of cholera forced it to surrender on 26 November 1855. In recognition of their heroism, the defenders were allowed to march out of the city with the honours of war and into captivity. Williams is the central figure in the composition, with the officers of his British staff around him.

Coatee with Company Officer's Epaulettes, *c*1845-55

70th (The Surrey) Regiment of Foot

NAM. 1991-11-40

Christopher Bakewell Bassano (1824-56) joined the 70th (The Surrey) Regiment of Foot as an assistant surgeon on 22 December 1848. He was appointed a staff surgeon, 2nd class on 10 August 1855 whereupon he travelled to the Crimea. He died at Balaklava on 1 February 1856. His coatee, with company officer's epaulettes, is of the standard pattern worn by the officers of infantry regiments; the distinguishing colour of the cuffs and the device on the buttons would have marked Bassano out as belonging to the Surreys.

Assistant Surgeon Christopher Bakewell Bassano and Children

Daguerreotype, 9cm. h x 6.7cm. w

NAM. 1992-04-218-1

Discharge certificate for Private Joseph Rook, 1856

Printed and manuscript, 25cm. h x 19.3cm. w

NAM. 1998-06-153-2

Joseph Rook (1832-57) enlisted in the Coldstream Guards at Lincoln on 8 January 1855. A labourer, five foot ten and a half inches tall, with light hair, blue eyes and a fair complexion, he was apparently an ideal recruit for the Guards. After four months in the Crimea during the winter of 1855-56, however, he contracted tuberculosis and was discharged 'as unfit for further service' on 5 August 1856.

[W. D. Form 64.]

E.

PARCHMENT CERTIFICATE.

Coldstream Regiment of *Guards*

THESE are to Certify that No. *5086.* *Private Joseph Rook* born in the Parish of *Saxilby* in or near the Town of *Lincoln* in the County of *Lincolnshire,* was enlisted at *Lincoln* for the *above Corps* on the *8 January 1855.* at the Age of *22 2/12* Years. That he has served in the Army for *One* Years, and *210* Days

That he is discharged in consequence of *being unfit for further service*

G. Upton for
Commanding Officer.

Dated at *London*
26 day of *July* 185*6.*

Horse Guards, *12* day of *August* 185*6.*
DISCHARGE of *Private Joseph Rook* confirmed *Reynolds*

CHARACTER.

Good G. Upton for

The Soldier's Character to be inserted only when recommendatory; if the general conduct of a Soldier, whilst in the Service, has been such as to give him no claim to have any thing said in his favour, the space for character in the above Certificate is to be cut off close under the black line following the confirmation of his Discharge, thereby leaving no opportunity for any addition to be made after the Certificate is given to the Man.

When a Soldier is *discharged* on account of *disgraceful conduct,* that will appear in the body of the Certificate.

F. & T. 5000. 3—56.

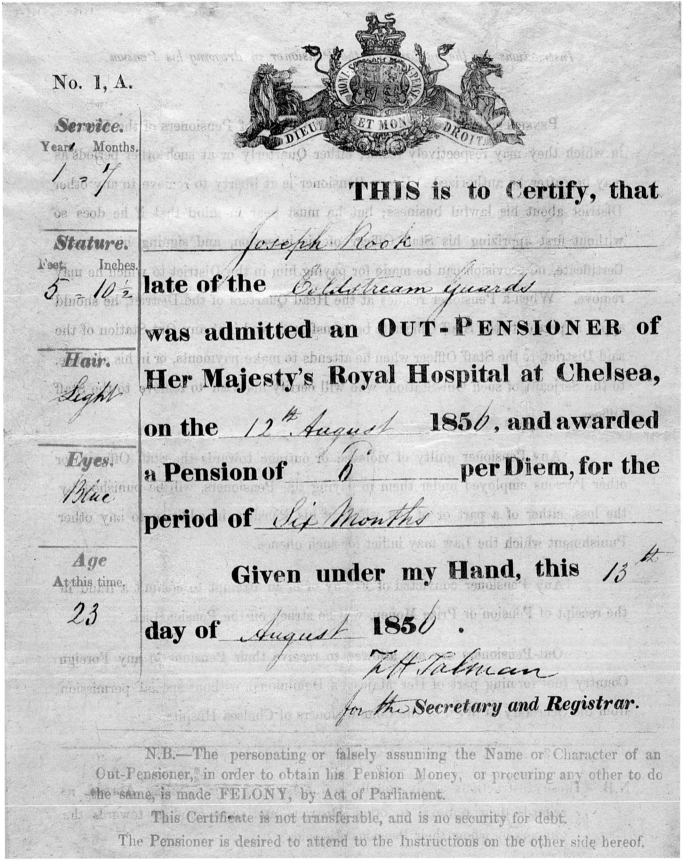

No. 1, A.

Service.
Years. Months.

Stature.
Feet. Inches.

Hair.

Eyes.

Age
At this time,

THIS is to Certify, that

Joseph Rook

late of the *Coldstream Guards*

was admitted an OUT-PENSIONER of

Her Majesty's Royal Hospital at Chelsea,

on the *12th August* **1856, and awarded**

a Pension of *6* **per Diem, for the**

period of *Six Months*

Given under my Hand, this *13th*

day of *August* **1856.**

T.H. Tolman

for the **Secretary and Registrar.**

N.B.—The personating or falsely assuming the Name or Character of an Out-Pensioner, in order to obtain his Pension Money, or procuring any other to do the same, is made FELONY, by Act of Parliament.

This Certificate is not transferable, and is no security for debt.

The Pensioner is desired to attend to the Instructions on the other side hereof.

Admission as an out-pensioner certificate for Joseph Rook, 1856

Printed and manuscript, 25cm. h x 20cm. w

NAM. 1998-06-153-3

Because Surgeon-Major James Monro, who examined Rook at the Coldstream Guards Hospital on 21 July 1856, adjudged him to have contracted his disease in the service, Rook was eligible to become an out-pensioner of the Royal Hospital, Chelsea. He received a pension of 6d per day for six months. Rook died of consumption in his home town of Saxilby, Lincolnshire on 28 February 1857.

Other Rank's Field Service Cap cover, *c*1855-56

Coldstream Guards

Linen

NAM. 1997-12-77

Cap covers had first been issued to the Army of the East in the summer of 1854 for use with the Albert Shako. By 1855, the Guards regiments (or at least the Coldstreams) had a cover intended for their unique field service caps: the inverted pleat across the crown allowed the cover to mould itself to the shape of the cap underneath, while the peak – made in two pieces – creates a pocket into which could fit one of the field service cap's down-turned flaps. On the inside of the underpeak the name J ROOK is embroidered in white cotton thread.

Officer's Shako Plate, *c*1855

British Foreign Legion

NAM. 2002-06-83

In addition to raising a British Swiss Legion, the Government also enlisted German and Italian legionaries. At first the German contingent was known as the British Foreign Legion, but Queen Victoria intervened to have the appellation changed, writing to the Secretary of State for War on 3 September 1855: 'The Queen wishes to remind Lord Panmure of the Foreign Legion being called the German Legion. .. She is sure that this will have a good effect in Germany and help the recruiting; the German papers have been taunting them with not being allowed to bear their own name.'

Officer's Sabretache badge, *c*1854-56

British German Legion (Light Cavalry)

NAM. 2002-06-85

The initial success of recruiting in Germany prompted George, Duke of Cambridge to suggest to Lord Panmure that the German contingent should include a cavalry arm of light dragoons. Panmure agreed and two regiments were eventually raised. They wore a blue hussar tunic with gold lace; their equipment, including the sabretache – on which was fastened this crown and cypher with triple scroll – was black leather.

Officer's Pouch Belt Plate, *c*1855-56

British German Legion

NAM. 2002-06-86

Whereas the British German Legion's shako plates and buttons are known to have at least initially borne the initials 'BFL' (for British Foreign Legion), it is apparent that by the time this gilt pouch belt plate was produced the cypher 'BGL' (British German Legion) ruled supreme.

Pattern 1827 Rifle Regiment Officer's Sword

100cm. l

Generously donated by Colonel G H Heaver

NAM. 1970-07-11

Ensign Kenrick Verulam Bacon was commissioned into the 2nd Jäger Corps, British German Legion on 17 August 1855 when he would have purchased this sword, a variant of the Pattern 1822 Infantry Sword with Rifle Regiment badge incorporated into the guard.

Notice of termination of employment, British German Legion, 1856

Printed and manuscript, 23.2cm. h x 20cm. w

Generously donated by Lieutenant-Colonel C R K Bacon

NAM. 1964-09-15-4

The British German Legion (BGL) had at the outset been reasonably well-disciplined: 40% of its personnel had prior military training and many of its officers were experienced. However, the BGL only started to leave for the East in October 1855 and had got no further than Constantinople by the time peace was declared. Upon its return to England, the BGL got into a series of fights with British troops; the Legion's officers, told that their

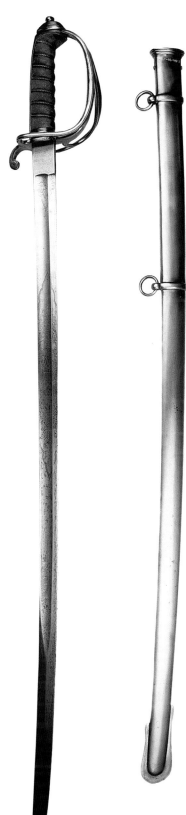

services were to be dispensed with, proved unwilling to impose order, claiming that promises to employ them for between three and five years had been reneged upon. The Government, however, was now more eager than ever to disband the BGL, and Ensign Bacon received notification of the termination of his employment in November 1856. Many of the BGL's rank and file went to Cape Colony as military settlers.

British German Legion.

War Department,
26th November 1856.

Sir,

I am directed by the Secretary of State for War to inform you, that your services as *Ensign* in the *2d* Regiment of *Jaegers* of the British German Legion, will not be required after the *30th of November 1856,* and are therefore dispensed with by Her Majesty from that date, under Section 15 of Articles of Capitulation for the formation of a British Foreign Legion.

I have the honour to be,

Sir,

Your obedient humble Servant,

John Kinloch
Inspector-General.

To *Kenrick Verulam Bacon Esq.*
Ensign 2d Jaeger Corps
British German Legion.

(184.)

'The camp of the Foreign Legion, near Hythe', Kent, 1855

Colour lithograph by T Picken after artist unknown, printed by Day and Son, *c*1856, 23.2cm. h x 30.2cm. w

NAM. 1974-03-144

In 1855, Great Britain raised a British German Legion of two regiments of light dragoons, three Jäger Corps, and six regiments of light infantry; a British Italian Legion of five regiments of infantry, and a British Swiss Legion of three regiments of light infantry. At the end of the war, these soldiers were entitled to return to their country of origin at the public expense, although some, fearing a hostile reception at home, settled in the Cape of Good Hope.

When the first German and Swiss legionaries arrived in England in May and June 1855, they were lodged in Dover Castle, but friction between the two led to the Swiss being encamped on the Western Heights above Dover and the Germans being sent to Shorncliffe Camp, near Hythe, as pictured here.

Saddle presented to HRH the Duke of Cambridge by the Turkish Sultan, *c*1856

60cm. l x 43cm. w x 51cm. h

Generously donated by the Royal United Service Institution

NAM. 1963-10-252-1

This beautifully made eastern saddle has a frame of metal and wood with silver bound edging. The seat is of padded and quilted yellow silk and is covered in maroon velvet. The Turkish Sultan presented it to the Duke of Cambridge following the Crimean War to express his appreciation of the Duke's services.

Pair of saddle holsters presented to HRH the Duke of Cambridge by the Turkish Sultan, *c*1856

40cm. l x 21.5cm. w x 16cm. h (each)

Generously donated by the Royal United Service Institution

NAM. 1963-10-252-3

Made of stitched red leather with gilt brass binding, this pair of pistol holsters is embroidered with the letters 'DC' for the Duke of Cambridge, to whom the Turkish Sultan presented them after the Crimean War.

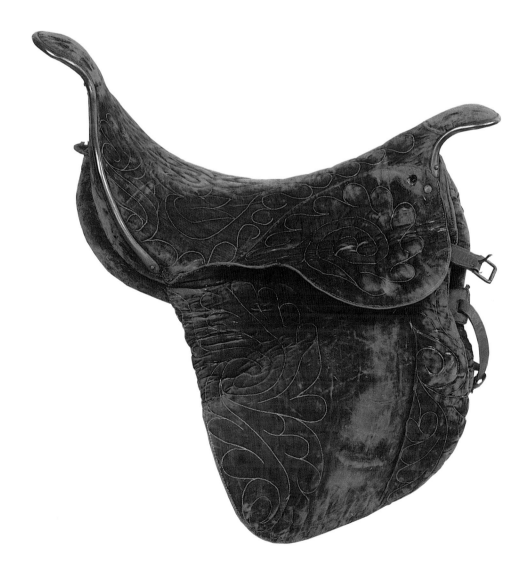

**Pair of stirrups presented to HRH the Duke of Cambridge by the
Turkish Sultan, *c*1856**

65cm. l x 14cm. w x 7cm. h

Generously donated by the Royal United Service Institution

NAM. 1963-10-252-6

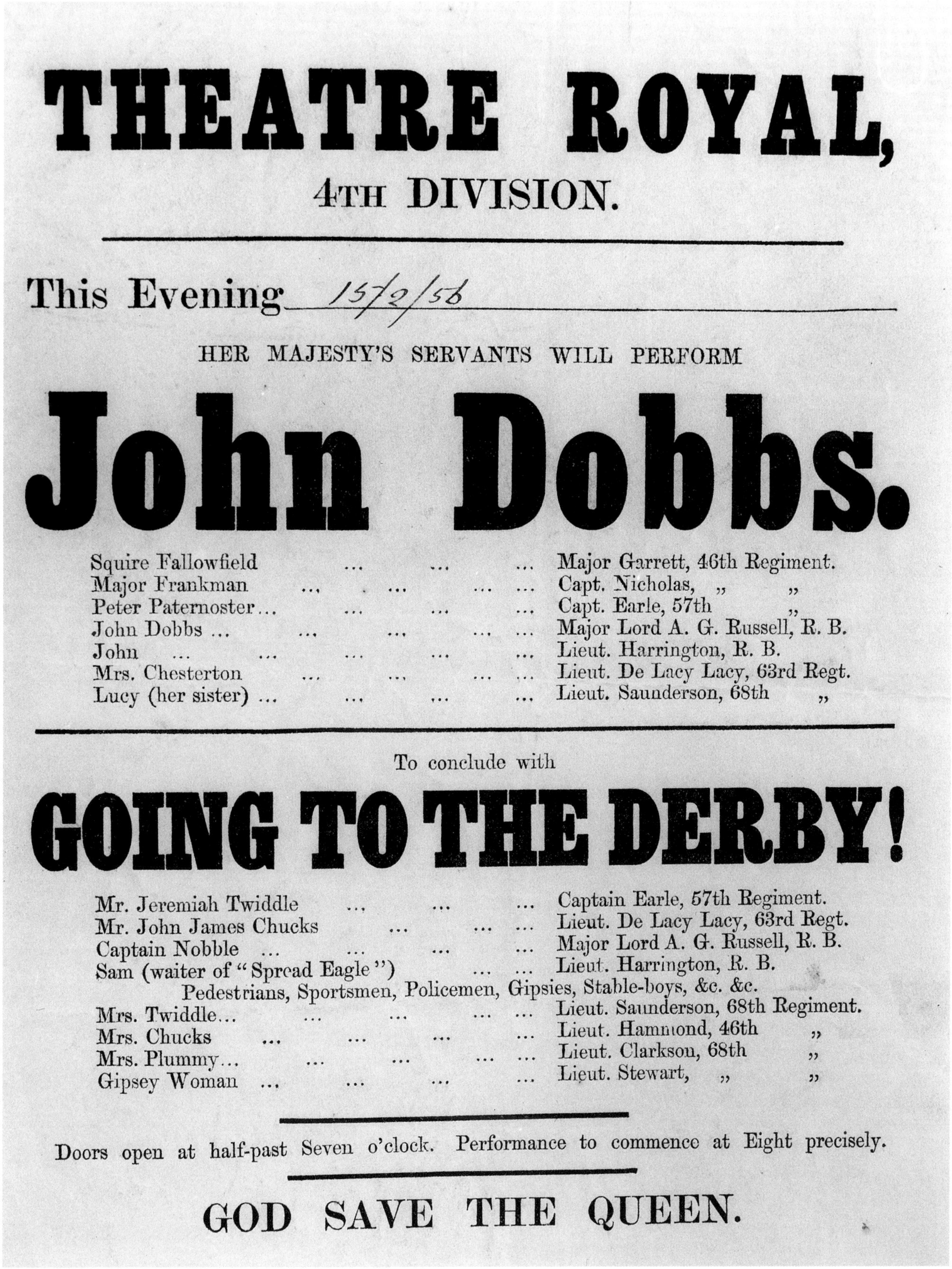

THEATRE ROYAL,

4TH DIVISION.

This Evening *15/2/56*

HER MAJESTY'S SERVANTS WILL PERFORM

John Dobbs.

Squire Fallowfield	... ...	Major Garrett, 46th Regiment.
Major Frankman	... ...	Capt. Nicholas, ,, ,,
Peter Paternoster	... ...	Capt. Earle, 57th ,,
John Dobbs	... ...	Major Lord A. G. Russell, R. B.
John	... ...	Lieut. Harrington, R. B.
Mrs. Chesterton	... ...	Lieut. De Lacy Lacy, 63rd Regt.
Lucy (her sister)	... ...	Lieut. Saunderson, 68th ,,

To conclude with

GOING TO THE DERBY!

Mr. Jeremiah Twiddle	... ...	Captain Earle, 57th Regiment.
Mr. John James Chucks	... ...	Lieut. De Lacy Lacy, 63rd Regt.
Captain Nobble	... ...	Major Lord A. G. Russell, R. B.
Sam (waiter of "Spread Eagle")	... ...	Lieut. Harrington, R. B.
Pedestrians, Sportsmen, Policemen, Gipsies, Stable-boys, &c. &c.		
Mrs. Twiddle	... ...	Lieut. Saunderson, 68th Regiment.
Mrs. Chucks	... ...	Lieut. Hammond, 46th ,,
Mrs. Plummy	... ...	Lieut. Clarkson, 68th ,,
Gipsey Woman	... ...	Lieut. Stewart, ,, ,,

Doors open at half-past Seven o'clock. Performance to commence at Eight precisely.

GOD SAVE THE QUEEN.

'Theatre Royal, 4th Division. This Evening 15/2/56'

Printed playbill, from an album of paintings, sketches and ephemera by Colonel (later General Sir) The Honourable George Cadogan (1814-80), 1st (or Grenadier) Regiment of Foot Guards, 1854-56, 19.8cm. h x 16cm. w

NAM. 1998-06-128-51

'Captn Earle in the part of Jeremiah Twiddle in going to the Derby. From nature', 1856

Pencil, from an album of paintings, sketches and ephemera by Colonel (later General Sir) The Honourable George Cadogan (1814-80), 1st (or Grenadier) Regiment of Foot Guards, 1854-56, 11.8cm. h x 6.8cm. w

NAM. 1998-06-128-52

'4th Division Theatricals. A scene from "John Dobbs"', 1856

Pen and ink, watercolour and pencil, from an album of paintings, sketches and ephemera by Colonel (later General Sir) The Honourable George Cadogan (1814-80), 1st (or Grenadier) Regiment of Foot Guards, 1854-56, 18.2cm. h x 25.4cm. w

NAM. 1998-06-128-53

Captain Maxwell Earle of the 57th (The West Middlesex) Regiment of Foot was a leading light of the 4th Division theatricals and was drawn in costume and painted on the stage (second from the left) by Colonel George Cadogan. Earle wrote to his father on 31 January 1856:

Our theatre, a handsome building is nearly completed and we hope to give another performance early next week. The 2nd Batt[alio]n of the Rifles performed two days ago, and gave great satisfaction especially to one person, a little more vulgar than the rest who stood up in the middle of the performance and declared that "it was much better than the 4th Div[isio]n". Comparisons are odious at any time, but on this occasion especially, for the person was surrounded by officers of the said 4th Div who had been invited to see the play. Fortunately we can bear comparison, for we have nearly 250 officers to select from and the others are confined to the officers & Non Com[missione]d officers of the 2nd Battn R[ifle] B[rigade]. I cannot see why men should be so jealous about which should make himself the greatest buffoon before an audience. We intend giving an evening over for the benefit of the Nightingale Fund, and we reckon on collecting nearly £150.

Poster announcing a rifle shooting competition, 1856

Printed, 32cm. h x 40cm. w

Generously donated by Lieutenant-Colonel A J Clark-Kennedy

NAM. 1963-02-4

A shooting competition was the kind of diversion for the troops which met with official approval. The Commander-in-Chief in the Crimea, Sir William Codrington, provided the winner's prize while the Headquarters Staff contributed the money awarded to the runners up. The adjudicator of the competition, Assistant-Adjutant-General Lieutenant-Colonel J Clark Kennedy, was a forebear of the donor.

RIFLE SHOOTING.

TOWARDS THE CONCLUSION OF THE WINTER PRACTICE, THE FOLLOWING PRIZES WILL BE GIVEN TO THE ARMY (THE MATCHES TO COMMENCE ON OR ABOUT MONDAY, 10th MARCH, 1856):—

Regimental Matches.

The Companies in each Regiment will compete for Three Prizes. Each Company to be represented by the Five best shots, who will each fire Five Rounds, at 300 Yards.

1st Prize - - - - 25 lbs. Tobacco.
2nd „ - - - - 20 „ „
3rd „ - - - - 15 „ „

Brigade Matches.

The Battalions in each Brigade will compete for a

PRIZE OF 25 lbs. OF CIGARS.

Each Battalion to be represented by Five Men, who will fire Five Rounds each, at 300 Yards.

The following conditions are to be strictly observed in the above Matches :—

1. The Targets to be the regulated size of 6 by 4 feet, with Two foot centre, and Eight inch Bull's Eye.
2. The value of Hits to be Bull's Eye, 3 ; Centre, 2 ; Outer, 1.
3. The Prizes to be gained by the highest collective score. Should any scores be equal, the Party having made the greatest number of Hits to be entitled to the Prize. Should both score and number of Hits be even, Ties will then be Shot off with an additional Round.
4. The Firing to be without Bayonets, each Man standing or kneeling at pleasure ; but no other position allowed.
5. The Prizes to be divided in the Companies and Battalions whose representatives gain them.

Match open to the whole Army,

For a Prize given by Gen. Sir Wm. Codrington, K.C.B., Commander of the Forces.

1. Two Entries allowed from each Battalion in the Army.
2. Each Man to fire Five Rounds :—viz. Two at 300 yards, Two at 200 yards, and One at 100 yards, at Targets of the regulated size.
3. The value of the Hits to be same as in the previous Matches, except that at 100 Yards, Outers will not count.
4. Should Scores be equal, the Individuals having the greater number of Hits to be entitled to the Prizes. Should both Scores and Number of Hits be even, Ties will be shot off with a single Round at each of the above-named distances.
5. The firing to be without Bayonets, each Man standing or kneeling at pleasure, at the 300 yards distance ; and standing at 200 and 100 yards. No other position allowed.

FOR THE BEST SHOT,
THE
COMMANDER OF THE FORCES' PRIZE OF £5 ;

To which will be added, by the Officers of the Head Quarters Staff, for the—

2nd Prize - - - - £2 10s.
3rd „ - - - - 2 0
4th „ - - - - 1 10
5th „ - - - - 1 0
6th „ - - - - 0 10

Due notice will be given for the Commencement of the Regimental and Brigade Matches ; and a day will be fixed for Shooting for the Prize given by Commander of the Forces.

In case of disputes arising, they are to be referred to Lieut.-Colonel CLARK KENNEDY, A.A.G., whose decision will be considered final.

Head Quarters ;
21st February, 1856.

J. CLARK KENNEDY,
Lieut.-Colonel & A.A.G.

354

'Sebastopol Spring Meeting' Race Card, 17 March 1856

Printed, 32.6cm. h x 20.3cm. w

Generously donated by Lieutenant-Colonel T Sutton

NAM. 1966-03-59

Horse racing was a popular diversion in the Crimea and meetings were being organised as early as the spring of 1855. Major Nigel Kingscote of Lord Raglan's personal staff wrote to his father on 15 May 1855 about one such race:

> We had a great match yesterday between a horse of Paulett Somerset's and one of young Barnard's, both having beaten everything else - 12 stone each - 1 1/2 mile. We got most soundly beaten and as I stood a 3rd of the money it was a bore. I laid out the course and flatter myself it was a very good one, a deal of trouble for worse than nothing.

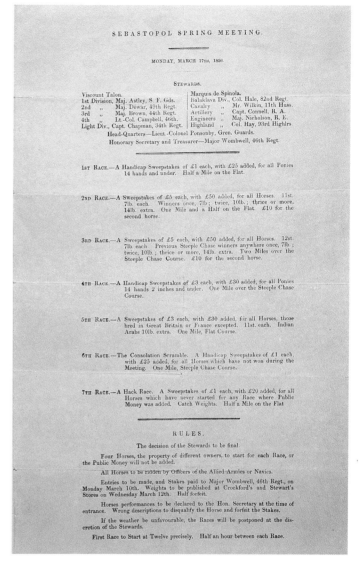

'Grand military steeplechase in the Crimea', 3 December 1855

Proof copy of a wood engraving after 'an officer of the 17th Regiment' for *The Illustrated London News*, c1856, which was subsequently published in *The Illustrated London News*, 9 February 1856, 28.3cm. h x 44.5cm. w

Generously donated by the Royal United Service Institution

NAM. 1968-06-331-1

This shows the kind of recreation that was pursued in the Crimea. According to the description published in *The Illustrated London News*:

> We have to thank a Correspondent (an officer of the 17th Regiment) in the Camp, Sebastopol, for the accompanying Sketch of the Grand Military Steeplechase, which took place on the 3rd of December last, and afforded capital sport. The race represented is the first of the "Grand International Steeplechase", which was won, in good style, by Captain Smith's "Muster-Roll".

Cornet Henry John Wilkin, 11th (or Prince Albert's Own) Hussars, 1855

Photograph by Roger Fenton, 19cm. h x 16.2cm. w

Generously donated by Major P D Mulholland

NAM. 1968-10-73-14

John Wilkin (d.1891) rode in the Charge of the Light Brigade as the 11th Hussars' Assistant Surgeon. On 2 February 1855 he purchased the rank of cornet in the 11th, and is photographed here in full hussar dress; even his horse has its throat plume. Wilkin was a skilful horseman and excelled in the races organised in the Crimea. On the race card reproduced on p355, he is listed as the steward representing the Cavalry Division.

11th Hussars disembarking their horses and stores at Portsmouth docks, on their return from the Crimea, 1856

Pencil and watercolour by George Housman Thomas (1824-69), artist for *The Illustrated London News*, 1856, 22.3cm. h x 33.9cm. w

NAM. 1980-05-37

The first detachment of the 11th (or Prince Albert's Own) Hussars sailed for England in June 1856 and the remaining detachment under Lieutenant-Colonel Edmund Peel left the Crimea on 4 July that year.

Although the artist, George Housman Thomas, produced a number of drawings for *The Illustrated London News*, it appears that this sketch was not selected for publication.

'Reception of Her Majesty's XXXIXth Regiment of Foot, on their arrival in Montreal from the Crimea... on passing under the Triumphal Arch at the Place d'Armes and Bank of Montreal', 28 June 1856

Silk printed with a wood engraving by J Walker after J Duncan, published by Salter & Ross, *c*1856, 72cm. h x 51cm. w

Anonymous donation

NAM. 1995-01-288

Britain's abortive attempt to recruit an American Legion – to join its Swiss, German and Italian legions – strained relations with the United States and, to help defend Canada in the event of war, five regiments under Major-General Sir William Eyre were shipped there directly from the Crimea. Among them was the 39th (The Dorsetshire) Regiment of Foot which left the Crimea on 1 May 1856 aboard the *Simoon* and, as this commemorative broadsheet shows, received an enthusiastic reception upon its arrival at Montreal.

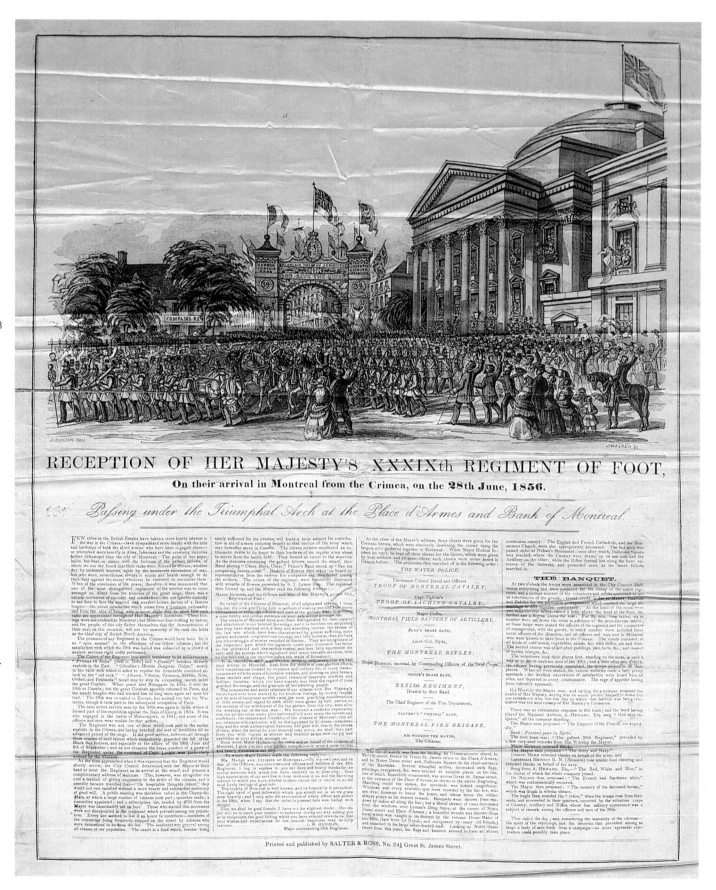

'Trumpeters Gritten and Lang, Royal Artillery'

Photograph by R Howlett, 23.9cm. h x 18.2cm. w

Generously donated by Lieutenant-Colonel N Lovett

NAM. 1964-12-154-6-22

When a body of men of the Royal Artillery arrived back in England from the Crimea in 1856, Queen Victoria and Prince Albert inspected them at Woolwich. The Queen was so pleased with the appearance of some of the men that she asked the photographers Robert Howlett (d. 1858) and Joseph Cundall (1818-95) to take their photographs. According to *The Illustrated London News*:

> The man, Trumpeter Gritten, arrived in England with an immense beard, which doubtless attracted Her Majesty's attention: unfortunately before the photographers arrived at Woolwich, he had cut off this ornament because it was so red. The lad, William Lang, was barely thirteen years old when he first heard the whistling of cannon-balls on the banks of the Alma. He says he was frightened for the first half hour, but has never been afraid of them since.

'Company Sergeant Christy and Serjeant McGifford, Royal Artillery'

Photograph by R Howlett, 18.6cm. h x 22.4cm. w

Generously donated by Lieutenant-Colonel N Lovett

NAM. 1964-12-154-6-23

Company Sergeant Christy (right) and Sergeant Samuel McGifford, both of the 4th Battalion, Royal Artillery, were also photographed at Queen Victoria's request. According to *The Illustrated London News*, 'The pictures, which they have converted into banners, were taken by these worthies from one of the churches of Sebastopol, where they decorated the wall. One picture is of St. Michael, the other of St. George and the Dragon. They are painted in a thoroughly Byzantine style, and in parts are illuminated with gold.'

Medal commemorating the end of the Crimean War 1856, issued by the City of Nottingham

Silver, 38 mm. diam

The obverse bears the figure of Britannia seated holding a palm branch and trident, with her shield and the British Lion beside her. On the reverse is a shield bearing the arms of the City of Nottingham, with its motto: VIVIT POST FUNERA VIRTUS (virtue lives after the grave), surrounded by the inscription: COMMEMORATED AT NOTTINGHAM 13TH MAY 1856.

NAM. 2001-04-58

This medal is unusual, as comparatively few 'public' medals commemorating the Crimean War were struck, in contrast to the output of medals following previous British military campaigns, notably the Peninsular War of 1808-14. A greater number of medals were produced to commemorate the reopening of the Crystal Palace in 1854 than events in the Crimea, suggesting that the interests of the emerging Victorian middle classes lay more in the fields of trade, industry and the accumulation of knowledge, than in military achievements.

Medal commemorating the Fall of Sevastopol and the Treaty of Paris, 1856

White metal, 51mm. diam

Generously donated by Major F G B Wetherall

NAM. 1963-07-37 (obverse)

Generously donated by Mr H R Walker

NAM. 1978-05-56 (reverse)

The obverse bears the inscription: THE ALLIES GIVE PEACE TO EUROPE MARCH 30TH 1856, within a circular laurel wreath entwined with ribbons bearing the names of the allied countries. The reverse depicts a view of Sevastopol, within a rectangle superimposed upon a trophy of flags, above which is a pair of scales between laurel sprays with rays in the background. Below is depicted a snake cut in two, among rushes with the words: SINOPE and HANGO below. Around the edge is the inscription: FALL OF SEBASTOPOL SEP 8TH.. 1855. (The names Sinope and Hango allude to naval engagements on 30 November 1853 and 5 June 1855).

THE PEACE of PARIS 31ST MARCH 1856.

'The Peace of Paris 31st March 1856.'

Printed textile, 5.9cm. h x 55.9cm. w

Generously donated by Ms Janet Kent

NAM. 2001-11-179-1

This ribbon is believed to have been designed to be worn across the body in the manner of a sash during the peace celebrations held in Britain in May 1856. A similar ribbon in the Collection is inscribed 'Peace and Goodwill to Men'.

(Opposite) 'Programme of the display of firework to be exhibited on the 29th May, 1856 on Primrose Hill', London, 1856

Printed silk, manufacture unknown, published for the Royal Artillery, 1856, 70.3cm. h x 50cm. w

Generously donated by Miss O M Boxer

NAM. 1983-08-66-2

On 29 May 1856 firework displays were held at a number of locations around Britain including Hyde, Green and Victoria Parks in London. This programme for those held on Primrose Hill details 24 separate sections called divisions, co-ordinated by Captain E M Boxer, Royal Artillery, Superintendent of Royal Laboratories.

On 31 May 1856, *The Illustrated London News* published a double issue on the peace celebrations which included views of the illuminated public buildings and the firework displays in London:

> The Government, having made up its mind for the celebration, managed the business with much tact and skill. It was necessary that the people should share, or appear to share, in the joy felt by the official mind that diplomacy had put an end to that very inconvenient and very troublesome war in which Great Britain was incurring such large expense, and reaping such small satisfaction. For, if the War were unpopular in official circles, the Peace was undoubtedly unpopular in those wider circles that form the nation. Hence it was resolved to celebrate the auspicious birthday of the Queen, and the inauspicious Treaty of Peace on the same evening. Thus loyalty was pressed into the service, and the illuminations that are customary to express the love and respect of the people for the person of the Sovereign did duty in another cause, and assisted the Government in celebrating its own triumphs.

On 7 June *The Illustrated London News* included a full-page illustration of the fireworks on Primrose Hill and recorded that:

> It was generally rumoured throughout the metropolis that the fireworks on Primrose-hill would be on a scale of magnitude surpassing those of the other centres of attraction, and there was an immense concourse to witness the pyrotechnic display which was announced to take place. The persons assembled within the inclosure were mainly of the middle and lower classes, but here was a much larger collection of "roughs" than might have been anticipated. The time appointed for the commencement of the display of fireworks was half-past nine o'clock. From that moment, in quick and unremitting succession, discharges of rocket, pearl streamers, parachute-shells, mines, squibs, tailed stars, and tourbillons, continued till a quarter past eleven o'clock. The people seemed highly delighted with the manner in which the display had been effected, and they gave expression to their satisfaction in loud and frequent applause.

Programme

OF THE

DISPLAY OF FIREWORKS

TO BE EXHIBITED ON THE 29th MAY, 1856,

ON

PRIMROSE HILL.

First Division.

Brilliant Illuminations with White, Red, Green, and Yellow Fires, and a continuous discharge of Maroons.

Second Division.

Order		Number
1.	Flight of Rockets	200
2.	Batteries of Pearl Streamers	4
3.	Parachute Shells	4
4.	Discharge of ½-lb. Rockets, Red and Green	100
5.	Discharge of 5½-inch Shells, Blue and Yellow	50

Third Division.

1.	Flight of Rockets	200
2.	Batteries of Mines, Squibs	4
3.	Tourbillons	40
4.	Discharge of ½-lb. Rockets, Parachute	100
5.	Discharge of 10-inch Shells, Serpents	100

Fourth Division.

1.	Flight of Rockets	200
2.	Batteries of Gold Streamers	4
3.	Parachute Shells	4
4.	Discharge of ½-lb. Rockets, Red and Green	100
5.	Discharge of 5½-inch Shells, Blue and Yellow	50

Fifth Division.

1.	Flight of Rockets	200
2.	Batteries of Mines, Squibs	4
3.	Tourbillons	40
4.	Discharge of 1-lb. Rockets, Red and Green	100
5.	Discharge of 10-inch Shells, Tailed Stars	100

Sixth Division.

1.	Flight of Rockets	200
2.	Batteries of Pearl Streamers	4
3.	Parachute Shells	4
4.	Discharge of ½-lb. Rockets, Red	100
5.	Discharge of 5½-inch Shells, Green	50

Seventh Division.

1.	Flight of Rockets	200
2.	Batteries of Mines, Squibs	4
3.	Tourbillons	40
4.	Discharge of ½-lb. Rockets, Parachute	100
5.	Discharge of 10-inch Shells, Brilliant	50

Eighth Division.

1.	Flight of Rockets	200
2.	Batteries of Gold Streamers	4
3.	Parachute Shells	4
4.	Discharge of ½-lb. Rockets, Blue and Yellow	100
5.	Discharge of 5½-inch Shells, Variegated	50

Ninth Division.

1.	Flight of Rockets	200
2.	Batteries of Mines, Squibs	4
3.	Tourbillons	40
4.	Discharge of 1-lb. Rockets, Blue and Yellow	100
5.	Discharge of 10-inch Shells, Crackers	50

Tenth Division.

1.	Flight of Rockets	200
2.	Batteries of Pearl Streamers	4
3.	Parachute Shells	4
4.	Discharge of ½-lb. Rockets, Green	100
5.	Discharge of 5½-inch Shells, Red	50

Eleventh Division.

1.	Flight of Rockets	200
2.	Batteries of Mines, Squibs	4
3.	Tourbillons	40
4.	Discharge of ½lb. Rockets, Parachute	100
5.	Discharge of 10-inch Shells, Gold and Silver Rain	50

Twelfth Division.

1.	Flight of Rockets	200
2.	Batteries of Gold Streamers	4
3.	Parachute Shells	4
4.	Discharge of ½-lb. Rockets, Blue and Yellow	100
5.	Discharge of 5½-inch Shells, Green and Red	50

Thirteenth Division.

1.	Flight of Rockets	200
2.	Batteries of Mines, Squibs	4
3.	Tourbillons	40
4.	Discharge of 1-lb. Rockets, Blue and Yellow	100
5.	Discharge of 10-inch Shells, Squibs	100

Fourteenth Division.

Order		Number
1.	Flight of Rockets	200
2.	Batteries of Pearl Streamers	4
3.	Parachute Shells	4
4.	Discharge of ½-lb. Rockets, Blue	100
5.	Discharge of 5½-inch Shells, Yellow	50

Fifteenth Division.

1.	Flight of Rockets	200
2.	Batteries of Mines, Squibs	4
3.	Tourbillons	40
4.	Discharge of ½-lb. Rockets, Parachute	100
5.	Discharge of 10-inch Shells, Tailed Stars	100

Sixteenth Division.

1.	Flight of Rockets	200
2.	Batteries of Gold Streamers	4
3.	Parachute Shells	4
4.	Discharge of ½-lb. Rockets, Green and Red	100
5.	Discharge of 5½-inch Shells, Variegated	50

Seventeenth Division.

1.	Flight of Rockets	200
2.	Batteries of Mines, Squibs	4
3.	Tourbillons	40
4.	Discharge of 1-lb. Rockets, Blue and Yellow	50
	" ½-lb. ditto	50
5.	Discharge of 10-inch Shells, Brilliant	50

Eighteenth Division.

1.	Flight of Rockets	200
2.	Batteries of Pearl Streamers	4
3.	Parachute Shells	4
4.	Discharge of ½-lb. Rockets, Yellow	100
5.	Discharge of 5½-inch Shells, Blue	50

Nineteenth Division.

1.	Flight of Rockets	200
2.	Batteries of Mines, Squibs	4
3.	Tourbillons	40
4.	Discharge of ½-lb. Rockets, Parachute	100
5.	Discharge of 10-inch Shells, Crackers	50

Twentieth Division.

1.	Flight of Rockets	200
2.	Batteries of Gold Streamers	4
3.	Parachute Shells	4
4.	Discharge of 1-lb. Rockets, Blue and Yellow	100
5.	Discharge of 5½-inch Shells, Green and Red	50

Twenty-first Division.

1.	Flight of Rockets	200
2.	Batteries of Mines, Squibs	4
3.	Tourbillons	40
4.	Discharge of 1lb. Rockets, Green and Red	100
5.	Discharge of 10-inch Shells, Gold and Silver Rains	50

Twenty-second Division.

1.	Flight of Rockets	200
2.	Batteries of Pearl Streamers	4
3.	Parachute Shells	4
4.	Discharge of ½-lb. Rockets, Green and Red	50
	" 1-lb. " Blue and Yellow	50
5.	Discharge of 10-inch Shells, Squib	100

Twenty-third Division.

1.	Flight of Rockets	200
2.	Batteries of Mines, Squibs	4
3.	Tourbillons	40
4.	Discharge of 1-lb. Rockets, Green and Red	100
5.	Discharge of 10-inch Shells, Tailed Stars	100

Twenty-fourth Division. Finale.

1.	Fountain of 12 Pr. Gerbes	3
2.	Flight of Rockets	200
3.	Batteries of Mines, Squibs	10
	" Pearl Streamers	6
4.	Parachute Shells	6
5.	Tourbillons	60
6.	Discharge of 1-lb. Rockets — Red	56
	Green	56
	Blue	56
	Yellow	56
7.	Discharge of 10-inch Shells, Brilliants	100
8.	Flight of Rockets, 210, 560, 840, 1120, 1400, 1680, 1960, 2240	10010

E. M. BOXER, Capt. R.A.

Superintendent Royal Laboratories.

Sunderland 'frog' mug, *c*1856

Earthenware, with transfer-printing and hand-colouring, made in Sunderland, *c*1856, 12.4cm. h x 9.3cm. w x 13.3cm. d

Generously donated by Captain J D Norie

NAM. 1998-02-170

This mug is decorated with flags and emblems of the United Kingdom and France beneath the motto, with a frog inside and a stanza of doggerel, or verse, verso.

The earliest examples of mugs containing frogs date from about 1775. They were extremely popular as a novelty item and were viewed as a form of rustic joke. An unsuspecting guest would be surprised as he drank from the mug to see a frog emerging from the beverage which would then appear to spit through the hole in its mouth as the mug is tilted.

Victoria Cross, 1856

Generously donated by the Royal
United Service Institution

NAM. 1963-10-59

At an early stage of the
Crimean War it had been
agreed that a new medal,
open to all ranks, would be
instituted for acts of gallantry:
it came to be known as the
Victoria Cross. This, the
original prototype, was struck for submission to and the
approval of Queen Victoria in February 1856; it was
subsequently donated to the Royal United Service Institution
by Lieutenant-Colonel M P Hancock DSO, whose grandfather
founded the firm which made and still makes this decoration.
The earliest crosses – of which 111 were awarded for service
in the Crimean War - were cast from the bronze of captured
Russian cannon.

'Victoria Cross the new order of valour for the Army', 1857

Colour lithograph with wood engraving after artist unknown,
published in *The Illustrated London News*, 20 June 1857,
39.6cm. h x 27.7cm. w

Generously donated by Mrs W H Duggan

NAM. 1956-02-855-4

On 20 June 1857, *The Illustrated London News* published a
list of the recipients of honours and awards for bravery in the
Crimean War. In addition, the newspaper devoted four pages
to illustrations of the acts of gallantry by members of the Army
and the Royal Navy for which the newly-instituted Victoria
Crosses were awarded. Six days later, on 26 June, Queen
Victoria presented the Victoria Cross to 62 servicemen at the
first investiture ceremony for the new decoration.

Letter of Captain Frederick Elton, 1855

Manuscript, 19.8cm. h x 25cm. w

Generously donated by Lady Elton

NAM. 1988-01-3-29

Among the acts of gallantry celebrated by *The Illustrated London News* (see p365) was that of Major Frederick Cockayne Elton (1832-88), 55th (The Westmoreland) Regiment of Foot. Elton was awarded his Victoria Cross for setting an example to his men when working in the trenches under heavy fire on 4 August 1855; the citation also mentioned his bravery on 7 June 1855 when he 'was the first of the party to leave our trenches leading his men; when in the Quarries, he several times rallied his men around him.' Yet ironically enough, writing to his father in July 1855, Elton had at the time complained of the lack of recognition given to him and his men of the 55th for their night's work the previous month:

> [We are awfully disgusted at Lord Raglan's despatch about the Quarries. Our party was not only there but was so desperately engaged that we lost 1 Officer and 27 men killed and 28 wounded and yet the number of the Regiment is not even mentioned while in every other instance] or nearly so, every single officer is mentioned as having greatly distinguished themselves while they were most of them not nearly so forward as we were nor were they in nearly so much danger. It is enough to disgust one of ever going to the front again if it can be avoided and I should not be surprised if it had that effect on the men for of course they look out for being mentioned as a body in the papers just as much as we do.

or nearly so,- Every single officer is mentioned as having greatly distinguished themselves while they were most of them not half so forward as we were nor were they in nearly so much danger. It is enough to disgust one of ever going to the front again if it can be avoided and I should not be surprised if it had that effect on the men for of course they look out for being mentioned as a body in the papers just as much as we do - Have you received your musket and bayonet yet? I should think you ought by this time. Every thing is going on much as usual and the advanced trenches are getting more and more dangerous from the pernicious habit the Russians have of throwing shells into them night and day. The number they send is perfectly wonderful and at night the air is sometimes alive with them -
Best love to everyone -
Believe me &c &c F. Elton

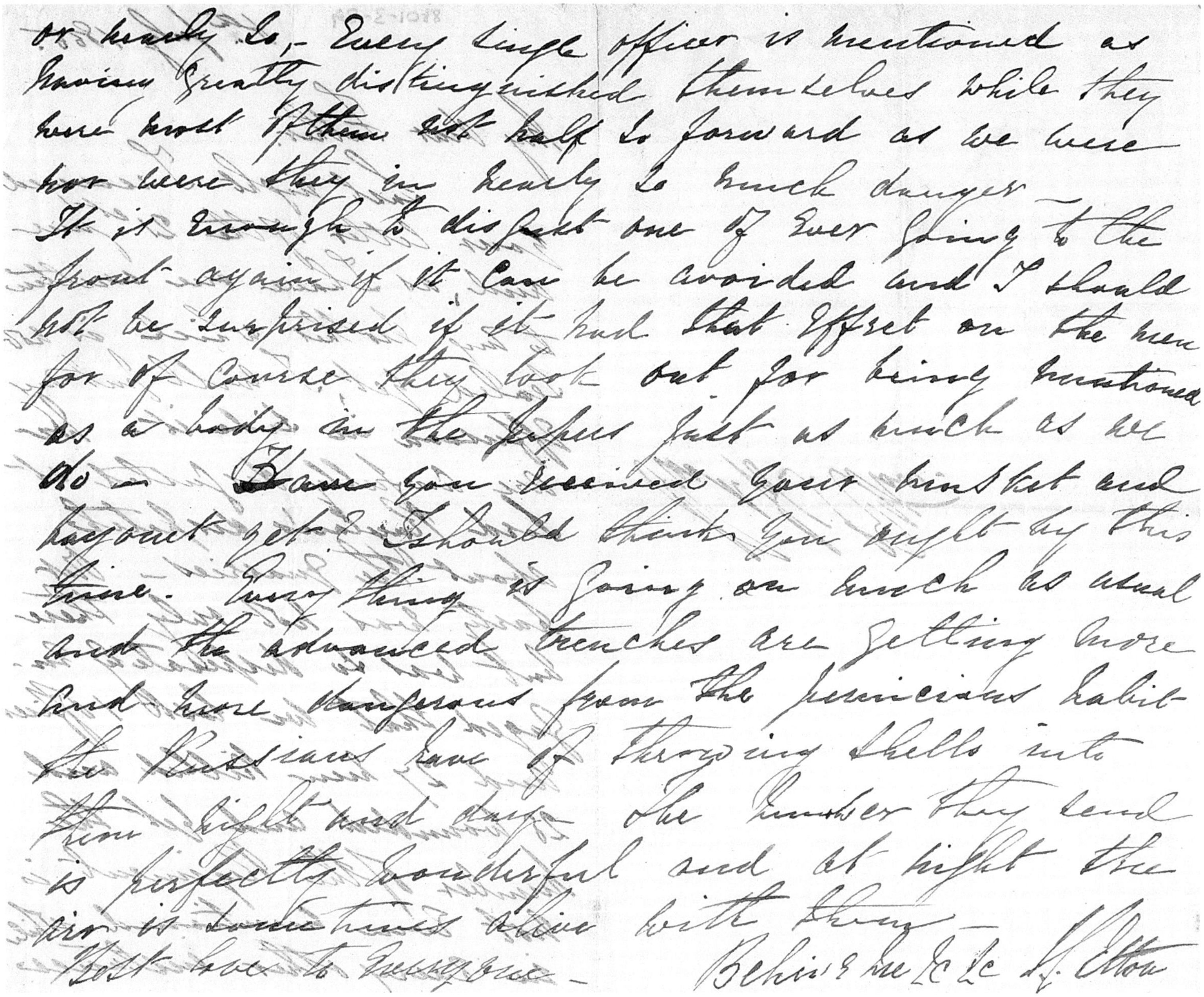

Alliance jug, *c*1856

Staffordshire pottery, with transfer-printed decoration, with the maker's mark 'GFS', 17cm. h x 17cm. w x 12cm. d

NAM. 1961-03-25

The jug bears the devices of two shields with the Royal Coats of Arms of the United Kingdom and France upon sprays of oak and laurel, with a rising sun in the background and above, the flags of the United Kingdom, Turkey and France emblazoned with Crimean battle honours.

selected members of the three Guards regiments who had performed outstanding service, at a time when insufficient official awards for gallantry were available. Ironically no member of the Coldstreams was ever to receive the medal, as the General had made the first presentation to the Grenadier Guards, whereupon the Coldstreams are said to have protested (on the grounds that the General, as an ex-Coldstream should have presented them with theirs first) and refused any awards. There are believed to have been 13 awards made, seven to the Grenadier Guards, two of whose recipients would later receive the VC, and five to the Scots Fusilier Guards. The thirteenth medal went to Pte John Alexander VC of the 90th Light Infantry, who had risked his life helping to save that of an officer in the Scots Fusilier Guards, in the trenches before Sevastopol on 6 September 1855.

Bentinck Medal, 1856

Silver, 35mm. diam

Awarded to Private John Main, Scots Fusilier Guards

The obverse depicts the Star of the Order of the Thistle, above which is the title: SCOTS FUSILIER GUARDS. On the reverse the medal is inscribed: FROM MAJ: GEN. BENTINCK TO PTE.. JOHN MAIN IN RECOGNITION OF THE RECIPIENT'S DISTINGUISHED CONDUCT DURING THE CAMPAIGN IN THE CRIMEA 1854-5. The inscription is in relief except for the recipient's name, which is engraved. The medal is attached to a foliate suspender similar to that of the Crimea War Medal.

NAM. 1982-07-31

The Bentinck medal was first presented in 1855 by Major-General Sir Henry Bentinck, formerly of the Coldstream Guards and Commander of the Guards Brigade in the Crimea. He intended to issue the medal in three different strikings to

Major-General Henry Bentinck

Photograph by Roger Fenton

NAM. Negative 46923

Major-General (later General Sir) Henry John William Bentinck (1796-1878) had first been commissioned into the Coldstream Guards in 1813 and led the Guards Brigade to the Crimea as a major-general. He was wounded in the arm at Inkerman and chose to return home to recover, which surprised the Army, Major-General William Codrington believing that his injury need not have kept him out of the saddle for more than ten days. He returned to the Crimea on I June 1855 to take command of the 4th Division, but he remained in post only until 10 October. 'Bentinck turned out an arrant imposter', concluded Captain Maxwell Earle, one of the 4th Division's brigade majors.

Memorandum calling for Explanations in regard to a section of the report of the Board of General Officers appointed to inquire into the statements contained in the reports of Sir John McNeill and Colonel Tulloch, animadverting upon the conduct of certain officers of the General Staff and others in the Army; together with the Explanation, and Appendix

Ordered, by the House of Commons to be Printed. 16 March 1857. 75pp, 32cm. h x 42.8cm. w

NAM. 33153

The commission of Sir John McNeill (1795-1883) and Colonel Alexander Murray Tulloch (1803-64) appointed by the Palmerston Government to inquire into the Commissariat in the Crimea had made its report in January 1856. While recognising that the lack of a metalled road between Balaklava and the camp before Sevastopol had been a contributory factor in the breakdown of supply to the Army, and that the home authorities had also been at fault for furnishing insufficient materials, it nevertheless criticised a number of Army officers and other officials for the delay in distributing stores. In response, the former commissary-general in the Crimea, William Filder (1789-1861), three generals – Lord Lucan, Lord Cardigan and Sir Richard Airey – and Colonel Alexander Gordon, demanded an inquiry into the report. A Board of General Officers sat at Chelsea from 3 April until 4 July 1856. All five aggrieved men were as a result cleared by the so-called 'Whitewashing Board'.

Filder had been vindicated because it was shown that the Treasury – at that date responsible for the Commissariat – had failed to meet his requests for supplies. Finding that the Treasury was blamed, the Government therefore called upon Sir Charles Trevelyan (1807-86) – the architect of the modern Civil Service - to furnish the additional explanations which the findings of the Chelsea tribunal apparently demanded, which he did in the course of this report, dated 2 February 1857.

Opening Address of Major-General Sir Richard Airey, K.C.B., Quartermaster-General of the Forces, before the Board of General Officers Assembled at the Royal Hospital, Chelsea

London, John Murray, 1856, 236pp, 20.5cm. h x 25cm. w

NAM. 13158

Airey's defence against the strictures of the McNeill and Tulloch Commission report was that the Quartermaster-General's Department had no responsibility for transport, a statement with which the Board of General Officers agreed. Major-General William Codrington had heard this line of reasoning before but had not been convinced, as he wrote on 21 January 1855:

> Lord Raglan and staff went about camp today and I rode along some time with him, and had much talk with Airey who somewhat surprised me by saying that he had nothing to do with the transport of the army - it was entirely under the Commissariat - this all sounded to me, funny. I am very glad I was not the Q[uarter] M[aster] G[eneral] though I think I should have considered all that the most essential part of my business.

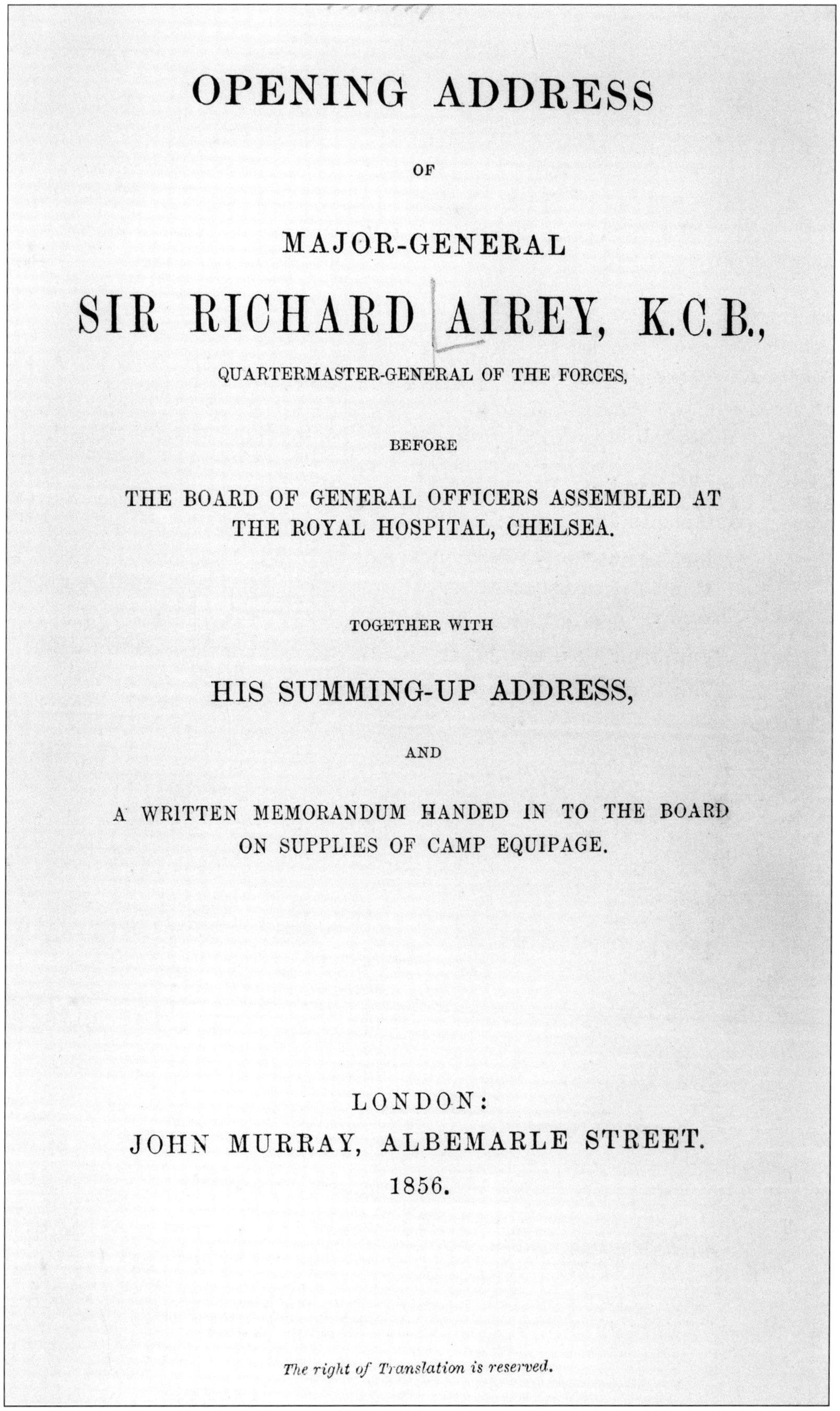

OPENING ADDRESS

OF

MAJOR-GENERAL

SIR RICHARD AIREY, K.C.B.,

QUARTERMASTER-GENERAL OF THE FORCES,

BEFORE

THE BOARD OF GENERAL OFFICERS ASSEMBLED AT THE ROYAL HOSPITAL, CHELSEA.

TOGETHER WITH

HIS SUMMING-UP ADDRESS,

AND

A WRITTEN MEMORANDUM HANDED IN TO THE BOARD ON SUPPLIES OF CAMP EQUIPAGE.

LONDON:
JOHN MURRAY, ALBEMARLE STREET.
1856.

The right of Translation is reserved.

'The Crimean Inquiry. - Examination of the Earl of Lucan', 1856

Wood engraving, artist unknown, published in *The Illustrated London News*, 19 April 1856, 17.5cm. h x 23.5cm. w

NAM. 18564

According to the report accompanying this illustration, the proceedings of the Board of General Officers held in the Great Hall of the Royal Hospital, Chelsea created more than a passing degree of interest: 'The attendance of the public has generally been pretty large, including a considerable number of ladies, who seem deeply interested in the inquiry into the causes of the frightful loss of life in the winter of 1854-5.'

Letters from Head-Quarters, or, the Realities of the War in the Crimea. By an Officer on the Staff

London, John Murray, 1856, volume 1 of 2, 445pp of 1004pp, 20.5cm. h x 29cm w

NAM. 8590

On 13 December 1856 Major Somerset John Gough Calthorpe, another of Lord Raglan's nephews to have served on his personal staff in the Crimea, published his two-volume history of the campaign. Lord Cardigan took exception to a number of its comments, particularly the allegation that when the Charge of the Light Brigade reached the Russian guns, at 'the moment when a General was most required, .. unfortunately Lord Cardigan was not then present'. It had been whispered for some time that before the third line of the Brigade even reached the guns, Cardigan had already been riding back to the British lines – which was true – but Cardigan nonetheless attempted to have Calthorpe court-martialled. After failing in this, Cardigan continued to harass Calthorpe until, in 1864, he decided to bring a case of libel against him. Although the judge's summing up was substantially in Cardigan's favour, the case was non-suited on the grounds that it was time-expired, five years having elapsed since publication of the book's third edition.

---

316   BATTLE OF BALAKLAVA.   CHAP. VII.

our handful of light cavalry advance down towards the Russian batteries. We all saw at once that a lamentable mistake had been made—by whose fault it was then impossible to say. Lord Raglan sent down two of his staff to ascertain the cause of all this, so little was it his intention that an attack of this nature should take place.

But to follow the fortunes of the light brigade. It consisted of scarce 700 horses, although composed of no less than five different regiments. In the first line were four squadrons of the 13th Light Dragoons and 17th Lancers; in the second were four squadrons of the 4th Light Dragoons and 11th Hussars. Again, in their rear was one squadron of the 8th Hussars, as a sort of reserve. As they started into a trot, poor Nolan galloped some way in front of the brigade, waving his sword and encouraging the men by voice and gesture. Before, however, they had gone any distance, the enemy's guns opened on them at long range. Nolan was the first man killed; some grape-shot hit him in the chest: his horse turned and carried him to the rear through our advancing squadrons. His screams were heard far above the din of battle, and he fell dead from his saddle near the spot where the order had been given for the charge. The pace of

CHAP. VII.   CHARGE OF LIGHT BRIGADE.   317

our cavalry increased every moment, until they went thundering along the valley, making the ground tremble beneath them. The awful slaughter that was going on, from the fire the enemy poured into them, apparently did not check their career. On they went, headlong to the death, disregarding aught but the object of their attack. At length they arrived at the guns, their numbers sadly thinned, but the few that remained made fearful havoc amongst the enemy's artillerymen. Scarce a man escaped, except those who crept under their gun-carriages, and thus put themselves out of the reach of our men's swords. This was the moment when a general was most required, but unfortunately Lord Cardigan was not then present. On coming up to the battery (as he afterwards himself described it), a gun was fired close to him, and for a moment he thought his leg was gone. Such was not the case, as he remained unhurt; however, his horse took fright — swerved round — and galloped off with him to the rear, passing on the way by the 4th Light Dragoons and 8th Hussars before those regiments got up to the battery. You may remember I mentioned that the enemy's cavalry were posted in rear of their guns. On our

Statement and remarks upon the affidavits filed by Lieut.-Col. Calthorpe in the Court of Queen's Bench; with some further evidence in contradiction of some of the statements contained in them

'Not Published', printed by John Mitchell, 33, Old Bond Street, London. 1864. 23pp, 30cm. h x 22.5cm. w

Generously donated by Mr G C Owen

In the libel action that he brought against Lieutenant-Colonel Calthorpe, Lord Cardigan printed the answers that he made in confutation of the sixteen affidavits submitted by the defendant. He printed at the same time nine statements gathered in support of his own claim that he had not retired from the combat prematurely. Among them was the testimony (shown here) of Private Robert Owen Glendwr of the 8th (The King's Royal Irish) Light Dragoons (Hussars).

NAM. 1977-06-6-6

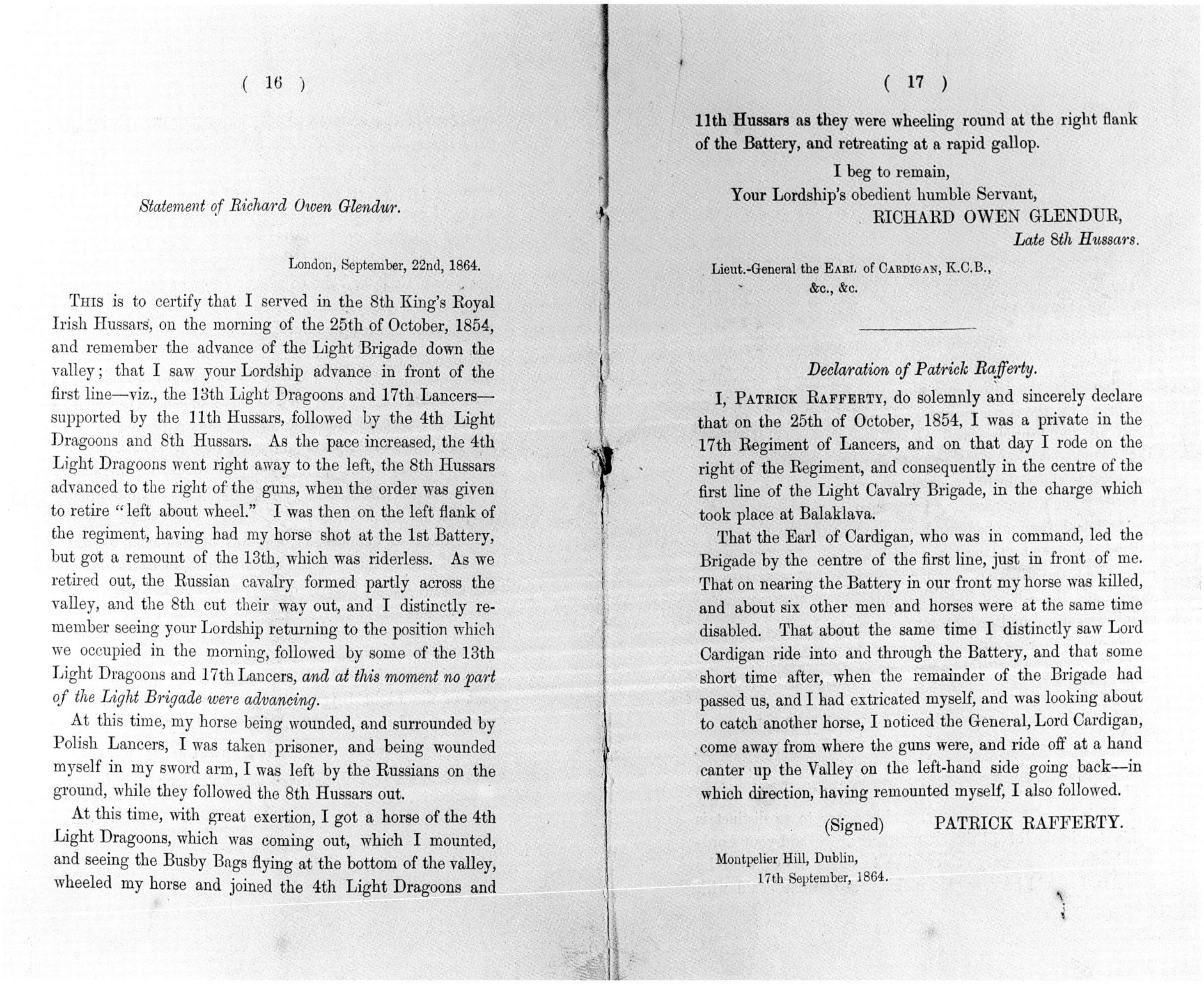

(16)

Statement of Richard Owen Glendur.

London, September, 22nd, 1864.

THIS is to certify that I served in the 8th King's Royal Irish Hussars, on the morning of the 25th of October, 1854, and remember the advance of the Light Brigade down the valley; that I saw your Lordship advance in front of the first line—viz., the 13th Light Dragoons and 17th Lancers—supported by the 11th Hussars, followed by the 4th Light Dragoons and 8th Hussars. As the pace increased, the 4th Light Dragoons went right away to the left, the 8th Hussars advanced to the right of the guns, when the order was given to retire "left about wheel." I was then on the left flank of the regiment, having had my horse shot at the 1st Battery, but got a remount of the 13th, which was riderless. As we retired out, the Russian cavalry formed partly across the valley, and the 8th cut their way out, and I distinctly remember seeing your Lordship returning to the position which we occupied in the morning, followed by some of the 13th Light Dragoons and 17th Lancers, *and at this moment no part of the Light Brigade were advancing.*

At this time, my horse being wounded, and surrounded by Polish Lancers, I was taken prisoner, and being wounded myself in my sword arm, I was left by the Russians on the ground, while they followed the 8th Hussars out.

At this time, with great exertion, I got a horse of the 4th Light Dragoons, which was coming out, which I mounted, and seeing the Busby Bags flying at the bottom of the valley, wheeled my horse and joined the 4th Light Dragoons and

(17)

11th Hussars as they were wheeling round at the right flank of the Battery, and retreating at a rapid gallop.

I beg to remain,
Your Lordship's obedient humble Servant,
RICHARD OWEN GLENDUR,
Late 8th Hussars.

Lieut.-General the EARL of CARDIGAN, K.C.B.,
&c., &c.

———————

Declaration of Patrick Rafferty.

I, PATRICK RAFFERTY, do solemnly and sincerely declare that on the 25th of October, 1854, I was a private in the 17th Regiment of Lancers, and on that day I rode on the right of the Regiment, and consequently in the centre of the first line of the Light Cavalry Brigade, in the charge which took place at Balaklava.

That the Earl of Cardigan, who was in command, led the Brigade by the centre of the first line, just in front of me. That on nearing the Battery in our front my horse was killed, and about six other men and horses were at the same time disabled. That about the same time I distinctly saw Lord Cardigan ride into and through the Battery, and that some short time after, when the remainder of the Brigade had passed us, and I had extricated myself, and was looking about to catch another horse, I noticed the General, Lord Cardigan, come away from where the guns were, and ride off at a hand canter up the Valley on the left-hand side going back—in which direction, having remounted myself, I also followed.

(Signed)   PATRICK RAFFERTY.

Montpelier Hill, Dublin,
17th September, 1864.

Medals awarded to Private Robert Glendwr, 1854-56

Crimea War Medal 1854-56, with clasps: Alma, Balaklava, Sebastopol; Turkish Crimean War Medal 1855, French issue.

Generously donated by Mr G C Owen

NAM. 1977-06-3

Robert Owen Glendwr was born c1833 and enlisted into the 8th (The King's Royal Irish) Light Dragoons (Hussars) in 1851. He embarked for the Crimea in the Horse Transport ship *Shooting Star* on 25 April 1854. Severely wounded during the Charge of the Light Brigade by two sabre cuts to his right arm, he also had two horses shot under him and was briefly taken prisoner before making his escape. He was invalided home on 22 December 1854.

Pattern 1853 Enfield Percussion Rifle Musket, .577 in., Windsor Pattern, 1856

Robbins & Lawrence, Windsor, Vermont

140cm. l

NAM. 1982-03-72

During the Crimean War there was a shortfall of Enfield Rifle Muskets. Insufficient numbers were being produced in the United Kingdom and, despite a contract for their manufacture being placed in Belgium, further assistance from both the United States and France was sought. An American contract was swiftly set up in February 1855 for 25,000 US rifle muskets, altered to the Enfield Bore, to be made by Robbins & Lawrence of Windsor, Vermont. Enfield Rifle Muskets made in Britain were variously stamped on the lock 'ENFIELD ' - for those made at the Royal Small Arms Factory at Enfield - 'LAC' for those manufactured by the London Armoury Company or 'TOWER' for other contract gunmakers. The American-produced Enfields were stamped with 'WINDSOR' on the lock.

Unforeseen financial difficulties at the company and complaints in Britain that the American Enfields were of inferior quality resulted in a total of only some 16,000 rifle muskets being produced in the US for the British Army.

Pattern 1856 Percussion Rifled Pistol, 1857

Tipping and Lawden, Birmingham

43cm. l

NAM. 1975-10-24

During the Crimean War, despite the widespread use of revolvers - which were largely purchased by officers - the higher echelons of the British Army remained unconvinced of their usefulness as a weapon. The general introduction of revolvers was consequently slow and for a time the Army even reverted to the single shot pistol.

This is an example of the rifled version of the Pattern 1842 Smoothbore Percussion Pistol which was introduced for lancers in 1856.

Pioneer Manners, and Guardsmen Webster and Lemmon, 1856 (right)

Photograph by J Cundall, 22.5cm. h x 18.7cm. w

NAM. 1964-12-154-6-4

Charles Manners, William Webster and Henry Lemmon of the Grenadier Guards wear the short-lived 1855 pattern double-breasted tunic. The latter two carry the Enfield Rifle.

Colour Sergeant's Full Dress Tunic, *c*1855-56 (left)

83rd Regiment of Foot

Generously donated by Mrs P G Mitchiner

NAM. 1953-06-15-1

The 83rd Regiment of Foot did not serve in the Crimea, although examples of the 1855 pattern tunic seen here were worn in the Crimea either by newly arrived regiments or by those troops already there who had received the new issue. The tunic was a considerable departure from the old coatee. Instead of being cut away at the front, the skirts of the tunic reached all the way round. Moreover, while the front of the coatee had been heavily covered in lace, the tunic was bereft. The collar too was lower and the buttons were made of brass rather than pewter.

This item of uniform was worn by Colour Sergeant J. Anderson, but he would not have done so for long: on 28 March 1856 it was announced that the double-breasted tunic would be replaced by a single-breasted version on 1 April the following year.

Drummer's Tunic and Epaulettes, *c*1855

Coldstream Guards

Generously Donated by H M Tower of London

NAM 1966-09-29, -1, -2

The Coldstream Guards' drummer's tunic, although ornate, was less heavily trimmed with white worsted lace than the coatee which it superseded. However, the lace retained its blue fleur de lys motif, which was common to all three regiments of the Guards. Among the Guards, the colouring of the blue and white worsted fringe to the collar and epaulettes was unique to the Coldstreams.

Shako, *c*1855-61

13th (1st Somersetshire) or Prince Albert's Regiment of Light Infantry

Black felt; black patent leather peaks

Generously donated by the Royal United Service Institution

NAM.1963-09-293

The French Pattern Shako introduced in 1855, although subtly different from the 'Albert' Shako which preceded it, still proved heavy and uncomfortable and was superseded by a lighter shako in 1861. The underside of the front peak bears the Adjutant-General's seal.

Knapsack, post-1856

Royal Artillery

40cm. w x 33cm. h x 10cm. d

NAM. 1997-05-5

An example of the type of knapsack produced at the end of the Crimean War, it has modified straps and a length of wood incorporated into the top inner edge, which acts as a strengthening stick. This improvement was officially introduced in 1856; however, it is known to have been applied to earlier knapsacks.

Markings on the knapsack indicate that it may have been stamped with a store or issue date of 1893, suggesting that this type of knapsack was still in use long after the introduction of valise equipment in 1871.

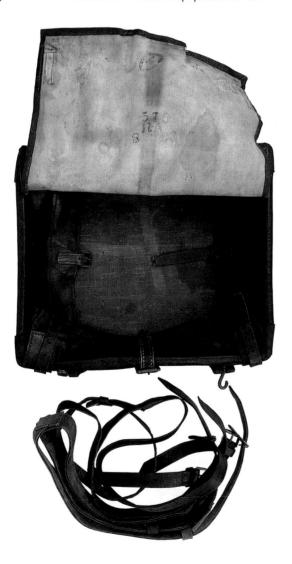

Infantry Ammunition Pouch, 1860; Pouch Belt and Percussion Cap Pouch, post-1855

23cm. l x 13cm. w x 11cm. d (pouch): 57cm. l x 6.5cm. w (belt); 10.5cm. l (cap pouch)

NAM. 1977-08-25-1, -2, –3

Although this British Army ammunition pouch is dated 1860, it is of the type worn in the Crimea. It is attached to a separate buff leather pouch belt, which was worn with the new waist belt. Some infantry troops were issued with the waist belt and pouch at the beginning of the Crimean War and gradually these replaced the old, uncomfortable cross straps. The interior of the pouch is fitted with a five-compartment tin tray and a black leather pocket for percussion caps is stitched to the inside front; the pocket is a feature which possibly was added after the Crimean War. The small buff leather pouch on the belt carried copper percussion caps and this example is stamped with the War Department mark, 'WD', which dates it after 1855.

The pouch belt passes through a loop in the back of the ammunition pouch and the cap pouch has an integral loop that allows it to slide onto the belt.

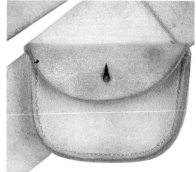

Other Rank's ankle boots, Universal Pattern, *c*1856

Coldstream Guards

Brown Leather

NAM. 1977-05-35-2

The British infantry adopted half boots, instead of shoes, in 1823. These boots were expected to be worn on alternate feet to give 'even' wear. No eyelet holes were punched; these had to be made individually by the wearer for comfort, hence the eyelet holes are not rimmed. In 1838 the half boot was replaced with the Cossack boot, which was similar in design. It was not until *c*1850 that the boots were constructed on individual lasts for each foot.

The inner quarters of the boots are marked inside with a large heavily impressed date of 1856 and the regimental details COLDST/GUARDS in slightly smaller lettering.

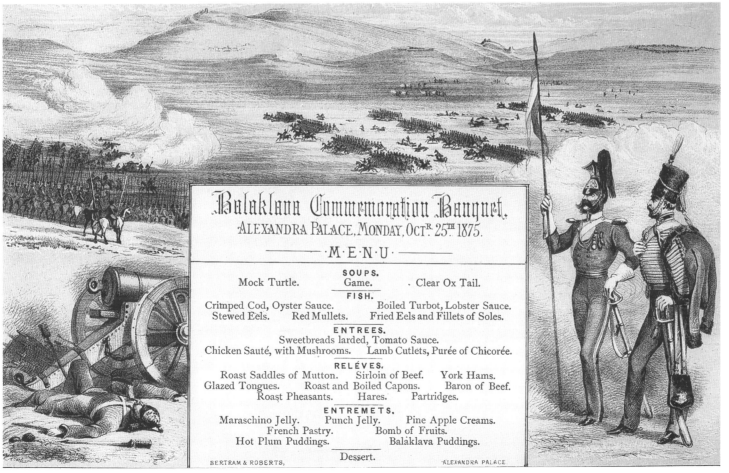

Menu for the Balaklava Commemoration Banquet, 1875

Printed, 25.2cm. h x 32.8cm. w

Generously donated by Mrs J C Forster

NAM. 1992-08-356-1

Although officers of the Light and Heavy Cavalry Brigades had held a reunion dinner in 1866, the Balaklava Commemoration Banquet held at Alexandra Palace on the 21st anniversary of the Charge of the Light Brigade was the first large-scale reunion of non-commissioned officers and other ranks, with 120 attending.

Invitation issued to R O Glendwr to attend the Balaklava Banquet, 1876

Printed and manuscript, 9cm. h x 12cm. w

Generously donated by Mr G C Owen

NAM. 1977-06-6-6

The resounding success of the 1875 banquet led to a repeat the following year on the twenty-second anniversary of the Charge of the Light Brigade. It was then decided to establish the 'Balaclava Commemoration Society', which organised the annual reunion in the years ahead.

'Some of the survivors of the Balaclava Charge 25th October 1854 XXXIII Anniversary Dinner 1887'

19cm. h x 24.5cm. w

NAM. 1987-10-56

In June 1887 the survivors had signed a Loyal Address to Queen Victoria to coincide with her Golden Jubilee celebrations. In 1897, on the occasion of the Diamond Jubilee, the survivors received honoured places overlooking the procession route.

Menu for the "Balaclava" Dinner held on the Battle's 59th Anniversary, 1913

Print and manuscript, 17.7cm. h x 21.6cm. w

Generously donated by Lady Thornton

NAM. 1967-11-23

This was the last annual dinner to be held and was attended by six survivors of the Charge of the Light Brigade. The menu is inscribed with the signatures of three of them: James Mustard (d.1916), 17th Lancers; William Henry Pennington (d.1923), 11th Hussars; and Henry Wilsden (d.1916), 4th Light Dragoons. The Charge of the Light Brigade, and the Crimean War as a whole, was increasingly slipping beyond living memory.

Soyer Stove, Sealed Pattern, 1953

Transfer from Ministry of Defence, Quality Assurance Directorate

NAM. 2002-12-6

The Soyer stove, named after its inventor Alexis Soyer (1809-58), was first used in the Crimean War. It was so successful that it continued in use in the British Army with minor modifications for over 100 years. This example, which was manufactured in Wolverhampton in 1953 as a sealed pattern for the Army, is of the same type as that used in the Crimea.

Alexis Soyer, the French chef of the Reform Club, had been troubled by reports of the difficulties encountered by soldiers trying to cook their food rations in the Crimea. In 1855 he travelled to the East at his own expense and, with the introduction of his new portable stove and easy to make recipes, he managed radically to improve the way the British soldiers were fed. His portable field stoves were very simple to use and economical.

According to Soyer's own calculations they could save an army of 40,000 men 90 tons of fuel per day. One stove could cook sufficient for fifty and be used either indoors or out, as they would work in all weather conditions, including heavy rain.

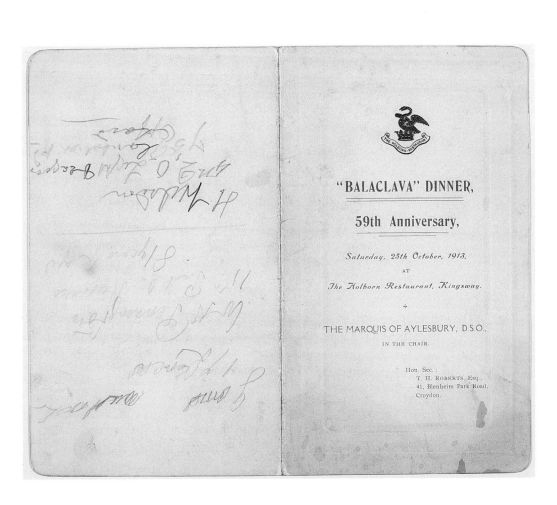

'Half a crown and a Pennyworth of ugly ribbon'?
How the Crimean War helped to shape the development of Britain's system of military awards

Lesley Smurthwaite

> The value attached by soldiers to a little bit of ribbon is such as to render any danger insignificant and any privation light if it can be attained.
>
> (Henry Pelham Pelham-Clinton, 5th Duke of Newcastle)[1]

Whether he appreciated it or not at the time, it is true to say that the British soldier serving in Her Majesty's Army before the start of the Crimean War had little to look forward to in the way of honours, medals or decorations to repay his endurance on campaign and bravery in the field.

Just as the War eventually would be seen by some as a watershed in British military history, influencing reforms in the organisation, tactics and weapons of the Army, as well as improvements in their dress and equipment, equally it was a time of significant developments in the field of honours and awards.

Among the factors that brought about these changes, not least was an unprecedented public awareness of the conditions under which British soldiers were fighting. Improved communications and the relative proximity of the War to Britain, as compared to recent campaigns in India, China and Africa, meant that eye witness accounts brought home with a new immediacy the extent of the hardships endured in the harsh Crimean winter and the signal acts of bravery and self sacrifice that were displayed by so many on the field of battle.

Another influence on public opinion was the discrepancy between the military honours available in this country and those decorations seen to be conferred by Britain's Allies. The Order of the Bath, open only to senior officers, did not compare favourably in terms of inclusiveness with France's Legion of Honour, which was awarded to her soldiers from the highest to the lowest rank.

Perhaps the most powerful and effective instrument of change was Queen Victoria herself and the personal interest and concern that she took in her army. Most of all, she paid close personal attention to everything to do with awards and medals and her correspondence bears witness to this.[2]

Ultimately, whilst there may be disagreement over who initiated it, there can be no doubt that without the Queen's intervention, and that of her husband Prince Albert, it is unlikely that Britain's most highly prized military award for gallantry, the Victoria Cross, would have come into being as we know it. The Crimean War was to provide the inspiration for its creation.

Existing awards at the start of the Crimean War

Gallantry awards to officers

After 1815 the only visible and tangible award for gallantry that most officers could expect was the Companionship of the Order of the Bath (CB). Even this, the Third and lowest class of the Order was limited to officers of field rank (i.e. majors) and above. Prince Albert highlighted its defects when he wrote in a memo to the Duke of Newcastle on 22 January 1855:

> It has been found open to the following objections, service officers feel, that their services may have been equally meritorious under those [sic] of their commander, and yet are left unremarked. The limitation of numbers must leave many cases of necessity unrewarded. The difficulty of distinguishing between the merits of different officers in responsible situations and the unwillingness on the part of Commanders to incur the odium of making the distinction, have led them to mention nearly everybody in their Dispatches and the Govt is then left, either to do possible injustice or to allow the reward to become a mere appendage of a certain rank.[3]

Indeed, when Queen Victoria received the very long list of proposed nominations to the Order in 1856 she returned it to Lord Panmure demanding 'an explanation of the services of the officers, and the reasons for which they were selected for the honour'.[4]

Another reward theoretically available to all officers for acts of gallantry or distinguished service was promotion to brevet rank, which gave the recipient a higher army rank than that enjoyed by him within his regiment. This was also limited, as virtually all promotions were conferred upon officers with staff appointments (as opposed to regimental officers in the firing line), although there was provision for one sergeant per regiment to earn a commission through distinguished service.

Another means of recognising gallantry, mentions in despatches, had long been a practice in the Army, but as with the Order of the Bath, it was indiscriminate, and like brevet promotions it was almost exclusively given to staff officers.

Not only was there effectively no gallantry award available to junior officers, other ranks also lacked any consistent form of recognition for outstanding service other than the gratuities and annuities that were awarded on a strictly limited basis to those receiving Long Service or

Meritorious Service medals (not in themselves gallantry awards). This would be addressed to some extent in 1854, with the creation of the Distinguished Conduct Medal (DCM).

Gallantry awards to other ranks

In 1830 the Long Service and Good Conduct Medal was authorised for soldiers who received a gratuity for 'meritorious conduct' on discharge and in 1845 the Meritorious Service Medal was instituted as an award for senior non-commissioned officers. Under the terms of the latter, £2,000 was made available annually for annuities not exceeding £20 each to be awarded to sergeants for 'distinguished or meritorious service'. At this time the conditions for award of the Long Service and Good Conduct Medal were that the recipient must 'have never been convicted by Court Martial, and must have borne an irreproachable character, or…must have particularly distinguished themselves by gallantry and zeal in Our Service'.[5]

In effect the Long Service and Good Conduct Medal was never awarded for 'gallantry and zeal', although the MSM appears to have been awarded for gallantry in a few instances. Even allowing for these conditions it would be fair to say that at the outbreak of the Crimean War no award exclusively for gallantry was available to corporals and privates, while for sergeants and above the Meritorious Service Medal was itself of limited and indeterminate status.

By a Royal Warrant of 4 December 1854[6] the total figure available for annuities was increased to £4,000, for which one sergeant in each cavalry regiment or battalion of infantry or Foot Guards was to be selected. Also, one sergeant, two corporals and four privates in each regiment were to receive a gratuity of £15 (sergeants), £10 (corporals) and £5 (privates), this gratuity to be accompanied by a medal. These provisions applied only to Raglan's army in the Crimea and the restriction on numbers and available finances was to cause confusion and resentment in the Army, especially as the Warrant made no mention of Artillery or Sappers and Miners. It was, however, eventually allowed that 64 medals should be given to the Royal Artillery (four with annuity) and 16 to the Royal Sappers and Miners (one with annuity).

On 21 December 1854 the Commander-in-Chief, Lord Hardinge, suggested that another medal should be struck, for gallantry, similar to the Long Service and Good Conduct, and that the inscription should read 'For Distinguished Conduct in the Field'. This medal would be available for award either with a gratuity or an annuity.[7]

A specimen medal was submitted to Queen Victoria on 25 January 1855 and on 2 February a quantity of medals was ordered for

'immediate issue'. A bulk consignment was sent to the Crimea on 26 March, followed by another on 3 April and a third on 14 May.
The United Service Gazette announced on 31 March 1855 'We are glad to announce that these Medals were forwarded to the Crimea this week. It is a very handsome medal with a red ribbon and blue centre'.

Sergeant Robert Turner, serving in the Royal Artillery, was awarded not only the Long Service and Good Conduct Medal with a gratuity of £10,

Sergeant Robert Turner's medals sewn onto his Royal Artillery full dress tunic. NAM. 1988-04-10

but also, according to his discharge certificate dated 21 January 1867[8] he was 'granted a Medal for "Distinguished Service in the Field" and a Gratuity of £5'. This was despite his having previously been convicted (for an unrecorded offence) by Court Martial, leading to imprisonment for 3 days in June 1851 and reduction in rank from corporal to gunner and driver. Turner, who also qualified for the Crimea War Medal with clasps for Alma, Inkerman and Sebastopol, and the Turkish Crimea Medal, as well as the MSM and Long Service and Good Conduct Medal, was to serve later in life as Assistant Master Gunner at Fort Belvedere, Windsor, where he died in 1910 at the age of 89.

The Victoria Cross

> Nothing could be more plain and homely, not to say coarse-looking… the whole cross is, after all, poor looking and mean in the extreme (*The Times*, 27 June 1857).

An aged Sergeant Robert Turner photographed as the Master Gunner at Fort Belvedere. NAM. 1980-03-93-1

The subject of a new gallantry award was raised in Parliament on 19 December 1854 by a Member named Capt George Treweeke Scobell, who moved in the House of Commons,

> That an humble address be presented to Her Majesty praying that she would be graciously pleased to institute an "Order of Merit" to be bestowed upon persons serving in the Army or Navy for distinguished and prominent personal gallantry during the present war and to which every grade and individual, from the highest to the lowest, in the United Services, may be admissible.[9]

A similar proposal was expressed by the Duke of Newcastle, Secretary of State for War. He wrote to Prince Albert on 20 January 1855;

> Your Royal Highness will recollect that some time ago I expressed an opinion that the circumstances of the present campaign and the alliance in which we have engaged in it seem to render either an extension of the Order of the Bath or the institution of some new Order of Merit…
>
> Your Royal Highness mentioned several objections to the proposition of adding to the three classes of the Order of the Bath, and I hope I am not taking too great a liberty if I ask Your Royal Highness's opinion upon the other suggestion, the institution of a new decoration to be confined to the Army and Navy, but open to all ranks of either service.
>
> I confess it does not seem to me right or politic that such deeds of heroism as this war has produced should go unrewarded by any distinctive outward mark of honour because they are done by Privates or by Officers below the rank of Major, and it is impossible to believe that HM troops fighting side by side with those of France do not draw an invidious contrast

between the rewards bestowed upon themselves and their allies.[10]

Prince Albert's response was favourable and on 29 January 1855 Newcastle announced in the House of Lords the decision to institute 'a Cross of Merit which would be open to all ranks of the Army in future'.[11]

Lord Panmure (Secretary of State for War in Palmerston's new government) wrote to Lord Raglan on 26 March 1855 'You know, I presume, that an order of merit is under preparation which will pervade all ranks.'[12] It was not until a year later however, when the War was about to end, that the Royal Warrant was drafted under which the Victoria Cross (VC) came into being. The Warrant, signed on the 29 January 1856 announced the institution of 'a New Naval and Military Decoration, which we are desirous should be highly prized and eagerly sought after by the officers and men of Our Naval and Military Services'. It was to be awarded only 'to those… who have served Us in the presence of the enemy, and…have performed some signal act of valour, or devotion to their country'.[13] The names of those on whom the decoration was conferred would be published in *The London Gazette*. Furthermore all VC winners below the rank of commissioned officer were to receive a pension of £10 a year to accompany the award and on receiving a bar, denoting a further act of gallantry, an extra £5 pension would be awarded.

The prototype VC, submitted to and approved by Queen Victoria, now in the National Army Museum (NAM.1963-10-59), was produced by the London jewellers, Messrs Hancock and Co. Its design, described by *The Times* as 'coarse looking' and 'mean in the extreme' consisted of a bronze cross pattée, referred to (incorrectly) in the Warrant as a 'Maltese Cross',[14] bearing on its obverse the Royal Crest, a crowned lion statant gardant upon a crown, beneath which a scroll bears the words 'For Valour', which the Queen herself is said to have preferred to the proposed motto: 'For the brave'. The reverse of the Cross was to be engraved with the date of the act of gallantry, with the name, rank and unit of the recipient on the reverse of the suspender bar. The earliest crosses were cast from the bronze of Russian guns captured in the Crimea, though later this metal would be superseded by the bronze of Chinese guns. The ribbon worn with the Cross was originally dark blue for awards to the Royal Navy and crimson (described in the Warrant as 'red') for the Army (this remained the case until 1918 with the formation of the Royal Air Force, when a crimson ribbon was adopted for all three services).

Awards of the new decoration were made retrospective to the start of the Crimean War, although the first act of gallantry to be so recognised occurred not in the Crimea but in the Baltic. Charles David Lucas, a midshipman in the Royal Navy, aged only 20, had the distinction of being the first VC winner, on 21 June 1854 during the bombardment of

As intended, the Victoria Cross became much sought after. In 1866 Lieutenant John Brophey, late of the 3rd Royal Lancashire Militia, who had received the Distinguished Conduct Medal for his actions as a colour-sergeant with the 63rd (The West Suffolk) Regiment of Foot at Inkerman twelve years before, unsuccessfully petitioned the Commander-in-Chief, the Duke of Cambridge, for the retrospective award of the VC.
NAM. 1975-04-79-1

THE ILLUSTRATED LONDON NEWS

JUNE 20, 1857.

ACTS OF BRAVERY DURING THE LATE WAR.

GERALD GRAHAM (LIEUT.) GALLANTLY BRINGING IN WOUNDED MEN.

MACGREGOR (PRIVATE) HAVING CROSSED THE OPEN IN BROAD DAYLIGHT, DISLODGED TWO RUSSIANS FROM THE RIFLE PITS.

ALEXANDER WRIGHT (PRIVATE) GALLANTLY REPELLING A SORTIE MARCH 22, 1855.

JOHN ROSS (CORPORAL) INTREPIDLY ASCERTAINING THE EVACUATION OF THE REDAN.

McWHEENEY, (SERGEANT) DIGGING WITH HIS BAYONET A COVER FOR HIS WOUNDED COMRADE, CORPORAL COURTNEY.

G. L. GOODLAKE (BREVET MAJOR) SURPRISING THE ENEMY'S PICKET AT WINDMILL RAVINE.

HONOUR · TO THE · BRAVE

Some of the acts of bravery which merited the award of the newly instituted Victoria Cross, as commemorated in *The Illustrated London News*.
NAM. 1969-10-349

Bomarsund. He was immediately commissioned lieutenant and eventually rose to the rank of rear admiral. Three naval VCs were awarded for this campaign. The first awards to be won in land operations were at the Alma in the Crimea on 20 September 1854, where six VCs were earned, four by the 1st Battalion, Scots Fusilier Guards (later the Scots Guards): Lieutenant J Knox, Major R J Lindsay, Sergeant J McKechnie and Private W Reynolds. The other two VC winners were Captain Edward William Derrington Bell and Sergeant Luke O'Connor, both of the 23rd (Royal Welsh Fusiliers) Regiment of Foot.

Lieutenant (later General Sir) Mark Walker, whose Victoria Cross is now in the National Army Museum (NAM. 2001-02-433), was one of thirteen soldiers to receive the VC for bravery at Inkerman on 5 November 1854.

Altogether 111 VCs were awarded for service in the Crimean War, of which 84 were won by the Army, 24 by the Royal Navy and three by the Royal Marines, the first and last awards being naval, in the Baltic on 21 June 1854, and in the Sea of Azov on 10 October 1855. Out of this number 62 officers and men received their crosses personally from Queen Victoria at a presentation ceremony held in Hyde Park on the morning of 26 June 1857, an event which had its precedent in the Queen's public presentation of Crimea War Medals at Horse Guards two years earlier.

Campaign medals

The Crimea War Medal

The Crimea War Medal was the first campaign medal to be struck and issued during hostilities to all troops serving in a particular theatre of war. Its genesis lay in a letter written by Queen Victoria on 30 November 1854 (when the Army had been in the Crimea for less than three months) urging that no time should be lost in announcing the intention of Her pleasure to confer a Medal on all those who have been engaged in the arduous and brilliant campaign in the Crimea. The Medal should have the word 'Crimea' on it with an appropriate device (for which it would be well to lose no time in having a design made) and Clasps, like to the Peninsula Medal, with the names 'Alma' and 'Inkermann' inscribed on them – according to who had been in one or both battles… The Queen is sure that nothing will gratify and encourage our noble troops more than the knowledge that this is to be done.[15]

The medal having been authorised under General Order No 638, Horse Guards 15 December 1854, designs were hastily submitted to the Queen for approval. The design of the medal was not particularly popular, being thought by some to be vulgar and ugly, while the unusually ornate clasps were compared by some officers to gin or port decanter labels. It is interesting to note that this fanciful design would not be adopted for clasps on any future campaign medals, most probably for reasons of practicality and expense. Eventually five clasps would be authorised for the Crimea War Medal: 'Alma', 'Balaklava', 'Inkermann', 'Sebastopol' and 'Azoff', the last being only awarded to naval personnel and marines. The ribbon chosen by the Queen was to be 'light blue with a yellow edge'.[16]

The first issues of the medal carried only the clasps: 'Alma' and 'Inkermann'. A clasp for Balaklava, although not initially approved - in view of the disastrous events that took place there - would be added in due course after intervention on the part of the Army's commanders in the field. On 22 January 1855 Newcastle wrote to the Queen referring her to 'a private letter from Lord Lucan urging that a Clasp should be given for the action at Balaklava – Lord Cardigan has since pressed the same request – so have several others' adding that he (Newcastle) was of the opinion that 'the Action was attended with sufficient success, so far as the result in its effect upon the Enemy was concerned, to justify this distinction, whilst the valour and conduct of the Troops were probably never surpassed on any occasion'.[17]

In her reply, written the following day, the Queen agreed to sanction the award, but with reservations:

> she will not withhold her consent, but she thinks that by doing so the value of the Clasps is lessened and the object of the Medal likewise to a certain degree effected. The 26th of October was a decided victory and the Queen thinks that Sir Lacy de Gurney [sic] and those under him will feel there is a want of justice in giving a Clasp for the 25th and not the 26th,

yet it would clearly be impossible to give a Clasp for every incident in a Campaign or Siege.[18]

The Balaklava clasp was authorised on 23 February and the first consignment of war medals was sent out to the Crimea in August 1855. One senior officer wrote 'I fear the Trenches are very hot just now… a Clasp should be granted for 'The Trenches' – it would be most popular with the army'.[19] The hard-earned clasp for Sevastopol which the Queen approved on 12 September would be sent later, separately, for attaching to medals already awarded. A memo of 5 December 1855 from Colonel G C Mundy, Under Secretary for War, records that Lord Panmure 'is of the opinion that Sevastopol Clasps should be sent out to the Crimea and fixed or attached to the Medals there. Sir James Simpson has reported that a skilful Armourer is employed for this purpose.'[20] Despite this there were many cases of individuals fitting their own clasp for Sevastopol or not attaching it at all and of course many who would have been eligible had died before they could receive it. In addition, medals to the Army are often found with their clasps in the wrong order, owing to the late award of the Balaklava clasp. They should correctly read upwards from the bottom: 'Alma', 'Balaklava', 'Inkermann', 'Sebastopol'.

Unlike most campaign medals awarded in the nineteenth century, the Crimea medal was not officially named before being issued, except in the case of casualties. This was done chiefly to avoid administrative delay. The recipient could return his medal free of charge to his unit for naming, or it could be done privately. However many preferred to retain their medals and have them privately named. This accounts for the great variety in forms of naming, both engraved and impressed to be seen on Crimea War Medals, and for the fact that in some cases the recipient's army number appears on the rim of the medal and in others it does not, a matter of frustration to medal collectors and researchers alike.

Queen Victoria's preoccupation with medals and her genuine concern for her troops was evident in a desire to present medals personally to those who had returned home. On 22 March 1855 she wrote to Panmure that she thought 'the value of the Medal would be greatly enhanced if she were personally to deliver it to the Officers and a certain number of men selected for that purpose'.[21]

Accordingly Lord Panmure wrote to Lord Raglan on 26 March that 'The Queen is to present the Crimea Medals publicly to detachments of Officers and Men from every Corps in the Crimea. You never saw anybody so entirely taken up with military affairs as she is.'[22] The presentation ceremony took place at Horse Guards at 10 am on 18 May

1855 and those honoured were, from each regiment or corps, all the officers, one non-commissioned officer and three privates, who were entitled to the medal. Victoria was to write of the event in her journal:

> The sight here was magnificent and overpowering… At first I felt so agitated, I could hardly hold the medal as I handed it with its blue and yellow edged ribbon…The Medals are to be given up again, so to have the Men's names engraved upon them, but they were most anxious not to do so, saying that they could not be sure of receiving the same medals back as I had given them. This is very touching.

Some 275,000 Crimea War Medals were issued in all, including a large number to the troops of Britain's allies, France, Turkey, and Sardinia. This in itself was unprecedented (and largely prompted by cordial relations between Queen Victoria and the allied Heads of State).

Queen Victoria presenting Lieutenant-Colonel Sir Thomas Troubridge, 7th Regiment of Foot (Royal Fusiliers) with his Crimea War Medal on Horse Guards Parade, 18 May 1855. Troubridge lost both feet at Inkerman.
NAM. 1960-12-322-27

The Baltic Medal

The Army played a small but not insignificant part in operations in the Baltic which, although they preceded the campaign in the Crimea, would not be recognised by a medal until 23 April 1856, eighteen months after the Crimea War Medal had been authorised. The institution of the Baltic Medal was officially announced in *The London Gazette* of 6 June 1856. The Army's contribution to the Baltic expedition consisted entirely of a contingent of Royal Engineers and Sappers and Miners and, even allowing for the limited numbers involved, very few soldiers would survive to receive a medal.[23] This was partly due to the high incidence of cholera in the Baltic, added to which a number went on to fight and become casualties in the Crimea.

Foreign awards

Britain's unprecedented generosity in issuing Crimea War Medals to the Allied forces inspired the other nations to respond with comparable or equivalent awards to our soldiers and sailors. Tancred's *Historical Records of Medals and Honorary Distinctions* [24] records that 'France decorated 543 officers in the British Army, and 166 in the Royal Navy with the Legion of Honour, and also gave her War Medal [*Médaille Militaire*] to 500 British soldiers. His Majesty the King of Sardinia had a medal struck for the Crimea, and presented it to 243 officers and 157 non-commissioned officers and privates of the army'. The author also records that 'Turkey, to show her gratitude to England, distributed the large number of nearly 1,200 Orders of the Medjidie to British Officers, and also gave a Silver Medal to every individual who had served in the Crimea before the surrender of Sebastopol.'[25] Although the Turkish Crimea Medal is commonly seen in conjunction with the Crimea War Medal awarded to British soldiers, Raglan's army did not in the event receive a full quota of some 75,000 Turkish Crimea Medals claimed. It should also be noted that unlike the British Crimea Medal the Turkish Medal was not issued to the next-of-kin of those who died.

The Duke of Cambridge presenting the British Crimea War Medal to French troops in Paris, 15 January 1856. NAM. 1988-06-77-6

Other more rarely seen Turkish medals were conferred on a limited number of British army personnel qualified to receive them, notably medals for the defence of Silistria (1854) and Kars (1855), and the Turkish General Service Medal, instituted in 1831. An example of the latter, awarded in gold to General William Fergusson Beatson is in the National Army Museum (NAM.1963-11-31).

Regimental Medals

Examples of unofficial medals for service in the Crimea, awarded privately or by regiments to deserving soldiers, are far less numerous than those produced during the Napoleonic Wars, when no official campaign awards were available. Three silver medals, each quite different in design are held in the National Army Museum. The Bentinck Medal, not strictly a regimental award, as it was intended for issue in different strikings to selected members of all three Guards regiments, was presented in1855 by Major-General Sir Henry J Bentinck, formerly of the Coldstream Guards, who during the War commanded the Guards Brigade, and later the 4th Division. He felt a need to reward those guardsmen who had performed outstanding service at a time when insufficient awards for gallantry were available. There are believed to have been 13 awards of the Bentinck Medal, of which seven were to the Grenadier Guards, (two of whose recipients would later receive the VC, Sergeant Alfred Ablett, - also awarded the DCM - and Private Anthony Palmer). Five medals went to the Scots Fusilier Guards, including Sergeant James Craig VC for attempting to save the life of Captain Buckley, an officer in his Regiment, at the Redan on 6 September 1855, and another to Private John Main, whose medal is in the National Army Museum (NAM.1982-07-31). The thirteenth medal was awarded to Private John Alexander VC of the 90th Regiment of Foot (Perthshire Volunteers) (Light Infantry) who had also risked his life in rescuing Captain Buckley.

The other two regimental medals in the Museum are both to soldiers in the 3rd (East Kent) Regiment of Foot (The Buffs). One of these was awarded to Private John Fahey, for bravery on 14 August 1855 when he was on picket duty and stood his ground throughout the night amidst heavy enemy fire, an act for which he was also awarded the Sardinian War Medal (NAM. 2001-08-94).

The second Buffs medal was awarded to none other than Private John Connors VC. A handsome, engraved medal with an ornate border, its design consisting of the numeral 3 between twin laurel sprays, with a crown above, surrounded by the words: 'A TOKEN OF ADMIRATION AND ESTEEM'. On the reverse are engraved the words: 'FROM HIS COMRADES To Pte J. Connors. In recognition of his remarkable Gallantry during the assault on the Redan SEPT. 8TH.. 1855' (NAM. 2001-08-210-4).

The Crimean War was by no means the only influence for change and development in nineteenth century British military awards, though it could be said to have paved the way for many future improvements and additions to the awards system. The War (and Prince Albert) undoubtedly influenced a number of reforms to the statutes governing the Order of the Bath, which included extending membership and, in the words of J C Risk, 'For the first time the Order was wrenched free from a purely domestic context and compared to similar foreign institutions'.[26] While the conditions for the award of the Victoria Cross would undergo numerous amendments and extensions, it continued to

be reserved only for the very highest level of bravery. It would be another 30 years before the introduction of the Distinguished Service Order (1886) brought recognition specifically to officers below field rank for gallantry and outstanding service, and not until the next century that the Military Cross (1914) and Military Medal (1916) met the need for a 'third level' of gallantry awards, reflecting the unprecedented scale of personal sacrifice made by officers, non-commissioned officers and men in the First World War.

Notes

1 Letter to Prince Albert of 20 Jan 1855. See - M J Crook, *The Evolution of the Victoria Cross*, Tunbridge Wells, Kent (1975) p13.

2 Sir George Douglas and Sir George Dalhousie Ramsay (ed), *The Panmure Papers*, Vols I & II, London (1908).

3 M J Crook, *Evolution of the VC*, p275.

4 J C Risk, *A History of the Order of the Bath and its Insignia*, London (1972) p69.

5 Royal Warrant, 19 Dec 1845.

6 *The London Gazette* 12 Dec 1854.

7 The National Archives: Public Record Office, WO 43/852.

8 TNA: PRO, WO 97/1353.

9 M J Crook, *Evolution of the VC*, p11.

10 *Ibid.* p13.

11 *Ibid.* p15.

12 *Panmure Papers*,Vol I p126.

13 TNA: PRO WO 98/1.

14 Its shape is similar to, and possibly inspired by that of the Army Gold Cross (1813), awarded for the Peninsular campaigns.

15 Royal Archives G20/4, Queen Victoria to the Duke of Newcastle.

16 RA G22/91, Victoria to Newcastle, 24 Jan 1855. The Duke of Newcastle had however stated in a letter of 19 January, that he believed 'the Prince prefers a single colour'.

17 G Tancred, *Historical Record of Medals and Honorary Distinctions*, London (1891 pp187-8.

18 RA G22/81, Queen Victoria is clearly referring to Sir George de Lacy Evans.

19 RA G37/12, General Sir A F Barnard to Colonel C B Phipps, 20 August.

20 TNA: PRO WO 6/130.

21 RA G27/6.

22 *Panmure Papers,* Vol 1 p126.

23 106 officers and men were entitled.

24 Tancred, *Historical Record* p191.

25 The names of 1,166 officers appointed to the Order of the Medjidieh were published in a Supplement to *The London Gazette* of 2 March 1858, together with the Queen's 'Royal license and permission that they may accept and wear the insignia of the several Classes'.

26 Risk, *op.cit.* p69.

Changes to the Weapons and Equipment of the British Army in the Crimea, 1855-56

Sara Jones

The weapons and equipment of the British soldier at the end of the Crimean War were different in several respects to those of 1854. It was a relatively short campaign, yet it marked a period of accelerated experimentation and modernisation for the British Army.

That said, the development of weapons and equipment and the introduction of new patterns was an on-going process and it is therefore difficult to ascertain exactly what was used by the British Army when in the Crimea. Two or more patterns were often in use at the same time and sometimes within the same regiment. Regiments could also be expected to manage with obsolete patterns until they wore out. It could take months, or years, before a new pattern of weapon or equipment was issued to the whole regiment. The standard arms or accoutrements on issue at any one time can be identified, but exactly what was in use in the field, and the unofficial modifications to which it had been subjected, may never be fully discovered.

Small Arms

Extensive trials took place in 1852 to develop a new, lighter arm as an improvement on the Pattern 1851 Minié Rifle Musket. The aim was to reduce the weight of the Minié bullet, and to do this the size of bore needed to be made smaller. Initially, a report by the Committee on Small Arms resulted in the Marquess of Anglesey, Master General of the Ordnance arranging for the manufacture of two rifle muskets modelled on the Minié, with bores reduced from .702in. to .530in..[1] Under Lord Hardinge, the Marquess of Anglesey's successor, the development grew more competitive. Five gunmakers each produced firearms designed to fire a lighter bullet, to be tested in the summer of

The bullets fired by the British in the Crimea included (from left to right): Pattern 1842 Smoothbore Musket ball; Pattern 1851 Minié Rifle Musket bullet with iron cup; and Pattern 1853 Enfield Rifle Musket Pritchett bullet with hollow base. NAM. Negative 98802

1852.[2] Further trials took place, and eventually led to the adoption of the Pattern 1853 Enfield Rifle Musket, which had a bore of .577in.. The new rifle was named after the place where it was to be manufactured, the Royal Small Arms Factory at Enfield. The first order for 20,000 Pattern 1853 Enfields was authorised in October 1853.[3]

The Pritchett bullet fired by the Enfield took its name from the London gunmaker who designed it. It differed from the Minié bullet in that the hollow base lacked an iron cup, but the bullet was still expanded into the rifling by the gasses from the exploding charge. Different versions of the bullet were later tried, including an iron cup, a boxwood plug and a baked clay plug.[4]

The Pattern 1853 Enfield cartridges were supplied in packets of ten, wrapped in light brown paper. Once the Enfield began to be issued, the Minié cartridge packets were given red paper wrapping to differentiate them.[5]

Supplies of Pattern 1853 Enfield Rifle Muskets arrived periodically in the Crimea during 1855. A Small Arms Office return of 11 April 1855 recorded that there were 33,886 Pattern 1851 Minié arms on issue and 16,361 of the new Pattern 1853 Enfields had left the store.[6]

The Enfield was a new service arm and in the Crimea it was not always viewed favourably. This may have been due to the lack of training with it given to those already on campaign, after they handed in their Miniés, and poor familiarisation with the new weapons for the reinforcements sent to the Crimea in 1855.

After the Crimean War various modifications were carried out to the Enfield and it achieved a far longer life than the Minié. The Enfield Rifle Musket remained the standard weapon of the infantry until breech-loading rifles were introduced in the mid-1860s. The Snider Rifle, which was adopted in 1866, was itself a breech-loading conversion of the Pattern 1853 Enfield.

New developments in infantry firearms were not mirrored by those for the cavalry. The cavalry encountered difficulties loading their carbines whilst on horseback and rarely used firearms. Following developments in France and Germany, however, in 1857 the British Army began testing breech-loading carbines for the cavalry, with the aim of achieving easier and faster loading.

The Royal Artillery carried the Pattern 1839 Carbine prior to the Crimean War, to be replaced by the Pattern 1842 Carbine. As the

Pattern 1853 Rifled Artillery Carbine of .577in. calibre, which also took the Pritchett bullet. In April 1855 almost half of the original 6,000 order had been completed and they were issued immediately. The gunners in the Crimea therefore received this arm before the Enfield Rifle Musket reached the infantry.[7]

In the absence of an organised transport system, and with the breakdown of supply during the hard winter of 1854, the Land Transport Corps was formed in 1855. Its new recruits were issued with smoothbore Pattern 1840 Constabulary Carbines, which had been fitted with the Lovell Pattern 1842 percussion lock.[8]

Soldiers of the 42nd (The Royal Highland) Regiment of Foot armed with the 1853 Pattern Enfield Rifle Musket.
NAM. 1964-12-154-6-11

Pistols and Revolvers

The 1851 Adams revolver was not official issue during the Crimean War, and was carried by officers who had purchased them privately. In 1855 and 1856, however, the Army placed contracts for Adams revolvers incorporating a new principle, patented by Lieutenant F B E Beaumont in 1855.[9] Beaumont's invention involved an additional facility, allowing the revolver to be manually cocked to afford greater accuracy when required. This was an improvement on the previous model, which could only be self-cocked. There are no instances recorded of Beaumont-Adams revolvers being used in the Crimean War and afterwards many of them remained in store. Little progress was made thereafter until the introduction of breech-loading centre-fire revolvers in the late 1860s; the new system being applied retrospectively to both Adams and Colt revolvers.

Although the Crimean War played its part in enabling revolvers to become recognised as an effective sidearm in the British Army, inherent conservatism and mistrust of revolvers made their general introduction slow. The Army reverted to the single shot percussion pistol with the introduction in 1856 of what was essentially a rifled version of the Pattern 1842 Lancers pistol. Eventually the breech-loading Enfield revolver was introduced in 1880.

The Sword and Lance

The various types of sword on issue during the Crimean War remained largely unchanged. The criticism of the Pattern 1853 Cavalry Sword grew after the Crimean War and a new sword was adopted in 1864. The Pattern 1846 Lance was in use until it was superseded by a new pattern in 1860.

With the establishment of the Land Transport Corps in 1855, officers carried the Pattern 1821 Light Cavalry Sword until the unit was re-formed as the Military Train in 1856.[10] Other ranks in the Land Transport Corps were issued with a sword resembling the French Model 1831 infantry sword, known in the French Army as the 'cabbage cutter'. There is, however, no evidence that it was used in the Crimean War.[11]

Artillery

By 1855 the strength of the British Artillery in the Crimea had increased significantly. It consisted of an additional troop of horse artillery, three more field batteries and over 100 siege guns.

In parallel with the development of the Minié Rifle Musket, trials in artillery applying the principle of the rifled barrel began in 1852. Initially a 9-pounder (pdr.) gun was produced with a four-groove barrel, and by a 9-pounder (pdr.) gun was produced with a four-groove barrel, and by the following year extensive experiments were being carried out to explore rifled cannon and elongated projectiles.[12]

The Lancaster rifling system, invented by Charles Lancaster (1820-78), had already been applied to small arms but was patented for ordnance use in 1850. Although still in the experimental stage, 68-pdr. and 8in. guns with Lancaster's elliptical oval bore were employed at Sevastopol.[13]

In September 1855, 183 large calibre British guns took part in the final attack on Sevastopol.[14] The heaviest of them, the 68-pdr., was reported to be the most effective: 'As perfect guns as can be desired … Their range is very great, and nearly as true as a rifle.'[15] Despite the strength of their barrels, and perhaps due to their immense power, three Lancaster guns and three 68-pdr. guns burst during the siege at Sevastopol.[16]

The Lancaster gun may not have made a huge contribution to the Crimean War, but it marked the beginning of the long awaited innovation in British artillery, which mirrored the developments in infantry arms. At this time Joseph Whitworth (1803-87) also conducted experiments with rifling and William George Armstrong (1810-1900) designed a stronger iron barrel for artillery guns, which was rifled and the first example of breech-loading artillery adopted by the British Government.

A 68-pounder Lancaster gun in the siegeworks outside Sevastopol.
NAM. 1971-02-33-490-10

Equipment

The issue equipment carried during the Crimean War did not change greatly. In the Crimea, however, generals, and the colonels of regiments, had a great deal of influence upon the equipment carried and how it was worn. This unofficial practice had been commonplace before equipment was standardised. Individual soldiers also often discarded, or adapted, their own equipment for comfort, or when the climate and conditions changed. When under fire at the Battle of the Alma the infantry discarded their packs, camp kettles and shakos and after the battle captured Russian knapsacks and boots to use in their place.[17] If equipment was damaged, lost or abandoned, replacements were often found on the battlefield from comrades or enemy troops who had become casualties.

The kit was far from perfect for the soldiers who carried it and the ill-fitting knapsack in particular received many complaints. It was at best uncomfortable and at worst crippling. General Estcourt expressed in several letters his opinion that the knapsacks were 'not very good' and that 'more attention should be drawn to the soldiers' mode of carrying their kit'.[18] In 1856 the knapsack was officially modified to include a strengthening stick, which was added 'across the inner and upper edge of the pack to give greater steadiness.'[19] This modification may, however, have been in use before it was officially adopted. Experimentation with the box knapsack continued until new valise equipment was gradually issued after its introduction in 1871.

As the Crimean War continued, the new waist belt, which had been worn by some regiments at the start of the campaign, was increasingly issued. In February 1855, however, Estcourt reported in a letter from Sevastopol that none of the regiments had received the new belts since arriving there.[20] When the waist belt was first adopted it was fitted with a 'V' shaped frog for the bayonet, which was later replaced with a sliding frog to allow greater movement along the belt.

In addition to the principal ammunition pouch that hung at the soldier's back, for active service the infantry were issued with a rectangular black leather pouch or ball bag, also for carrying cartridges and percussion caps. It was in use from 1855-56, and was carried in the Crimea. The pouch was attached to the front right side of the waist belt, providing an immediate, more easily accessible supply of ammunition.

The ammunition for the Pattern 1853 Enfield Rifle Musket was of smaller diameter than the Minié round; the Enfield ammunition pouch therefore carried 60 rounds, in packets of ten, instead of 50 for the Minié. A 60 round pouch for infantry was declared obsolete in 1859,

In 1860 a new 50 round pouch with tin compartments was proposed by the Adjutant-General.[22] A purpose-designed black leather pocket for percussion caps stitched to the inside right face of the ammunition pouch was adopted but may not have been introduced in time for the Crimean War.[23]

The equipment of the cavalry remained essentially unchanged during the Crimean War, although new developments in saddlery were taking place. Captain Louis Edward Nolan (c1820-54), 15th (The King's) Regiment of Light Dragoons (Hussars), had designed his own saddle using knowledge gained in part from his earlier service in an Austrian cavalry regiment.[24] Under his influence, a standard saddle for the cavalry was developed, and in 1856 the Universal Wood Arch Saddle was introduced. In 1860 a universal pattern bridle was introduced as a replacement for the light and heavy cavalry bridles.

The Crimean War coincided with, and to a certain extent accelerated, a period of change in the British Army's weaponry and equipment. Thereafter, the pace of change slowed, or even, as in the case of sidearms (with the effective setting aside of the revolver) and of the artillery (following the abandonment of breech-loading) went into reverse. The technological revolution could not be kept at bay, however, and ten years after the end of the Crimean War the infantry received the Snider, its first breech-loading rifle, and twenty years after that the Lee-Metford, its first bolt action magazine rifle.

Officers and men of the 3rd (East Kent) Regiment of Foot (The Buffs) photographed by Roger Fenton. The two soldiers standing in the centre wear the waistbelt with black leather ball bag attached to its front; their ammunition pouch and pouch belt is carried over the left shoulder.
NAM. 1964-12-151-6-13

Notes

1   C H Roads, *The British Soldier's Firearm, 1850-1864*, London (1964) p48.

2   For details of gunmakers, see W S Curtis, 'Infantry Shoulder Arms of the Crimean War, Part Nine – Great Britain, Rifled Musket Pattern 1853' *The War Correspondent* Vol 15, No 3, Oct 1997 p14.

3   C Robins 'Muskets and Rifles', *The War Correspondent* Vol 12, No 1, Apr 1994 p19.

4   Information supplied by Mr D F Harding and Dr D W Bailey.

5   W S Curtis 'Infantry Shoulder Arms of the Crimean War, Part 11 – Great Britain, Some Notes Upon Ammunition for the 1853 Rifle', *The War Correspondent* Vol 16, No 1, Apr 1998 pp25.

6   Roads, *op. cit.* p39.

7   W S Curtis 'Shoulder Arms of the Crimean War, Part Fifteen – Great Britain, Rifled Artillery Carbine Pattern 1853', *The War Correspondent* Vol 17, No 1, Apr 1999 p13.

8   W S Curtis 'Shoulder Arms of the Crimean War, Part Seventeen – Great Britain, Carbine of the Land Transport Corps', *The War Correspondent* Vol 17, No 4, Jan 2000 p9.

9   W H J Chamberlain & A W F Taylerson, *Revolvers of the British Services, 1854-1954,* Ontario & New York (1989) p4.

10   B Robson, *Swords of the British Army*, London (1996) p240.

11   *Ibid.* pp240-41.

12   H Strachan, *From Waterloo to Balaclava, Tactics, Technology, and the British Army, 1815-1854,* Cambridge (1985), p139.

13   *Ibid.* p139.

14   *Ibid.* p134.

15   Mordecai, *Military Commission to Europe, in 1855 and 1856*, p66; in Strachan, *op. cit.* p134.

16   W E M Reilly, *An Account of the Artillery Operations Conducted by the Royal Artillery and Royal Naval Brigade Before Sebastopol in 1854 and 1855,* London (1859) p208.

17   M Barthorp, *The British Army on Campaign (2) The Crimea*, London (2001) pp24 & 36.

18   NAM. 1962-10-97 Letters of Gen Estcourt, Adjutant-General of the Army of the East, to Gen Wetherall, from Scutari, 15 June 1854 and the camp before Sevastopol, [Oct 1854].

19   Horse Guards Circular 2 Aug 1856.

20   NAM. 1962-10-97 Estcourt to Wetherall, camp before Sevastopol, 3 Feb 1855.

21   I D Skennerton, *Lists of Changes in British War Material, Vol I, 1860-1886*, Margate (1980); p3 LoC No 60, 23 Nov 1859 & LoC No 61, 16 Dec 1859.

22   *Ibid.* p4; LoC No 127, 2 May 1860.

23   J L Summers, *Tangled Web, Canadian Infantry Accoutrements 1855-1985*, Ontario & New York (1992) pp9-10.

24   G Tylden, *Horses and Saddlery*, London (1965) p137.

Sources and Select Bibliography

Manuscript and other unpublished material in the National Army
Museum Archive

NAM. 1980-11-54 : Alderson letters

NAM. 1976-06-10 : Annesley journal

NAM. 1994-01-215 : Bell letters

NAM. 1989-01-33 : Boldero letters

NAM. 1968-03-45 : Butler journal

NAM. 1968-07-375 to-381 & 1978-08-90 : Codrington papers

NAM. 1993-06-51 : Dennison letter

NAM. 1994-03-154 : Earle letters

NAM. 1981-11-30 : Edwards letters

NAM. 1988-01-3 : Elton letters

NAM. 1986-02-75 : Firkins letter

NAM. 1976-06-38 : Fisher memoirs

NAM. 1963-09-5 : Forrest letters

NAM. 1963-05-162 : Fowle-Smith letter

NAM. 1983-10-132 : Gordon letter

NAM. 1997-07-47 : Harvey letters

NAM. 1972-08-51 : Howell letter

NAM. 1967-07-16 : Hutton letters

NAM. 1973-11-170 : Kingscote papers

NAM. 1959-03-128 : Layard letters

NAM. 2002-02-1409 : Lewes letter

NAM. 2002-05-2 : Lynden Bell letters

NAM. 1984-09-31 & 2002-03-36 : Mundy papers

NAM. 2002-03-167 : Newman letters

NAM. 1989-06-41 : Nolan journal

NAM. 1996-05-4 : Pine letters

NAM. 1982-12-29 : Radcliffe letters

NAM. 1968-07-280 to-305 : Raglan papers

NAM. 1983-11-9 : Seager letters

NAM. 1965-01-183 : Steevens letters

NAM. 1956-06-96 : Stirling diaries

NAM. 1970-06-8 : Wellesley diary

NAM. 1962-10-94 to-97 : Wetherall papers

Books and periodicals

Adkin, M, *The charge : why the Light Brigade was lost*, London (1996)

Agnew and sons, T, *Agnew's 1817-1967*, London (1967)

Airlie, Countess of (ed), *With the Guards we shall go : a Guardsman's letters in the Crimea, 1854-55*, London (1933)

Anderson, O R, *A Liberal state at war : English politics and economics during the Crimean War*, London (1967)

Anglesey, Marquess of (ed), *'Little Hodge' : being extracts from the diaries and letters of Colonel Edward Cooper Hodge, written during the Crimean War, 1854-1856*, London (1971)

Atkinson, C T, *The Dorsetshire Regiment : vol I : The Thirty-Ninth*, Oxford (1947)

Bailey, D W, *British military longarms 1815-1865,* London (1972)

Barthorp, M, *Crimean uniforms : British infantry*, London (1974)

Barthorp, M, *The British Army on campaign 1816-1902 (2) : the Crimea 1854-56*, London (1987)

Barthorp, M, *Heroes of the Crimea : the battles of Balaclava and Inkerman*, London (1991)

Baudelaire, C, *The painter of modern life,* London (1964)

Baudens, J B L, *On military and camp hospitals, and the health of troops in the field, being the results of a commission to inspect the sanitary arrangements of the French Army, and incidentally of other armies in the Crimean War,* New York (1862)

Bayley, C C, *Mercenaries for the Crimea : the German, Swiss and Italian Legions in British service, 1854-1856,* Montreal (1977)

Bentley, N (ed), *Russell's despatches from the Crimea 1854-56*, London (1966)

Blackmore, H L, *British military firearms 1650-1850*, London (1969)

Blackwood, Lady A, *A narrative of personal experiences and impressions during a residence on the Bosphorus throughout the Crimean War,* London (1881)

Boase, F, *Modern English biography,* London (1965 reprint)

Brackenbury, G, *The campaign in the Crimea*, London (1855 & 1856)

Brown, D K, *Before the ironclad : development of ship design, propulsion and armament in the Royal Navy, 1815-60,* London (1990)

Bustarret, C, *et al, Crimée 1854-1856 : premiers reportages de guerre,* Paris (1994)

Caldwell, G and Cooper, R, *Rifle green in the Crimea,* Leicester (1994)

Calthorpe, S J G, *Letters from Head-Quarters; or, the realities of war in the Crimea,* London (1856)

Calthorpe, S J G & Cadogan, Sir G, *Cadogan's Crimea,* London (1979)

Campbell, C F, *Letters from camp to his relatives during the siege of Sebastopol*, London (1894)

Carver, M (ed), *Letters of a Victorian army officer : Edward Wellesley, Major, 73rd Regiment of Foot 1840-1854,* Stroud (1995)

Chamberlain, W H J & Taylerson, A W F, *Revolvers of the British services, 1854-1954,* Ontario (1989)

Clifford, Sir H H, *Henry Clifford, VC : his letters and sketches from the Crimea*, London (1956)

Colebrooke, Sir T E, *Journal of two visits to the Crimea in the autumns of 1854 and 1855 : with remarks on the campaign,* London (1856)

Compton, P, *Colonel's lady and camp-follower : the story of women in the Crimean War*, London (1970)

Cooke, B, *The grand Crimean central railway,* Knutsford (1990)

Crook, M J, *The evolution of the Victoria Cross,* Tunbridge Wells (1975)

Crowe, Sir J, *Reminiscences of thirty-five years of my life,* London (1895)

Curtiss, J S, *The Russian Army under Nicholas I 1825-1855,* Durham North Carolina (1965)

Curtiss, J S, *Russia's Crimean War*, Durham, North Carolina (1979)

David, S, *The homicidal Earl : the life of Lord Cardigan*, London (1997)

Douglas, Sir G & Ramsay, Sir G D (eds), *The Panmure papers*, London (1908)

Duberly, F, *Journal kept during the Russian war*, London (1856)

Edgerton, R B, *Death or glory : the legacy of the Crimean War*, Boulder, Colorado (1999)

Evans, R J W and von Strandmann, H P, *The revolutions in Europe, 1848-1849 : from reform to reaction*, Oxford (2000)

Eyre-Todd, G (ed), *The autobiography of William Simpson RI (Crimean Simpson)*, London (1903)

Ffoulkes, C & Hopkinson, E C, *Sword, lance and bayonet,* London (1938)

Fuller, W C, *Strategy and Power in Russia 1600-1914,* New York (1992)

Gernsheim, H & Gernsheim, A, *Roger Fenton, photographer of the Crimean War : his photographs and his letters from the Crimea*, London (1954)

Goldie, S M (ed), *Florence Nightingale : letters from the Crimea,* Manchester (1997)

Gooch, B D, *The new Bonapartist generals in the Crimean War : distrust and decision-making in the Anglo-French alliance*, The Hague (1959)

Gough, B M, *The Royal Navy on the northwest coast of North America*, 1810-1914, Vancouver (1974)

Griffith, P, *Military thought in the French Army, 1815-51*, Manchester (1989)

Hamley, E B, *The story of the campaign of Sebastopol,* Edinburgh (1855)

Harris, S M, *British military intelligence in the Crimean War, 1854-1856*, London (1999)

Hayward, J B (ed), *Casualty roll for the Crimea*, London (1976)

Hibbert, C, *The destruction of Lord Raglan : a tragedy of the Crimean War, 1854-55*, London (1961)

Hibbert, C, *The Illustrated London News social history of Victorian Britain*, London (1975)

Higginson, Sir G, *Seventy-one years of a Guardsman's life*, London (1916)

Hughes, B P, *British smoothbore artillery,* London (1969)

James, L, Crimea, 1854-56 : *the war with Russia from contemporary photographs*, Thame (1981)

Kagan, F W, *The military reforms of Nicholas I: the origins of the modern Russian army*, Basingstoke (1999)

Kagan, F W & Higham, R (eds), *The military history of Tsarist Russia*, Basingstoke (2002)

Kagan, J L H, *Soldiers of the Tsar: Army and Society in Russia 1462-1874,* Oxford (1985)

Kelly, Sir R D, *An officer's letters to his wife during the Crimean War*, London (1902)

Kerr, P *et al, The Crimean War,* London (1997)

Kinglake, A W, *The invasion of the Crimea : its origin, and an account of its progress down to the death of Lord Raglan*, 6th edition, London (1885)

Kingsford, C L, *The story of the Duke of Cambridge's Own (Middlesex Regiment)*, London (1916)

Knight, C R B, *Historical records of the Buffs East Kent Regiment (3rd Foot) formerly designated the Holland Regiment and Prince George of Denmark's Regiment 1704-1914* : part two : 1814-1914, London (1935)

Lake, A, *Kars and our captivity in Russia*, London (1856)

Lambert, A D, *The Crimean War : British grand strategy against Russia, 1853-56*, Manchester (1990)

Liddell, R S, *The memoirs of the Tenth Royal Hussars (Prince of Wales's Own)*, London (1891)

Longmore, Sir T, *The sanitary contrasts of the British and French armies during the Crimean War*, London (1883)

Lummis, W M and Wynn, K G, *Honour the Light Brigade,* London (1973)

Lysons, Sir D, *The Crimean War from first to last,* London (1895)

Manfredi, C, *La spedizione Sarda in Crimea nel 1855-56*, Rome (1896)

Maude, Sir F S, *Letters from Turkey and the Crimea,* printed for private circulation (1896)

Mawson, M H, *Eyewitness in the Crimea : the Crimean War letters (1854-1856) of Lt. Col. George Frederick Dallas*, London (2001)

Maxwell, E H, *With the Connaught Rangers in quarters, camp and on leave,* London (1873)

Miller, D, *Victorian watercolours and drawings in the collection of Her Majesty The Queen*, London (1995)

Mitchell, A, *Recollections from one of the Light Brigade*, Canterbury (1885)

Mollo, J & Mollo, B, *Into the Valley of Death : the British Cavalry Division at Balaclava 1854*, London (1991)

Nolan, E H, *The history of the war against Russia*, London (1857)

Pack, R, *Sebastopol trenches and five months in them*, London (1878)

Paget, C S (ed), *The Light Cavalry Brigade in the Crimea : extracts from the letters and journal of the late Gen. Lord G. Paget... during the Crimean War*, London (1881)

Peard, G S, *Narrative of a campaign in the Crimea; including an account of the battles of Alma, Balaklava, and Inkermann*, London (1855)

Pearse, H, *The Crimean diary and letters of Lieut.-General Sir Charles Ash Windham*, London (1897)

Ragsdale, H (ed), *Imperial Russian foreign policy*, Cambridge (1993)

Reilly, W E M, *An account of the artillery operations conducted by the Royal Artillery and Royal Naval Brigade before Sebastopol in 1854 and 1855*, London (1859)

Rich, N, *Why the Crimean War? : a cautionary tale,* London (1985)

Risk, J C, *A history of the Order of the Bath and its insignia*, London (1972)

Roads, C H, *The British soldier's firearm, 1850-1864*, London (1964)

Robins, C D (ed), *The murder of a regiment : winter sketches from the Crimea, 1854-55*, Bowdon (1994)

Robson, B, *Swords of the British Army*, London (1996)

Royle, T, *Crimea : the great Crimean War, 1854-1856*, London (1999)

Russell, W H, *The British expedition to the Crimea*, London (1858)

Russell, W H, *The great war with Russia*, London (1895)

Ryan, G, *The lives of our heroes of the Crimea*, London (1855)

Ryan, G, *The life of Major-General Estcourt, Adjutant-General of the Army in the East*, London, 1856

St Arnaud, L de, *Lettres du Maréchal Saint-Arnaud 1832-1854*, Paris

St Arnaud, L de, *Lettres du Maréchal Saint-Arnaud 1832-1854*, Paris (1858)

Sandwith, H, *A narrative of the siege of Kars*, London (1856)

Seacole, M, *The wonderful adventures of Mrs Seacole in many lands*, London (1999)

Seaton, A, *The Crimean War : a Russian chronicle*, London (1977)

Skene, J H, *With Lord Stratford in the Crimean War*, London (1883)

Skennerton, I D, *Lists of changes in British war material : vol 1 : 1860-1886*, Margate (1980)

Slade, Sir A, *Turkey and the Crimean War : a narrative of historical events*, London (1867)

Smith, K W & Guys, C, *Crimean War drawings 1854-1856*, Cleveland, Ohio (1978)

Sterling, A, *The story of the Highland Brigade in the Crimea,* London (1895)

Strachan, H, *Wellington's legacy : the reform of the British Army 1830-54*, Manchester (1984)

Strachan, H, *From Waterloo to Balaclava : tactics, technology, and the British Army, 1815-1854*, Cambridge (1985)

Summers, J L, *Tangled web : Canadian infantry accoutrements 1855-1985*, Ontario (1992)

Sweetman, J, *War and administration : the significance of the Crimean War for the British Army*, Edinburgh (1984)

Sweetman, J, *Raglan : from the Peninsula to the Crimea*, London (1993)

Tancred, G, *Historical record of medals and honorary distinctions*, London (1891)

Taylor, A J P, *The struggle for mastery in Europe 1848-1918*, Oxford (1954)

Taylor, A J P, ed Wrigley, C, *From Napoleon to the Second International: essays on nineteenth century Europe,* Harmondsworth (1993)

Temperley, H W V, *England and the Near East : the Crimea*, London (1936)

Terrot, S A, *Reminiscences of Scutari hospitals in winter 1854-55*, Edinburgh (1898)

Thomas, R H G & Scollins, R, *The Russian army in the Crimean War, 1854-56*, London (1991)

Tolstoy, Leo, *Tales of army life*, Oxford (1935)

Tylden, G, *Horses and saddlery*, London (1965)

Ward, S G P, *The Hawley letters : the letters of Captain R B Hawley, 89th, from the Crimea, December 1854 to August 1856*, London (1970)

Waterfield, G, *Layard of Nineveh*, London (1963)

Whinyates, F A, *From Coruña to Sevastopol*, London (1884)

Wilkinson-Latham, R J, *Crimean uniforms : 2. British artillery*, London (1973)

Wilkinson-Latham, R J, *Uniforms and weapons of the Crimean War*, London (1977)

Wirtschafter, E K, *From serf to Russian soldier*, Princeton, New Jersey (1990)

Woodham-Smith, C, *Florence Nightingale 1820-1910*, London (1950)

Woodham-Smith, C, *The reason why*, London (1953)

Woods, N W, *The past campaign : a sketch of the war in the East*, London (1855)

Woollright, H H, *Records of the Seventy-Seventh (East Middlesex), the Duke of Cambridge's Regiment of Foot, now the Second Battalion The Duke of Cambridge's Own (Middlesex Regiment)*, London (1907)

Periodicals

The Illustrated London News

The Journal of the Society for Army Historical Research

The London Gazette

The War Correspondent : the Journal of the Crimean War Research Society

Index

Ranks indicated are those held in the Crimea